D1596257

DANGEROUS MINDS

POLITICAL PSYCHIATRY IN CHINA TODAY
AND ITS ORIGINS IN THE MAO ERA

Human Rights Watch

Geneva Initiative on Psychiatry

DANGEROUS MINDS

Political Psychiatry in China Today and its Origins in the Mao Era

**Human Rights Watch and
Geneva Initiative on Psychiatry**

Addresses for Human Rights Watch
350 Fifth Avenue, 34th Floor, New York, NY 10118-3299
Tel: (212) 290-4700, Fax: (212) 736-1300, E-mail: hrwnyc@hrw.org

1630 Connecticut Avenue, NW, Suite 500, Washington, D.C. 20009
Tel: (202) 612-4321, Fax: (202) 612-4333, E-mail: hrwdc@hrw.org

2-12 Pentonville Road, Second Floor, London N1 9FP, UK
Tel: (44) 20-7713-1995, Fax: (44) 20-7713-1800, E-mail: hrwuk@hrw.org

15 Rue Van Campenhout, 1000 Brussels, Belgium
Tel: (32) 2-732-2009, Fax: (32) 2-732-0471, E-mail: hrwbe@hrw.org

Web Site Address: http://www.hrw.org

Listserv address: To subscribe to the Human Rights Watch news e-mail list, send a blank e-mail message to subscribe@igc.topica.com.

Addresses for Geneva Initiative on Psychiatry
P.O. Box 2182 1200 BG Hilversum, The Netherlands
Tel: (31) 35 6838727, Fax: (31) 35 6833646, E-mail: gip@geneva-initiative.org

Zenevos Iniciatyva Psichiatrijoje
Oginskio 3, 2040 Vilnius, Lithuania
Tel: (370) 2-715-760, Fax: (370) 2-715-761, E-mail: zip@zenevos-iniciatyva.lt

Zhenevska Iniciativa v Psihiatriata
1, Maliovitsa Str., Sofia 1000, Bulgaria
Tel/fax: (359) 2-987-7875, E-mail: zhip@Zhenevska-IniciativaBG.org

HUMAN RIGHTS WATCH

Human Rights Watch is dedicated to
protecting the human rights of people around the world.

We stand with victims and activists to prevent
discrimination, to uphold political freedom, to protect people from inhumane
conduct in wartime, and to bring offenders to justice.

We investigate and expose
human rights violations and hold abusers accountable.

We challenge governments and those who hold power to end abusive practices
and respect international human rights law.

We enlist the public and the international
community to support the cause of human rights for all.

HUMAN RIGHTS WATCH

Human Rights Watch conducts regular, systematic investigations of human rights abuses in some seventy countries around the world. Our reputation for timely, reliable disclosures has made us an essential source of information for those concerned with human rights. We address the human rights practices of governments of all political stripes, of all geopolitical alignments, and of all ethnic and religious persuasions. Human Rights Watch defends freedom of thought and expression, due process and equal protection of the law, and a vigorous civil society; we document and denounce murders, disappearances, torture, arbitrary imprisonment, discrimination, and other abuses of internationally recognized human rights. Our goal is to hold governments accountable if they transgress the rights of their people.

Human Rights Watch began in 1978 with the founding of its Europe and Central Asia division (then known as Helsinki Watch). Today, it also includes divisions covering Africa, the Americas, Asia, and the Middle East. In addition, it includes three thematic divisions on arms, children's rights, and women's rights. It maintains offices in New York, Washington, Los Angeles, London, Brussels, Moscow, Tashkent, Tblisi, and Bangkok. Human Rights Watch is an independent, nongovernmental organization, supported by contributions from private individuals and foundations worldwide. It accepts no government funds, directly or indirectly.

The staff includes Kenneth Roth, executive director; Michele Alexander, development director; Reed Brody, advocacy director; Carroll Bogert, communications director; John T. Green, operations director, Barbara Guglielmo, finance director; Lotte Leicht, Brussels office director; Michael McClintock, deputy program director; Patrick Minges, publications director; Maria Pignataro Nielsen, human resources director; Malcolm Smart, program director; Wilder Tayler, legal and policy director; and Joanna Weschler, United Nations representative. Jonathan Fanton is the chair of the board. Robert L. Bernstein is the founding chair.

The regional directors of Human Rights Watch are Peter Takirambudde, Africa; José Miguel Vivanco. Americas; Mike Jendrzejczyk (Acting), Asia; Elizabeth Andersen, Europe and Central Asia; and Hanny Megally, Middle East and North Africa. The thematic division directors are Joost R. Hiltermann, arms; Lois Whitman, children's; and LaShawn R. Jefferson, women's.

The members of the board of directors are Jonathan Fanton, Chair; Robert L. Bernstein, Founding Chair, Lisa Anderson, David M. Brown, William Carmichael, Dorothy Cullman, Gina Despres, Irene Diamond, Fiona Druckenmiller, Edith Everett, Michael Gellert, Vartan Gregorian, Alice H. Henkin, James F. Hoge, Jr., Stephen L. Kass, Marina Pinto Kaufman, Wendy Keys, Bruce J. Klatsky, Joanne Leedom-Ackerman, Josh Mailman, Joel Motley, Samuel K. Murumba, Jane Olson, Peter Osnos, Kathleen Peratis, Catherine Powell, Bruce Rabb, Sigrid Rausing, Orville Schell, Sid Sheinberg, Gary G. Sick, Malcolm Smith, Domna Stanton, John Studzinski, Maureen White, Maya Wiley. Emeritus Board: Roland Algrant, Adrian DeWind, and Malcolm Smith.

GENEVA INITIATIVE ON PSYCHIATRY

Geneva Initiative on Psychiatry is the main development agency working in mental health care in Central and Eastern Europe and the New Independent States (CCEE/NIS), and it focuses its efforts on the principle of empowerment of local mental health reformers and their organizations.

Geneva Initiative on Psychiatry engages in a wide spectrum of mental health related work: pilot projects, policy development, structural projects, training and publication programs, NGO development and exchange of experience and know-how between mental health reformers in the CCEE/NIS.

Geneva Initiative on Psychiatry collaborates, internationally, with mental health organizations such as the World Health Organization and the World Psychiatric Association, and strives, at local level, to promote and deepen cooperation between mental healthcare facilities and their users, family members and user organizations.

Geneva Initiative on Psychiatry monitors the human rights situation in mental health in all countries where it operates, and combats the political abuse of psychiatry wherever it is found to occur.

Geneva Initiative on Psychiatry
General secretary: Robert van Voren

The international foundation Geneva Initiative on Psychiatry sprang to life in 1980 to combat the political abuse of psychiatry which at that moment was widely used as a tool of repression in the Soviet Union and in a number of Eastern European countries. Its campaigns helped to force the Soviet All-Union Society of Psychiatrists and Neuropathologists (AUSPN) to withdraw from the World Psychiatric Association (WPA) in early 1983.

In 1989 the situation was changing dramatically in the countries of Central and Eastern Europe and the Soviet Union. In the preceding two years, virtually all political prisoners had been released from prisons, camps, exile and psychiatric hospitals, the latter group being the last ones to be set free. When increasing numbers of Soviet psychiatrists contacted the organization with the request to assist them in reforming mental health care in their country, it felt it had a duty to respond positively and to help end the legacy of Soviet totalitarian psychiatry.

In 1993, the Network of Reformers in Psychiatry was established, which developed into a support group and think tank for mental health reform for countries of Central and Eastern Europe and the New Independent States (CCEE/NIS). It now unites some 600 mental health reformers in 29 countries. It is multi-disciplinary: among its members are psychiatrists, psychologists, psychiatric nurses, social workers, sociologists, lawyers, relatives of the mentally ill as well as a growing number of users. More than a hundred non-governmental mental health organizations in the CCEE/NIS are linked to the Network.

Geneva Initiatives strives to improve the lives of the users of mental health care services, users being both consumers and their relatives and dependents alike. However, Geneva Initiative also strives for a *structural* improvement of their situation, and thus tends to concentrate on programs with a structural nature, such as policy reform, institutional reform, care program reform and educational reform. In addition, we try to combine the positive sides of pioneering and taking risks with the need to achieve sustainability – daring programs do not make sense if there is no chance of future funding from regular financial sources. However, at the same time, without daring programs the barrier of stagnation and inertia often cannot be overcome.

Board of Directors
Prof . Robin Jacoby (UK, Chairman); Drs. Robert Van Voren (NL, General Secretary); Drs. Rudi Rust (NL, Treasurer); Dr. Jim Birley (UK, Past President); Prof. Richard Bonnie; Drs. Gerard Doornkate (NL); Dr. Ray Freebury (CDN); Dr. Dorothea Holman (UK); Ms. Pien de Lange (NL); Mr. Lars Olof Ljungberg (S); Ms. Ellen Mercer (USA); Ms. Jane Salvage (UK); Mr. Joel Slack (USA); Drs. Conny Westgeest (NL).

GIP Staff
Hilversum: Robert Van Voren (Director); Jan Veldmeijer; Maaike Hooghoudt; Mariska Kools; Rob Keukens, Ella Terburg; Cisca Goedhart.
Vilnius: Dana Migaliova (Director); Irena Kuldos; Alexander Avramenko.
Sofia: Elena Dimitrova (Director); Galina Veshova; Valentina Hristakeva.

ACKNOWLEDGEMENTS

This report was researched and written by Robin Munro, a London-based expert on China human rights issues who served as principal China researcher and director of the Hong Kong office of Human Rights Watch during 1989–1998. Munro also selected and translated the documents appearing in the appendices. Robert van Voren, secretary general of the Geneva Initiative on Psychiatry, wrote the section titled, "The Soviet Case: Prelude to a Global Consensus on Psychiatry and Human Rights."

The chapter titled "Judicial Psychiatry in China and its Political Abuses" was first published in the *Columbia Journal of Asian Law*, vol. 14, no. 1, 2000 (actual publication date: January 2001) and is used with permission. While writing it, Munro was a Senior Research Fellow at the Law Department and Centre of Chinese Studies, School of Oriental and African Studies (SOAS), University of London, and a member of the School's Law and Public Health in Developing Countries Research Group. He gratefully acknowledges the kind assistance of Dr. James Birley, former president of the U.K. Royal College of Psychiatrists; Richard J. Bonnie, John S. Battle Professor of Law and Director of the University of Virginia Institute of Law, Psychiatry and Public Policy; Professor Donald C. Clarke of the University of Washington School of Law; Dr Frank Dikötter, Director of the Contemporary China Institute, SOAS; John Gunn CBE, Professor of Forensic Psychiatry, Institute of Psychiatry, King's College, London; Professor Michael Palmer, Head of the Law Department, SOAS; Leonard S. Rubenstein J.D., Executive Director of Physicians for Human Rights, Boston; and Robert Van Voren of the Geneva Initiative on Psychiatry; all of whom provided valuable comments on earlier versions of the Columbia Journal article. Munro also gratefully acknowledges the generous assistance of Sir Joseph Hotung, member of the Governing Body of SOAS, in providing financial support for the research fellowship that produced the article.

Jim Birley also provided expert commentary on the documentary appendices to this report, and Richard Bonnie and Leonard Rubenstein gave important advice on the drafting of the Recommendations.

Sidney Jones, then Executive Director of the Asia Division of Human Rights Watch, and Cythnia Brown, consultant to Human Rights Watch, edited the report. Copy editing assistance was provided by Neelangani De Soyza and Liz Weiss, Human Rights Watch associates.

TABLE OF CONTENTS

Judicial Psychiatry in China and its Political Abuses

Appendices

Preface

> *In the former Soviet Union during the Khrushchev–Brezhnev era, the KGB used its forensic psychiatric institutions to brand, arbitrarily and for political reasons, large numbers of political dissidents as suffering from "schizophrenia" and "paranoid psychosis" and then incarcerated them for long periods in "special psychiatric hospitals." In 1976, the Soviet Union was severely censured on this account by psychiatrists from all over the world at a conference in Hawaii of the World Psychiatric Association. Only after Gorbachev's rise to power were these errors rectified. We have now discovered that similar practices have also occurred in certain parts of China."* [1]
> — Jia Yicheng (China's top forensic psychiatrist), 1998

In January 2001, the first detailed study of the political misuse of psychiatry in the People's Republic of China as a means of silencing peaceful political dissidents and others appeared in a U.S. law review.[2] The subject quickly attracted wide international attention, prompting a strong public denial by the Chinese Ministry of Foreign Affairs.[3] It also led to the formation of a

---

[1] Jia Yicheng, "A Discussion of Certain Legal Issues Concerning the Hospitalization of the Mentally Ill," *Shanghai Archives of Psychiatry*, no.1 (1998), pp.6-10. (Two factual corrections should be made here: first, the Hawaii conference of the WPA took place in 1977, not 1976 as stated by Professor Jia; and second, the political misuse of psychiatry in the Soviet Union went well beyond the forensic psychiatric domain. In perhaps a majority of cases, political dissidents and others were committed to regular mental institutions without the involvement of the forensic authorities. For an explanation of the term "forensic psychiatry," see Note 6 below.)

[2] Robin Munro, "Judicial Psychiatry in China and its Political Abuses," *Columbia Journal of Asian Law*, vol. 14, no.1 (2000), pp.1-128. (The journal cover date notwithstanding, the article itself was completed in November 2000, and the journal issue was published in January 2001.) See also Robin Munro, "Political Psychiatry in Post-Mao China and its Origins in the Cultural Revolution," *Journal of the American Academy of Psychiatry and the Law*, vol. 30, no.1 (2002), pp.97-106. The same issue of the AAPL Journal contains several other articles and commentaries on the China political psychiatry question (by Richard J. Bonnie, Robert van Voren, Jim Birley, Frederick Hickling, Alan Stone, Arthur Kleinman and Sing Lee, and Sunny Y. Lu and Viviana B. Galli).

[3] See, for example, Erik Eckholm, "China's Crackdown on Sects Stirs Alarm Over Psychiatric Abuse: Rights Groups Cite Rise in Medical Detentions," *New York Times*, February 18, 2001; and Isabel Hilton, "The China Scandal," *The Guardian*, February 22,

1

growing advocacy campaign in several countries to pressure the Chinese medical and legal authorities to investigate and put a stop to these ethically wrong practices.

This report seeks to advance the current debate within the world psychiatric and human rights communities, bringing the issue of politically abusive psychiatry in China to a much wider audience. It provides important new documentary evidence showing that such abuses were more common in China during the Cultural Revolution (1966-76) and the subsequent decade than in the former Soviet Union or any other country where similar phenomena have occurred in the past, and that, moreover, official psychiatric theory in China continues to condone and encourage such practices in the twenty-first century. To set these recently uncovered documents in their proper historical and analytical context, we also reproduce here the full text of the *Columbia Journal of Asian Law* article that launched this latest round in the longstanding controversy over China's abusive human rights record in general.

As if to emphasize the continuing seriousness of the political-psychiatric abuse problem, the Chinese authorities since mid-1999 have forcibly sent detained Falun Gong activists to mental asylums throughout the country; as of March 2002, Falun Gong sources reported that more than three hundred of their members had been subjected to this treatment and three had died as a direct consequence; no independent verification of these figures has been possible. The authorities' current attempt to partially "psychiatrize" the Falun Gong question by claiming that the group's spiritual doctrines and practices drive its members insane represents only the most recent phase in a now well-documented history of political psychiatric abuse in China stretching back almost half a century.[4]

Overview

Since the earliest years of the People's Republic, political dissidents, religious nonconformists, "whistle-blowers," and other dissenting citizens have consistently been viewed by the Communist Party of China as posing a major political threat to society. Even in today's economically more open China such people continue to be arrested and imprisoned as enemies of the state. (Until

---

2001. The same week, Zhu Bangzao, spokesman of the PRC Ministry of Foreign Affairs, stated: "Such allegations are totally groundless and unacceptable…There is no evidence to support it" ("China Slams Study Alleging Psychiatric Abuse," *Reuters*, February 20, 2001). See also "Contortions of Psychiatry in China" (editorial), *New York Times,* March 25, 2001.

[4] Human Rights Watch, *Dangerous Meditation: China's Campaign Against Falungong*, (New York: Human Rights Watch, 2002).

1997, the criminal charge of choice was "counterrevolution," while nowadays the less political-sounding charge of "endangering state security" is most often applied.)[5]

The official psychiatric literature in China unequivocally records that in many cases since the late 1950s, however, detained dissidents, non-conformists, "whistle-blowers," and other dissenters have additionally been subjected to forensic psychiatric evaluation by the legal authorities, found to be criminally insane and then forcibly committed to various types of psychiatric institutions.[6] In essence, the question placed before psychiatric examiners by the police in all these cases has been: are the detainees "bad," "mad" or (in certain borderline cases) a combination of both? Freedom – pursuant to a finding that the forensic examinee is sane and also innocent – is rarely an option for those concerned, since even today the acquittal rate for people accused of political crimes in China is virtually nil; and if found non-prosecutable or not guilty by reason of insanity, they are in most cases sent for long-term custodial care. In the

---

[5] For a detailed account of China's legislation in this area, see Human Rights Watch/Asia and Human Rights in China "Whose Security?: 'State Security' in China's New Criminal Code," *A Human Rights Watch Report*, vol. 9, no. 4 (C), April 1997.

[6] The term "forensic psychiatry" refers to the field of professional cooperation between psychiatrists and the police or judicial systems. They may cooperate, for example, in cases where police officers suspect that a detainee may be mentally ill and so seek expert psychiatric opinion as to mental capacity to undergo further legal proceedings. Although forensic psychiatry is commonly applied, in China as elsewhere, within both the civil and the criminal sectors of the legal system, the focus of the present report is on its nature and political misuses within the Chinese criminal justice system. The closely related term "judicial psychiatry" refers more narrowly, in most countries, to the involvement of psychiatrists in formal court proceedings. In China, however, the Public Security Bureau (the police) is officially viewed as being a constituent part, together with the courts and the prosecution authorities, of the country's "judicial organs" (*sifa bumen*). Therefore, the terms "judicial psychiatry" and "forensic psychiatry" are used interchangeably in this report to denote all cases where police and psychiatrists work together, including those in which the courts and judiciary may have no professional involvement, direct or otherwise. In China, significantly, the majority of crime-related psychiatric cases are still handled solely by the police, with only a small proportion proceeding to the stage of formal prosecution and trial. For a brief account of the history of forensic psychiatry in China, see below, "Judicial Psychiatry in China and its Political Abuses," section III., "The Early Years of the People's Republic." For a detailed overview of the role of forensic psychiatry within the Chinese legal system today, see section V., "Legal Norms and Judicial Process." As is discussed in further detail below, the majority of cases involving the political abuse of psychiatry in China appear to occur within the forensic or police-related branch of the country's psychiatric profession. Although there has been a resurgence of such abuse within the ·general psychiatric domain since 1999, it is important to note that the wider field of general psychiatry in China nowadays conforms, in the main, to internationally accepted standards of mental healthcare diagnosis and treatment.

authorities' view socially dangerous acts have "objectively" been committed, and so society must be protected from any further such threat.

As the documents presented below indicate, China's official psychiatric literature records clearly that the Communist Party's notion of "political dangerousness" was long ago institutionally grafted on to the diagnostic armory of Chinese psychiatry and incorporated into the key concept of psychiatric dangerousness.

It is important to stress that we adopt, in this report, an agnostic position on the question of whether some or perhaps even many of the victims of China's "political-psychiatric dangerousness" policy are in reality suffering from some form of mental illness or impairment. The truth of this matter can be established conclusively only by the Chinese government agreeing to allow qualified outside observers full access to places of psychiatric detention, so that their alleged mentally-ill political, religious and labor activist inmates can be given an independent medical evaluation. It is entirely possible that at least some of those concerned will prove to be suffering, or to have suffered in the past, from conditions ranging from minor personality quirks or abnormalities all the way through to full-blown mental illness.

The bottom line, however, is that most of these people should not have been arrested or brought for forensic psychiatric evaluation (formal or otherwise) in the first place, since in the overwhelming majority of recorded cases their only "offense" was to have expressed views or beliefs which served to offend the political sensitivities of the Chinese Communist Party. Any of them who are indeed mentally ill should be offered suitable medical care and treatment, on an outpatient or in-patient basis as appropriate. Involuntary confinement in mental hospitals (whether civilian or police-run) should be contemplated only in the case of those meeting the internationally agreed minimum criteria for mentally ill persons who pose a direct danger to themselves or others. The Chinese authorities' frequent imposition of this extreme measure on individuals (mentally normal or otherwise) whom they regard as posing only a "political threat" to society stands in clear and direct violation both of the World Psychiatric Association's 1996 Declaration of Madrid and of the U.N.'s 1991 Principles for the Protection of Persons with Mental Illness and for the Improvement of Mental Health Care.[7]

---

[7] For further information on these important documents, see below, "Judicial Psychiatry in China and its Political Abuses," Section II.

The real cause of politically abusive psychiatry in China today is to be found in the more intractable problem of the Chinese authorities' longstanding insistence upon viewing the peaceful expression of dissident or nonconformist viewpoints as constituting "political crimes" that must be sternly punished by law. Until this fundamental impediment to the observance of internationally recognized human rights in China can be removed, a small but significant proportion of those arrested on such charges will no doubt continue to be diagnosed as having committed their "heinous offenses" as a result of mental illness rather than from any politically "hostile" intent. Any genuinely mentally disturbed dissidents and religious believers – and also any non-dissident individuals who happen to express their mental disturbances in the form of politically-colored thought, speech and action – should be given the benefit of humane and appropriate medical care in a non-forensic, regular psychiatric care setting. Many Chinese psychiatrists now publicly acknowledge that most of those in the latter categories (a quixotic but seemingly quite large group that might best be described as "pseudo-counterrevolutionaries") became mentally disturbed or were driven insane as a direct result of the incessantly persecutory political campaigns of China's recent past. For the legal and medical authorities to treat such people also as being "dangerously mentally ill criminals" is an affront to human dignity.

Analysis of New Documentary Evidence

The previously known evidence of political misuse of psychiatry in China is set forth in extensive detail in the first main item of this report: the article titled "Judicial Psychiatry and its Political Abuses in China." The remainder of the report consists of hitherto unknown material shedding important new light on two key aspects of the psychiatric abuse problem in China: first, its origins and development during the Cultural Revolution decade, and second, how China's law-enforcement and psychiatric establishments have continued to pursue similarly abusive policies (albeit on a substantially reduced scale) against political dissidents and others during the post-Mao reform era and right up to the present day.

DOCUMENTS 1-7: The Cultural Revolution and the Late 1970s

The first two documents appearing in the Appendices date from April 1966 – the eve of the Cultural Revolution – and provide a tantalizing glimpse of the tectonic upheaval that was about to hit the Chinese psychiatric profession and whose dire effects were to last for the ensuing decade and more. As DOCUMENT 1, an editorial from the *Chinese Journal of Neurology and Psychiatry*, notes, "Many problems still exist in our work, foremost among them being that some psychiatric workers are still quite heavily influenced and affected by bourgeois medical ideology...[However,] an ardent high tide in the universal study of Chairman Mao's works has been unleashed, allowing us to raise our level of ideological awareness, to give full prominence to politics, and to criticize and condemn the bourgeois ideological preference for working in isolation from politics, the masses and reality."

DOCUMENT 2, an article from the same journal, written by staff at a Gansu Province mental hospital, elaborates on this theme, stating: "In the course of the 1957 Anti-Rightist Movement and the struggle to annihilate capitalism and assert the proletarian worldview,[8] the level of ideological awareness among our medical personnel rose greatly and we made initial progress in critiquing the bourgeois viewpoint that 'mental illness is protracted and incurable' and so nothing much can be done about it."

Intriguingly, in common with much of the reforming zeal that arose in other walks of life during the opening months of the Cultural Revolution, Chinese psychiatry appears at this time to have addressed certain real and pressing problems in the care of the mentally ill – in particular, the over-reliance on medication and institutional confinement that was also found in most other parts of the world at that time – and moreover, to have done so in a way that might, if political circumstances had been more favorable, have turned out rather differently. For the first time in China, for example, the non-biological approach of "psychotherapy" (*xinli zhiliao*) began to be used as an alternative therapy within the mental healthcare system. As this document and others show, however, the form of psychotherapy actually used from early 1996 onwards consisted of increasingly intense political indoctrination sessions in which mental patients were exhorted to cure themselves by studying the works of Mao and adopting a "proletarian" political outlook:

> [T]he everyday atmosphere in the sick wards is increasingly
> brisk, lively and dynamic. One mental patient, for example,
> wrote to us after being discharged from hospital: "My stay in
> hospital this time was just like being in a political study school
> – you cured both my physical illness and also my ideological

---

[8] "The struggle...worldview" in Chinese: "*fan youpai, xing-wu mie-zi de douzheng.*" The Anti-Rightist Movement was the Communist Party's first post-1949 campaign of mass repression against Chinese intellectuals. In the course of the campaign, hundreds of thousands of intellectuals were imprisoned or sent into internal exile, often for periods of up to twenty years.

sickness. I want to thank the Party for all the warmth and concern it has shown me.[9]

DOCUMENTS 3-7, taken from a "restricted circulation" medical journal published in China between 1972 and 1978, chart in vivid and painful detail the practical outcome of the quickly thwarted moves to reform Chinese psychiatry in the direction of a more patient-centered approach. They take the form of a crucial debate among several leading Chinese psychiatrists on the question of what constituted the "essential nature of mental illness." By the late 1960s, Mao's insistence upon the Promethean role and virtue of human will and subjective political ideology attained its apotheosis in a corollary belief, on his part, that *incorrect* thinking or mentality was therefore tantamount to a crime against the revolution. This punitive doctrine pervaded all walks of life in China during the Cultural Revolution, but it found especially fertile soil for development within the field of Chinese psychiatry. In the Chinese language, fortuitously or not, the words for "ideology" and "mentality" are one and the same (*sixiang*.) The outcome of all this was that individual mental problems soon came to be seen, in simplistic and reductionist fashion by the ultra-Maoists, as being not merely reflective of, but actually caused by, incorrect or deviant political thinking on the part of the sufferer. Three short extracts from the 1972-78 debate, the conclusion of which marked a fundamental return by the mainstream of Chinese psychiatry toward more internationally accepted standards of psychiatric diagnosis and ethics, should suffice to illustrate its overall contours.

First, let us see the viewpoint that prevailed throughout most of the 1970s. DOCUMENT 3 – "Analysis of a Survey of 250 Cases of Mental Illness" – was published in August 1972 and presented the "model findings" of a wide-ranging psychiatric study carried out by a group of ultra-Maoist civilian and military psychiatrists some months earlier.

---

[9] Elsewhere in the same issue of the psychiatric journal in question, another patient was reported as saying:

> In the past, when the doctor told me that "to cure your sickness you must be guided by correct ideology," I felt quite upset and offended. How could correcting one's ideology ever make one recover from mental illness? Would this not mean that in fact I had an ideological sickness? Now that I've gained an understanding of the dialectical relationship between ideology and illness, however, I know why the medicine I used to take had no effect and I've become confident of being able to cure myself. (*Chinese Journal of Neuropsychiatry*, vol. 10, no.2, (1966), p.114.)

> Under the socialist system, a clash will inevitably develop
> between the concept "public" and [certain people's]
> preoccupation with the concept "private," engendering a
> contradiction within their minds between these two things.
> And unless this contradiction can be correctly resolved, the
> ideological struggle within their minds will intensify and may
> produce partial imbalances in the functioning of their cerebral
> cortexes; so people like this can very easily develop mental
> illnesses... The reason why most patients become mentally ill
> is connected to the class struggle, and the fundamental causal
> factor in the majority of cases is that they still retain a
> bourgeois worldview and methodology...

Some five years later, Jia Rubao, a psychiatrist from Shaanxi Province and
one of those who had participated in the original "250 cases" survey, further
elaborated (in DOCUMENT 6) on the highly influential psychiatric theory that had
emerged from that study:

> The process goes exactly like this: under the socialist system,
> it is impossible for these people to satisfy their selfish desires
> and so the "boil" cannot be lanced; at first, the normal
> thoughts and the pathological thoughts coexist side by side,
> but as the pathological thoughts steadily gain the ascendant in
> their minds, they begin to sing, dance and run around
> aimlessly, tearing off their clothes and going around naked,
> and sometimes injuring or killing people – that is, they
> become mentally ill. We see, therefore, that bourgeois
> worldview and methodology are the fundamental causal
> factors in the emergence of mental illness; indeed this is the
> essential nature of mental illness.

> Some people will ask the question: in capitalist society, then,
> is mental illness more commonly found among the bourgeois
> class? Yes, there are certainly more mentally ill people from
> this class background than elsewhere... [However,] if we use
> class education and political-line education to profoundly re-
> educate the mentally ill in the proletarian worldview...and
> raise their awareness of the class struggle, the struggle over

political line and the need to continue the revolution under the dictatorship of the proletariat...and dig out the roots of mental illness by overthrowing the concept of private ownership and implanting the principle of public ownership...then the overwhelming majority (90 percent) of mentally ill people can be completely cured.

The following intervention (DOCUMENT 7) by a psychiatrist who was himself persecuted during the Cultural Revolution and who is now one of the most respected and influential psychiatrists in China, was made on the eve of Deng Xiaoping's return to national power, at a time when scholars in all fields had begun to receive license from the Communist Party to fundamentally rethink the future policy contours of post-Mao China.

Yang Desen, Hunan Medical College, August 1978:

After the founding of New China, the Party and the People's Government made great efforts to improve the health of the population... [However,] after Lin Biao and, especially, the Gang of Four[10] started to peddle their reactionary political line – a line that was "left" in form but right in essence – the country was plunged into deep disaster. Every aspect of official life in China suffered the noxious consequences of their doctrines, and the damage wrought in the field of psychiatry was certainly no less serious and profound than elsewhere... As a result of all this, in the worst-hit mental hospitals, recovery rates and sickbed rotation rates began to decline and medical staff became so demoralized that they left psychiatry altogether.

Eventually, [the ultraleftists] began claiming that the real reason people became mentally ill was that their heads were filled with an "excess of selfish ideas and personal concerns"

[10] Marshall Lin Biao was Mao's close second-in-command and designated successor until September 1971, when he was said to have tried to defect to the Soviet Union. In what the Chinese government subsequently termed the "Lin Biao Self-Explosion Incident," he died when his aircraft crashed in a remote part of the Mongolian People's Republic, presumably en route to Moscow. The "Gang of Four," arrested in October 1976, a month after Mao's death, consisted of Mao's former close political colleagues Zhang Chunqiao, Yao Wenyuan, Jiang Qing and Wang Hongwen.

and that it was the product of "an extreme development of individualism." Simplistic techniques of ideological re-education then became the principal form of treatment and cure for mental illness in China. Mentally ill people were made to undergo re-education at the hands of the medical staff and ordered to dig out, from within their own minds, the "ideological roots" of their illnesses. In some mental hospitals, patients who uttered [politically] banned thoughts or engaged in banned forms of behavior because of their illnesses were held criminally responsible, and even their families were wrongfully implicated. This conception of mental illness as being an ideological sickness and a disease of the bourgeoisie, the belief that it is a product of the capitalist social system, holds in lofty disdain the sufferings of countless numbers of working-class mentally ill people and has served to consign psychiatry to the distant margins of public health work in our country. Is it not now incumbent upon us, therefore, to expose and criticize to the fullest extent possible all these absurd theories and pernicious policies of the Gang of Four, these perversions of medicine that have inflicted such harm and damage upon the mentally ill and upon the great majority of those working in our profession?

Two years earlier, in August 1976, one month before the death of Mao and at the height of the power of the "Gang of Four," Yang had expressed broadly similar views, albeit in a less adamant and forthright manner.[11] (See DOCUMENT 5.) It would be hard to overstate the degree of personal bravery he showed at that time in frontally challenging the Cultural Revolution orthodoxy whereby all mental illness was said to be caused by politically deviant thinking on the part of the sufferer. As the full exchange of views between Professor Yang and his ultra-Maoist colleagues eloquently shows, the depth and extent of the politicization of Chinese psychiatry that occurred during the Cultural Revolution

---

[11] It is worth noting that even Yang, in his August 1976 intervention in this debate, felt it necessary to state that thoughts and ideas expressed by mentally ill people that had "adverse influence and effects upon society...must not be permitted to spread unchecked or to threaten public order and stability." In his view at that time, those concerned "should be subjected to compulsory treatment and we should reinforce management over them..." (See DOCUMENT 5, below.)

decade went well beyond anything of a similar nature found in the former Soviet Union. According to one of China's leading forensic psychiatrists, for example,

> Political cases...are very seldom mentioned in the literature of other countries. According to a survey done by this author of forensic psychiatric appraisal cases carried out at the Shanghai Municipal Mental Health Center over the period 1970-71, however, political cases accounted for 72.9 percent of the total. This had to do with the particular historical circumstances of that time.[12]

In other words, the numbers of detained political activists sent to institutes for the criminally insane during the Cultural Revolution far exceeded the combined total of psychotic murderers, rapists, arsonists and other violently mentally ill offenders dealt with under China's forensic psychiatric system at that time. And as further official testimony provided below shows, many genuinely mentally ill people were sent to prison or shot as "counterrevolutionaries" in the course of Mao's "revolution to touch men's souls." Any attempt to defend Chinese psychiatry against the current allegations of political abuse on the basis of the acknowledged fact that some psychiatrists were themselves persecuted for upholding ethical standards during the Cultural Revolution must also, unavoidably, take on board the equally significant fact that other psychiatrists were, for whatever reason, active participants in the wholesale ethical abuses of that period.

Over the past two decades, mainly as a result of the courageous stance taken by Yang Desen and other veteran Chinese psychiatrists around the time of Mao's death, the Chinese psychiatric profession has steadily evolved to the point where, nowadays, its theory and practice is in general based on internationally accepted diagnostic and ethical standards. The recent decision of the Chinese Psychiatric Association to remove homosexuality from the country's list of officially recognized mental disorders provides a clear illustration of this trend.[13]

---

[12] Shen Zheng, ed., *Falü Jingshenbingxue* (*Legal Psychiatry*), (Beijing: China University of Law and Politics Publishing House, 1989), p. 314.

[13] As in earlier versions of the American psychiatric profession's *Diagnostic and Statistical Manual* (DSM), the residual category of disorders caused by lack of self-acceptance on the part of homosexuals has still been retained in China.

DOCUMENTS 8-11: The Deng Xiaoping and Jiang Zemin Eras

Where Chinese forensic psychiatry was concerned, however, the deeper conceptual and institutional roots of the late-Maoist psychiatric orthodoxy that equated mental illness with political deviancy survived substantially intact. At best, it underwent what can be termed a "nuanced reversal": Whereas, during the Cultural Revolution decade, more or less *all* mentally ill people were seen as being that way because of their "bourgeois ideological defects", from the late 1970s onwards the view became that *some* people who displayed these same ideological defects (namely a subgroup of political and religious dissidents) held the offending views in question *because they were mentally ill.*

This revised theory, entailing a return to the classic "hyperdiagnosis" (or politically-inspired overdiagnosis of mental illness) model found in Soviet psychiatry, persisted in China during the 1980s and then steadily declined in influence during most of the 1990s, in line with the sharp fall in the numbers of "counterrevolutionary offenders" arrested in China at that time. But the basic doctrine remained intact within the forensic branch of Chinese psychiatry, and since the start of the campaign against Falun Gong in mid-1999, it has been pressed back into widespread service by the Chinese police and their forensic psychiatrist colleagues. (We shall consider the Falun Gong caseload in more detail shortly.)

DOCUMENT 8 is the most detailed retrospective survey so far published in China on the question of the nature and main targets of forensic psychiatric appraisals work carried out across the country from the 1950s to the late 1980s. According to its author, Jia Yicheng, who is currently China's senior authority on such matters, the average incidence of "political cases" dealt with under the system throughout this four-decade period was more than 20 percent of the total criminal psychiatric caseload. Jia's commentary on this state of affairs also provides a useful summary of the broader historical trend:

> As can be seen from the statistical data provided in the twelve articles [under study], altogether 1,621 (or 21.05 percent) of the 7,699 criminal cases under examination involved reactionary or counterrevolutionary speech or action (*fandong huo fan'geming yan-xing*), placing this category in a high second position [after murder: 23.03 percent] on the overall statistical list of dangerous behaviors. However, when viewed from a periodic perspective, a very clear distinction emerges. Six of the articles contained statistical data on appraisals carried out during the post-Cultural Revolution period of

1981-86, and among the 2,019 criminal defendants who were appraised during this period, only 59 (or 3.12 percent) had engaged in counterrevolutionary speech or action. The other six articles contained statistical data from the period beginning in the 1950s and ending in 1976, and among the 5,680 criminal defendants appraised during this period, the relevant figure was 1,562 persons, or as much as 27.5 percent. This was clearly a product of the Cultural Revolution period and of the ultraleftist ideological trend that preceded it.

As the statement by Jia Yicheng presented at the beginning of this report vividly shows, he was acknowledging by 1998 that these cases were of a "similar" politically abusive nature as those that used to occur in the Soviet Union. It is important to note, however, that Jia's figure of 3.12 percent for "political cases" during the early to mid-1980s was substantially lower than the average incidence of such cases (10–15 percent) found in numerous local forensic psychiatric studies carried out during the 1980s as a whole by other researchers. And crucially, it was only with the sharp percentage reduction in such cases that occurred in the early 1990s, to a level of between 1 and several percent, that China's level of political psychiatric abuse began, finally, to fall to approximately the same level as that found at the height of similar phenomena in the Soviet Union during the 1960s and 1970s. Hitherto, China's incidence rates for "political cases" appear to have been much higher than those found under Soviet psychiatry. Equally important, moreover, with the current psychiatric detention of Falun Gong protestors, the incidence curve in China has again started to move upwards.

In DOCUMENT 9, an article published in a Shanghai psychiatric journal in 1996, we are given a rare glimpse into the workings of China's police-run network of institutes for the criminally insane, the so-called Ankang hospitals, which were first set up in 1987 and of which there are so far twenty around the country. According to the authors, who worked at the Hangzhou city facility, "Ankang hospitals...are meant to be specialized hospitals that serve the goals of public order by taking in and treating mentally ill people who create disastrous incidents of various kinds. As the Ministry of Public Security calculated in 1993, there are approximately 12 million severely mentally ill people in China, more than 1.3 million of whom pose a serious danger to public order; it is therefore essential that every province in China should establish its own Ankang hospital." As other documents discussed in the Columbia Journal article presented below show, alleged mentally ill political dissidents figure prominently on the authorities' target list of those who "create disastrous incidents" and who must therefore, for the protection of society, be incarcerated in Ankang facilities. The article as a whole paints a depressing picture of conditions within the Ankang hospital system as of early 1996: a very high patient-to-doctor and nurse ratio, severe underfunding by the government, and serious lack of capacity leading to a dense overcrowding of inmates. This scenario would be broadly familiar to those working in high-security institutes for the criminally insane in most countries, but in China's case it serves to dramatize the plight of the peaceful and non-violent dissidents and religious nonconformists who end up being confined in such conditions alongside genuinely dangerous psychotic offenders.

The official psychiatric literature is also quite specific in noting that persons arrested for dissident activities who are then found non-prosecutable or not guilty by reason of insanity are, in most cases, sent for involuntary and indefinite psychiatric committal – either in an Ankang hospital or (in the many areas of China which do not yet have this kind of specialized police-run facility) the closed wards of general mental hospitals. For example, according to DOCUMENT 10 – "An Analysis of Forty-One Mentally Ill People Involved in Cases of a Political Nature,"

> Instances whereby mental illness sufferers, owing to the severe weakening or outright loss of their powers of recognition and control, become involved in cases of a political nature are by no means rare. After committing these crimes, once ascertained in the course of forensic-psychiatric evaluation as being not legally responsible for their actions, the majority of such people are sent to Ankang hospitals. During the period 1978-89, the Hangzhou Ankang hospital admitted 41 patients of this kind, accounting for 7.8 percent of all admissions. The largest numbers were admitted in 1978 and 1989, when they accounted for 17.1 percent and 14.6 percent of total admissions respectively – markedly higher than in other years...

As the authors of this article themselves obliquely indicate, the reason why so many "political case" admissions took place in 1978 and 1989 was that the former was the year of the Democracy Wall movement (the first phase of China's modern dissident/human rights movement) and the latter was the year of the Tiananmen Square pro-democracy movement. The article continued,

According to reports in the Chinese literature, the proportion
of mentally ill persons subjected to expert judicial appraisal
who have committed political offenses is between 15.7 percent
and 20.5 percent; this is second only to cases of murder and
injury, although there has been a marked decrease in such
cases since the 1980s. The majority of those in the case group
had schizophrenia, but unlike the situation in other kinds of
criminal cases, they were all suffering from the paranoid
variety. This shows that paranoid schizophrenics tend to
commit "anti-government" activities much more readily than
those suffering from other variants of the disease, probably as
a result of their delusions of persecution, relational delusions,
and delusions of grandeur, as well as their impaired thought
processes.

Literally dozens of similarly specific references to "political case"
percentages among forensic psychiatric sample groups in China appear
throughout the professional literature. Virtually all of the leading specialist
authorities in the field have written about it at length over the past twenty years.
As we also learn in DOCUMENT 10, the most frequent diagnosis made by police
psychiatrists in this context is of either "schizophrenia" or "paranoid psychosis"
leading to the following kinds of "crimes" by the alleged sufferers: "sending
reactionary letters," "writing reactionary slogans," "petitioning and litigating,"
"shouting reactionary slogans" and "spreading rumors to delude the masses."
And as the authors conclude, "Cases of political crime created by the mentally
ill usually exert a highly negative influence in society and have extensive
ramifications. They take up large amounts of human and material [police]
resources and pose a definite disruptive threat to the normal functioning of state
offices and to the political stability of the country."

DOCUMENT 11, a chapter taken from a major two-volume study on mental
illness and crime published in August 2000 and written by a law researcher at
the Chinese Academy of Social Sciences, represents the current "state of the art"
thinking within Chinese forensic psychiatry on the question of "political crimes"
committed by alleged mentally ill dissidents. Titled "On Negative Political
Speech and Action," the chapter begins by stating,

Acts that endanger the nation and threaten the social system
can, when severe in nature, constitute crimes. Offenses of this
type are customarily referred to as political crimes... Mentally
ill people, owing to the pathological factors that beset them,

may also engage in behavior that endangers the state and the
social system, and the most commonly seen forms of such
behavior are the writing of banners, distributing leaflets and
flyers, sending letters, making speeches, and shouting out
slogans... [However,] to describe [this] as
"counterrevolutionary behavior" or as "behavior that
endangers state security" would obviously [since those
concerned are mentally ill] be "inappropriate." To call it
"reactionary behavior" would also not be good, since the term
"reactionary" has excessively vague connotations. In the end,
this writer has decided to use the term "negative political
speech and action" [to denote such behavior].

So far so good: the author appears to be making an effort to "downgrade"
the seriousness of the political offenses committed by dissidents in cases where
they are perceived by the authorities to be suffering from mental illness.
However, while he brings to his topic a degree of analytical sophistication going
well beyond that found in most other Chinese forensic-psychiatric discussions of
this question, he remains severely hampered in this endeavor by the awkward
fact that all the dissident activities in question are still held under China's
criminal law to constitute the most serious possible forms of crime. Hence, his
adoption of the slightly more liberal and user-friendly rubric of "negative
political speech and action" in place of the formerly prevalent terms
"reactionary" and "counterrevolutionary" to denote such activities turns out to
have no practical legal consequences for the detainees concerned: they must still
be sent either to institutes for the criminally insane or to locked wards in general
psychiatric hospitals.

One of the more interesting aspects of DOCUMENT 11 is the author's
discussion of the seemingly large subgroup of such "offenders" whom we earlier
called the "pseudo-counterrevolutionaries": people who were driven insane by
China's past campaigns of political persecution and whose psychiatric
symptoms have taken the form of "reactionary" or "counterrevolutionary"
thoughts, speech and behavior. (Since the late 1950s, according to the official
psychiatric literature, these symptoms have consisted primarily of political
"ravings" against Mao, the Cultural Revolution and the current Chinese
leadership.) There is, nonetheless, a strongly oxymoronic quality to his account
of this topic.

For example, if those who become mentally abnormal as a
result of suffering political persecution then develop delusions
of persecution, the content of these delusions may have a
negative political coloration, and such people may therefore
develop hostile feelings toward the political environment.
However, the fact that such a history existed before the mental
illness arose by no means implies that the negative political
speech and action expressed by the mentally ill person
concerned is necessarily rational in nature. For sufferers of
this kind, the influence of the pre-illness history occurs at the
unconscious level.

In other words, even though "sufferers" of this type were in fact the targets
of severe political persecution in the past, their resultant long-term feelings of
persecution are still, in the author's view, to be attributed to mental illness
("unconscious delusions" against the Party) rather than to any rational or
accurate subjective construal of their past traumatic experiences. Any hapless
bona fide dissident who had encountered previous episodes of official
persecution on ideological grounds would be hard-pressed indeed to argue that
he or she was not, contrary to the official perception, "pathologically deluded"
in the present. Considerable caution is therefore called for when evaluating even
this subgroup of what the authorities colloquially term "political lunacy"
(*zhengzhi fengzi*) cases in China today.

As the author of DOCUMENT 11 further explains,

Among the various categories of delusion, the ones that most
readily give rise to negative political speech and action are
delusions of persecution and delusions of grandeur. If the
identity of the persecutor that is fabricated [in the mind of the
detainee] by virtue of the delusions of persecution happens to
be either the ruling political party, the state institutions, or
individual members of the leadership, then inevitably the
sufferer will develop feelings of hostility and over-vigilance
toward the ruling political party, the state institutions or
individual leaders, and they may then start "exposing,"
"denouncing" and "condemning" the latter's various
"conspiracies" and "crimes." In general, the targets of these
delusions of persecution are limited to certain specific
individuals, but in some cases the scope of hostility may
become constantly amplified in the sufferer's mind,

progressing from one individual to a number of different
people, and then onward to include a whole organization, the
government, or even the whole of society.

Forensic psychiatrists in most developed countries are familiar with a
specific subcategory of violent criminal offenders who commit their crimes
because they suffer from systematic paranoid delusions broadly related to
politics: they may believe, for example, that the Queen of England or the
President of the United States is trying to persecute and punish them, or (most
commonly in the case of schizophrenics) that they have had electronic bugging
devices implanted in their brains by the security services; they then feel
compelled to fight back, sometimes in a violent and indiscriminate manner.

The crucial distinction in China's case, however, is that in the great
majority of officially reported cases no internationally recognized criminal
offense has taken place, and the alleged mentally ill detainees in question are
found criminally insane solely on account of their peacefully expressed "anti-
government" thoughts and viewpoints. Again, if genuinely mentally ill, such
people should in all cases be afforded humane and appropriate medical care in a
non-coercive psychiatric setting. They should not be incarcerated in high-
security mental institutions simply because their political or religious views
happened to upset the Chinese Communist Party. Finally, the author poignantly
cites yet another subcategory of this type: "In the case of those suffering from
depressive illness who engage in negative political speech and action,
sometimes their aim in doing so is to commit an indirect form of suicide (self-
punishment.)" This formulation speaks volumes as to the wider state of freedom
of political thought and expression in China today.

DOCUMENTS 12 and 13: The Anti-Falun Gong Crackdown

These two documents shed important light on the situation of detained
Falun Gong practitioners who have been forcibly confined to mental institutions
since the start of the government's crackdown against this unorthodox
traditional spiritual sect in July 1999. The first document discusses the mental
condition, first discovered by Chinese psychiatrists in the early 1980s and later
(in 1989) incorporated as a "culture bound disorder" into the Chinese
Classification of Mental Disorders, known as "qigong-induced or qigong-related
mental disorder." Qigong is a traditional Chinese form of mind-body exercises
that shares certain features of yoga, meditation and other non-Western self-
cultivation practices; according to Chinese psychiatry, if practiced improperly or
too intensively, it can produce, alongside its many acknowledged benefits, a

series of mental imbalances ranging from minor cognitive disorders to occasionally more serious, psychosis-like conditions. Since all Falun Gong followers practice a variant form of qigong, it was previously believed that this particular diagnosis served as the Chinese authorities' main medical justification for psychiatrically detaining large numbers of Falun Gong activists. A number of Western commentators have even argued that no unethical misuse of psychiatry or other human rights abuse has been involved in these cases because those concerned probably were suffering from qigong-related mental disorders.[14]

In fact, psychiatric studies published in China over the past year or so have contradicted this assumption by stating that the diagnosis of qigong-related mental illness is not to be used in the case of Falun Gong detainees, since (according to DOCUMENT 13), "Falun Gong is entirely different from ordinary body cultivation techniques, and no clear definition of the type of mental disorder that it produces can be found within China's currently used body of diagnostic criteria for mental illness." Instead, the entirely new diagnostic label of "evil cult-induced mental disorder" (*xiejiao suo zhi jingshen zhang'ai*) has now been coined by Chinese psychiatry, for exclusive use against the Falun Gong and any other unorthodox spiritual movements in China that happen to have been banned by the Communist Party and government.

In effect, the legal authorities' post-Mao formulation that "some dissidents commit political crimes because they are mentally ill" has now been supplemented by the issuance of a Chinese government "health warning" to the public: "Spiritual or religious beliefs banned on political grounds can drive people mad." The close similarity between this and the Cultural Revolution doctrine that mental illness is caused by politically deviant thinking should be readily apparent.

Falun Gong "psychopathology" – the official version

Four specific cases are presented in DOCUMENT 13 – "A First Look at the Forensic Psychiatric Evaluation of Falun Gong Cases" – and each illuminates in different ways the politically persecutory essence of this new forensic diagnosis. Since the Falun Gong caseload represents the most recent and conspicuously serious phase in China's decades-long history of the misuse of psychiatry as a tool of political repression, and since so much controversy currently surrounds

---

[14] See, for example, Arthur Kleinman and Sing Lee, "Psychiatry in its Political and Professional Contexts: A Response to Robin Munro," *Journal of the American Academy of Psychiatry and the Law*, vol. 30, no.1 (2002), pp.120-125. See also Robin Munro, "On the Psychiatric Abuse of Falun Gong and Other Dissenters in China: A Reply to Stone, Hickling, Kleinman and Lee," *Journal of the American Academy of Psychiatry and the Law*, vol. 30, no.2 (2002), pp.266-274.

this particular group of detainees, it is well worth examining these four cases in some detail.

The first case discussed concerns a 45-year-old woman who (according to the two psychiatrists who wrote the article) "went to Beijing to petition the authorities and was then placed under criminal detention, but still she persisted in practicing Falun Gong." In other words, the reason for her arrest was not that her mental condition had posed any immediate physical or psychological danger to herself or to anyone else, but rather that she had been brave or foolhardy enough to openly express her peaceful opposition to the government's relentless campaign of suppression. The forensic examiners' conclusion was: "Mental disorder caused by practicing an evil cult; no capacity to bear legal responsibility [for her crimes]; recommend medical treatment." The mental symptoms cited by the examiners to justify this conclusion consisted almost entirely of a list of the patient's Falun Gong-inspired spiritual beliefs. (While some of these admittedly would strike a Western observer as being highly unusual, it is surely not the job of psychiatrists to pass judgment on their patients' spiritual or religious convictions.) The remaining "symptoms" cited by the forensic examiners included: "flagrantly telling everyone how much she was benefiting from her practice of Falun Gong" and "refusing to be dissuaded from her beliefs and continuing to gather people to practice Falun Gong...even after the government declared it to be an evil cult."

The second case concerns a 62-year-old man who, after suffering from insomnia for a long time, took up Falun Gong in 1995. According to the forensic case report,

> He soon became solitary and untalkative, and he began giving people valuable presents for no reason. He always ate less than other people and would buy the cheapest of foods, to the point even of buying and taking home items that others had turned down. He said that [this was because] he wanted to be a genuinely "truthful, compassionate and forbearing" person.[15]

There was nothing in the case account that would plausibly indicate that the detainee posed any psychiatrically related danger to himself, others or society. Again, the sole reason for this person's arrest was that, according to the forensic report, "After the government declared Falun Gong to be an evil cult, he not only ignored all efforts to dissuade him from continuing to practice Falun

---

[15] "*zhen shan ren*": the three cardinal teachings of Falun Gong.

Gong, but also joined with other practitioners in traveling to Beijing to 'uphold the dharma' on behalf of Falun Gong." It is clear from the final diagnosis – "mental disorder caused by practicing an evil cult; should bear partial legal responsibility for his crimes" – that the examining psychiatrists partially acknowledged that the "danger" he posed was basically unrelated to his alleged mental condition; however, the immediate consequence of the detainee's being found only "half mad" was that, in their view, he must face criminal trial for his non-violent beliefs.

Here we see the ethical dilemma faced by Chinese psychiatrists in all such cases: had they found, as international standards require, that the patient was basically quite sane, he would certainly have been sent to prison for his "crime" of peacefully demonstrating in Beijing. A finding of complete insanity would have been ethically absurd in this case, so they instead opted for the middle course. While we are not told about the final disposition of this case, being set free was certainly not an option: the detainee would either have received a reduced prison sentence or, perhaps more likely, have been sent for some form of custodial psychiatric care.[16]

The third case concerns a young male worker and Falun Gong practitioner who appears to have been genuinely mentally ill: said by the forensic examiners to have already been suffering from symptoms of schizophrenia prior to taking up Falun Gong, he claimed that he "could tell what was going on in people's minds without the use of any instruments of detection; and that his soul had been fully realized and he was able to maintain frequent contact with aliens from outer space." The examining psychiatrists' verdict was: "[S]chizophrenia; behavior and actions completely dominated by pathological factors, and hence no capacity to bear legal responsibility." From the case details supplied, this forensic conclusion seems to be an accurate and ethically appropriate one. But we still need to look further. Why was the person arrested? It was because, once again, he had gone to Beijing to petition peacefully against the crackdown on Falun Gong – "thereby exerting an extremely bad influence in society" – and not because his schizophrenic symptoms or behavior had posed any perceptible threat to public safety. Having been accused of this grave "national security" offense, the inevitable outcome of the forensic diagnosis was that he would be sent to a custodial facility for criminal offenders (either the locked ward of a regular mental hospital or an Ankang facility – most parts of China do not yet

---

[16] Purists might argue that the examining psychiatrists' only ethically correct course of action in this case would have been to inform the police: this man is both sane and also innocent of any crime; in reality, though, the psychiatrists would probably have suffered harsh retribution from the political authorities had they dared to suggest any such thing.

have the latter, which appears to be why most Falun Gong psychiatric detainees have ended up in the former).

Perhaps the greatest irony here is that, as most expert outside observers acknowledge, China's national psychiatric care system is so severely under-funded that the great majority of mentally ill people, even schizophrenia sufferers, currently receive no medical care, institutional or otherwise. The schizophrenic worker discussed above, in common with countless other Falun Gong practitioners suffering from other medical ailments for which they simply cannot afford to be treated under China's increasingly expensive government-run healthcare system, was recommended to join the Falun Gong because it claims dramatically to improve practitioners' health.[17] Is it ethically appropriate that extremely scarce psychiatric resources should be allocated in such a way that a schizophrenic posing no evident threat to society, and who would otherwise probably have gone totally untreated, is sent by the police for custodial medical care of a kind which, according to all accounts so far provided by Falun Gong psychiatric detainees, amounts to an extrajudicial form of physical and psychological punishment?[18]

The final case illustrates yet another permutation of the whole sorry business. It concerns a 41-year-old female government official who began practicing Falun Gong in 1996 and then went on to become a leader and organizer of the movement in her area of residence. According to the forensic report issued after her arrest, "Consciousness clear and alert; thinking logical and well-ordered...apart from being emotionally over-excited, she showed no signs of hallucination, delusions or other conspicuous mental abnormalities. Forensic finding: not mentally ill; should be held legally responsible for her crimes." On the face of it, no ethical abuse was involved in this case because the

---

[17] Incidentally, several wide-ranging medical surveys conducted by numerous top Chinese physicians prior to the July 1999 crackdown on Falun Gong concluded that, in the case of most common illnesses, it actually does so; schizophrenia, of course, is quite another matter, but it should also be noted that this particular detainee apparently had the condition well before taking up Falun Gong. For details of two of the pre-crackdown medical surveys, see below, Note 267.

[18] On a related point, several Western commentators offer an alternative "scarce resources" argument against the political abuse allegations. They consider it to be highly improbable that the Chinese authorities would send mentally normal dissident offenders for custodial psychiatric care, when prison is a much cheaper and more obvious option. In fact, it costs the government a substantial amount nowadays to house a convicted prisoner, whereas Falun Gong and other dissenting involuntary inmates of psychiatric institutions are usually billed, directly or through their families, for all hospitalization and treatment charges.

examinee was found to be mentally normal and hence no psychiatric treatment was ordered. However, the key issue highlighted here concerns Chinese forensic examiners' attitude toward the question of a detainee's "legal responsibility" for peaceful dissident offenses. Had the psychiatrists involved in the examination of this and other similar cases simply confined their conclusions to the medical side of things, then the issue of psychiatric abuse would not have arisen and it would have been just another case of political persecution under the Chinese criminal justice system. But no, the examining psychiatrists first confirm that the only reason for the female Falun Gong practitioner being placed under police arrest was that, "rejecting all efforts to persuade and educate her away from the cult, she continued to organize groups of practitioners to carry out petitioning activities on its behalf." They then, in the medical diagnostic portion of their report, saw fit to make the wholly political comment and judgment: "she defended with extreme vigor the various advantages of practicing Falun Gong, and in so doing slandered and vilified [China's] present social realities." In other words, the psychiatrists appear to have felt under intense political pressure to endorse – enthusiastically and without reservation – the spurious criminal charge that had been laid against the detainee. Either that, or they did so freely and willingly.

As if to underscore this same point, the authors of this report on the four Falun Gong cases conclude by saying: "If we exercise comprehensive judgment, it is usually not difficult to make a diagnosis of evil cult-induced mental disorder. At the same time, [recently established criteria] will help us to identify and maintain our guard against any die-hard Falun Gong elements who might try to feign mental illness as a way of escaping legal punishment for their crimes." So there we have it: the examining psychiatrists evidently saw it as being one of their most pressing concerns to help weed out, on the government's behalf, any Falun Gong detainee who might deviously wish to pretend to be mad as a means of avoiding stern punishment for what, by international standards, was the entirely non-criminal act of belonging to an unorthodox spiritual group. It is in cases like this that one sees perhaps the most striking evidence of complicity and collaboration by Chinese psychiatrists in the Chinese government's continuing repression of peaceful political and religious belief.

A Call to the World Psychiatric Community

As the foregoing discussion has sought to explain, China's forensic psychiatrists unavoidably still find themselves, wherever political dissident cases or ones involving Falun Gong detainees and the like are concerned, at the ethically invidious intersection of modern medical principles and an unreconstructed criminal justice system whose overriding concern remains the arbitrary suppression of dissent. We do not yet know how many, or even what general proportion of, Chinese psychiatrists are directly involved in these ethically abusive practices, but it seems clear that they form a relatively small minority within the profession as a whole.[19] Furthermore, it is possible that many of the Chinese psychiatrists who have written extensively on the topic of "political cases" dealt with in the forensic domain since the early 1980s have been motivated to do so by a desire to bring the existence of this still sizeable ethical problem to a wider domestic, and possibly also international, audience. If so, the absence of overt value judgments in most of their reports would mirror their need to protect themselves against charges of disloyalty to the Party.

From all of this, we can begin to discern the outlines of an appropriate response by the international psychiatric community to the problem of politically abusive psychiatry in China: on the one hand, to stand in firm solidarity with the ethically sound mainstream of the Chinese psychiatric profession, while recognizing that current political conditions in China make it largely impossible for psychiatrists there, individually or collectively, to speak out openly themselves against these abuses; and on the other hand, to work in a targeted manner, through the World Psychiatric Association and its national member associations, to put pressure upon the Chinese authorities to end the political misuse of psychiatry within the forensic evaluations domain, the Ankang police custodial network, and the relatively few corners of the general psychiatric system where it still persists.[20]

At their annual general meeting in July 2001, the members of the Royal College of Psychiatrists overwhelmingly passed the following resolution on the China question:[21]

> Bearing in mind the available evidence that political dissidents in The People's Republic of China (PRC) are being systematically detained in psychiatric hospitals, we propose

---

[19] There are still relatively few full-time forensic psychiatrists in China; probably a majority of the forensic cases are examined and dealt with by general psychiatrists who work part-time for the police.

[20] As indicated earlier, it is likely that only a relatively small minority of Chinese psychiatrists are involved in political abuses of the profession. However, it is vital to remember that this was also the case in the former Soviet Union; in both countries, political and religious dissidents have accounted, naturally enough, for only a small part of the overall psychiatric caseloads.

[21] Annual General Meeting of the Royal College of Psychiatrists, London, July 11, 2001; in the final vote on the China resolution, there were two abstentions and no votes against.

that the Royal College of Psychiatrists takes the following action:

1) to join with the World Psychiatric Association (WPA) to arrange a fact-finding visit to the PRC;
2) if this visit and other evidence confirm political abuse of psychiatry, to ask the WPA to reconsider the constituent membership of the Chinese Society of Psychiatrists;
3) to work with the WPA to provide support for those Chinese psychiatrists who are committed to ethical and evidence-based practice.

It should be stressed that, under the terms of the WPA's 1996 Madrid Declaration, the need to reconsider China's constituent membership of the WPA would follow automatically from any finding of systematic political abuse of psychiatry in China, so the inclusion of point 2), above, in no way served to prejudge the issue. Rather, the attention of the world psychiatric community should presently be focused on the other two proposals: that a WPA-led fact-finding mission be undertaken to establish the veracity or otherwise of the allegations, and that meanwhile the hand of professional friendship and support be extended to all Chinese psychiatrists not directly involved in the abuses concerned. This carefully worded resolution from the Royal College expresses, we believe, priorities that should now be weighed and acted upon by psychiatrists everywhere.

Recommendations

To the Chinese Government:

- The Chinese government should permit an international investigative mission led by the World Psychiatric Association (WPA) and composed of acknowledged international experts in the fields of general and forensic psychiatry, criminal law and human rights to visit China, hold workshops and seminars, carry out independent and confidential medical evaluations of a representative selection of persons, visit secure psychiatric detention and treatment facilities where political or religious dissidents are believed to be held, and publish a report on their findings and recommendations. In addition, international human rights groups and concerned medical organizations other than the WPA should be allowed freely to investigate the alleged abuses.

- The Chinese government should conduct a systematic review of the country's existing national and local-level legislation and administrative regulations governing forensic psychiatric assessment, interactions between police and prosecution agencies and the psychiatrists, and psychiatric custody of persons determined to be dangerously mentally ill. Aside from clarifying these procedures and assuring the professional independence of psychiatrists, the government should remove all provisions stating or implying that dissident or nonconformist political or religious beliefs provide a medically or legally acceptable basis for the diagnosis of severe or dangerous mental illness.

- The Chinese legislature should promptly formulate and enact the long-delayed Mental Health Law of the People's Republic of China, in such a form as to incorporate fully the minimum international provisions for safeguarding the rights and interests of involuntary mental patients, as laid down by the WPA and the U.N. and also in the World Health Organization's 1996 document, "Mental Health Care Law: Ten Basic Principles." The Mental Health Law should contain specific provisions stating unequivocally that deviation from, or inability to conform to, the country's prevailing political or religious orthodoxies as upheld by the Chinese government and Communist Party does not provide a medically or legally acceptable basis for the diagnosis of mental illness, psychiatric custody, or involuntary treatment.

26

- A coordinated campaign should be carried out throughout China's police and prosecutorial and court system, to inform law-enforcement and judicial officers at all levels that previous policies or practices, whether formal or ad hoc in nature, that either permitted or encouraged involuntary psychiatric examination or custody of persons holding peaceful dissident or religious views will no longer be officially tolerated or condoned. Chinese translations of both the WPA's Madrid Declaration and the U.N.'s 1991 Principles should be widely disseminated within the police and judicial systems.

- The Chinese judicial authorities should conduct a comprehensive nationwide review of all cases in which citizens have been diagnosed as severely mentally ill and then psychiatrically detained mainly or solely on account of their non-violent political or religious viewpoints or activities. All such persons should be relieved of any outstanding criminal charges or convictions and should be promptly released from psychiatric or police custody. Any such persons found, after fresh medical examination, to be suffering from genuine mental illness should be afforded humane and appropriate medical care in a non-forensic setting and (unless posing a clear and verifiable danger to themselves or others) on a voluntary basis.

- The Chinese government should extensively revise the provisions of the Criminal Law concerning offenses of "endangering state security," in such a way that they no longer provide a basis for the criminalization of political or religious freedom of expression, or can otherwise be used as a means of punishing those who engage in peaceful acts of public protest, assembly or demonstration or who attempt to form non-violent dissident groups of various kinds.

To the Chinese Psychiatric and Mental Healthcare Community:

- Acknowledging that most Chinese psychiatrists are not involved or complicit in the abuses described in this report: China's mental healthcare professionals should resist any pressure or inducement from the country's law-enforcement and judicial agencies to become personally involved in the legal handling or psychiatric assessment of persons detained by the police solely or mainly on account of their peaceful and non-violent political or religious views or activities.

Chinese psychiatrists should decline to make diagnoses of severe mental illness on the above-mentioned grounds, whether asked by the authorities to do so in a formal forensic appraisals setting or in the context of a regular psychiatric treatment facility. Where direct conflicts of interest are encountered between their ethical obligations and their professional duty to examine police detainees, they should refuse to participate. They should also refrain from commenting on the specific criminal charges laid by the police, in cases where these clearly conflict with internationally agreed standards of human rights and due process.

- Those working either as fulltime police psychiatrists or as part-time forensic consultants to the police, prosecutorial and judicial agencies in China should take the lead in repudiating past abuses within their sphere of professional competence and in systematically removing the theoretical, medical-diagnostic and treatment bases for any continuance of such practices in the future. This should include an extensive revision of the country's existing training and reference literature in the field of forensic psychiatry, as well as the long-term vocational retraining of those already employed in this field.

- In the specific case of psychiatrically detained Falun Gong activists who have been "unofficially" handled by the police authorities on a non-forensic track and within the general psychiatric care domain, general psychiatrists who are called upon by the police to diagnose such cases should decline to do so on the grounds that the requisite legal process for criminal psychiatric committal has not been observed.

- Recognizing the Chinese Psychiatric Association's recent decision to remove homosexuality from the Chinese Classification of Mental Disorders (CCMD-III), we call upon the Chinese psychiatric community to further improve its diagnostic and treatment regime by supplementing CCMD-III with a specific provision stating that a person's disagreement with, deviation from, or inability to conform to the country's currently prevailing political, religious or other ideological orthodoxies should never be viewed as grounds for making a diagnosis of severe mental illness.

- The Chinese Psychiatric Association (a constituent body of the Chinese Medical Association) should invite the World Psychiatric Association, through its Review Committee and other relevant bodies, to provide professional assistance and advice aimed at furthering and enhancing its own efforts to systematically remove all elements of politically motivated psychiatric abuse from within its professional ranks. The assistance of the WHO's Mental Health Division in this process would also be useful.

To the International Psychiatric Community:

- At its forthcoming world congress in Yokohama, Japan, in August 2002, the World Psychiatric Association should seriously and systematically address the issue of political psychiatric abuse in the People's Republic of China. Its national constituent bodies should debate and vote on a formal resolution at Yokohama expressing the WPA's concern over this issue, calling upon the Chinese government to allow a WPA-led international psychiatric investigative mission to visit China, and declaring that steps will be taken, as mandated under the terms of the Madrid Declaration, to expel the Chinese Psychiatric Association from the WPA should the Chinese government fail to cooperate fully in the WPA's attempts to investigate the alleged abuses or if the authorities then fail to adopt effective remedies.

- National psychiatric associations throughout the world should continue to develop and expand their professional contacts and exchanges with Chinese psychiatrists and Chinese mental health facilities of all kinds. While expressing their firm solidarity with the ethically minded mainstream of contemporary Chinese psychiatry, national psychiatric bodies should also use all such bilateral events and exchanges as a forum for raising clearly with their Chinese counterparts their deep concern over the Chinese authorities' continued misuse of psychiatry as a means of dealing with certain categories of peaceful political or religious dissidents.

To Other Governments and International Bodies:

- In human-rights dialogues with the Chinese government, governments should discuss the issue of political psychiatric abuse in China. Where known, the names of individual Chinese political or religious dissidents currently being detained in psychiatric asylums in China should be presented to the Chinese side and requests made for clarification of their status and for their release.

- Both the U.N. Special Rapporteur on Torture and the U.N. Working Group on Arbitrary Detentions should take up the issue of political psychiatric abuse in China.

- The U.N. Sub-Commission on Prevention of Discrimination and Protection of Minorities should begin compiling and studying the available evidence of political psychiatric abuse in China, with a view to preparing a detailed report and set of practical recommendations aimed at bringing Chinese government practice into conformity with established U.N. rules and guidelines in the field of compulsory psychiatric detention and the rights of the mentally ill.

The Soviet Case: Prelude to a Global Consensus on Psychiatry and Human Rights[22]

When in 1971 the Soviet dissident Vladimir Bukovsky sent his first documentation of several prominent Soviet psychiatric-abuse cases to the World Psychiatric Association (WPA), the Soviet delegation threatened to withdraw from the international body, and the notion that this would hurt the WPA instead of the Soviets themselves was so strong that the issue was shelved. Bukovsky was subsequently sentenced to twelve years' imprisonment, but a Pandora's box had now been opened, and in the next twenty years the attitude of world psychiatry towards the problem of political psychiatric abuse would change almost 180 degrees. Professional bodies such as the WPA, which had initially strongly resisted getting involved in the issue, would be triggered into adopting firm, clear ethical codes and setting up investigative bodies that would ensure that these new codes of conduct would be adhered to and any violators sanctioned.

During the six years between Bukovsky's revelations and the next WPA congress in Honolulu, increasing numbers of well-documented cases reached the West and international protests started to mount. The first committee against the political abuse of psychiatry was founded in 1974 in Geneva, lending the Geneva Initiative on Psychiatry its current name. National psychiatric associations became active, in particular the British Royal College of Psychiatrists and the American Psychiatric Association, and when the next World Congress convened in Honolulu in 1977, the question of Soviet political psychiatric abuses could not be kept off the agenda. This congress led not only to the first official international condemnation of those abuses, but also to the Declaration of Honolulu, a document that for the first time set forth a set of basic ethical standards guiding the work of psychiatrists everywhere. Soviet psychiatric abuse had begun to have an impact reaching far beyond the issue itself.

After Honolulu, pressure on the Soviets continued to mount, led by rights groups and psychiatrists. The campaign had two main goals: to pressure the Soviet authorities to a point where they would decide that it would be more profitable to end the abuses and send political prisoners only to labor camps, and to mobilize world psychiatry to take a stand against such abuses in general and to take measures to prevent them from occurring elsewhere. The latter goal

---

[22] This account of the Soviet-era psychiatric abuses was written by Robert van Voren, secretary general of the Geneva Initiative on Psychiatry.

proved to be quite difficult, as many psychiatrists felt that the issue was a "political" rather than an ethical one, and it was several years before the realization sank in that the campaign against politically abusive psychiatry in the Soviet Union was in fact aimed at taking politics out of psychiatry, rather than at bringing it in. In the corridors of power in Moscow, however, this campaign of public pressure worked quite well. Those hospitalized by the police were increasingly less-prominent political prisoners, and soon after international campaigns began on particular cases, those concerned were either released or moved to "normal" places of detention. In 1982, facing imminent expulsion from the WPA, the Soviets withdrew voluntarily from the world body, and the following year a resolution was adopted at the WPA's World Congress in Vienna placing strict conditions on their return.

Over the next six years, the Soviet authorities tried to find a compromise position between campaigning for a return to the WPA – showing that they saw their forced departure as a loss of face – and continuing the abuses in a less conspicuous manner. As in China in recent years, documenting cases of political psychiatry became increasingly difficult due to the intensified crackdown on the dissident movement in the early to mid-1980s, but after Mikhail Gorbachev assumed power and started his campaign of *glasnost*, the Soviet press itself soon started publicly to address the issue. Increasingly cornered by their own newspapers, by evidence from victims of political abuse freed under the policy of *perestroika*, and by a damaging report issued by a 1989 U.S. State Department mission to Moscow to investigate the political abuse of psychiatry, the Soviet delegates to the WPA's 1989 World Congress in Athens finally agreed to acknowledge that the systematic abuse of psychiatry for political purposes had indeed taken place in their country. As a condition for its return to the WPA, the Soviet psychiatric association (the All-Union Society of Psychiatrists and Neuropathologists) promised to discontinue these abuses, rehabilitate the victims, and democratize the psychiatric profession. The latter proved to be an unnecessary promise, since three years later the Soviet Union itself fell apart and new national psychiatric associations soon sprang up across the country. When a WPA delegation visited the USSR in 1991, they met newly founded associations in Lithuania and Ukraine, set up by psychiatrists who were to play a key reforming role in all areas of the profession in the years that followed. Conditions remained generally poor in most parts of the mental healthcare system, and it soon became clear that the twenty-year-long international campaign had been directed at only the tip of an iceberg: massive human rights abuses were found to have occurred at all levels, in a highly institutionalized and biologically oriented system of psychiatry that had taught society to ostracize its mental patients and see them as distinctly second-class citizens. But the misuse of psychiatry as a tool against political dissent had finally come to an end

Moreover, the campaign against politically abusive psychiatry had helped put the issues of human rights and medical ethics high on the agenda of post-Soviet countries, and these concerns now form the cornerstone of the work of mental health reformers there. Internationally, too, the issue has continued to have an impact. In 1996 the WPA adopted the Madrid Declaration at its World Congress in the Spanish capital, further deepening and fine-tuning the Honolulu Declaration adopted nine years earlier – and when during that congress reports reached the West of new cases of political psychiatric detention in Turkmenistan, one letter of protest from an international group that included psychiatrists from the former USSR sufficed to immediately halt those abuses. Today, with the issue of political abuse of psychiatry in China placed on the agenda, there is no discussion as to whether or not it is an issue that the WPA should address. To the contrary, the WPA is taking an active role in this campaign, through its Review Committee and other relevant bodies, and its discussions with organizations such as Geneva Initiative on Psychiatry concentrate on matters of tactics, not of content.

Judicial Psychiatry in China and its Political Abuses[23]

I. INTRODUCTION

In the Soviet Union today, whoever takes a proletarian standpoint, upholds Marxism-Leninism, and dares to speak out and resist is...arrested and imprisoned, or declared 'mentally ill' and thrown into 'lunatic asylums.'
— People's Daily, 1964[24]

The content of Zhu's "theories" was conceptually chaotic... [They were] a form of "political delusion," a pathological mental disorder...
— Chinese forensic-psychiatric case report, March 1987

Without a correct political standpoint, one has no soul.
— Mao Zedong

During the 1970s and 1980s, reports that the security authorities in the Soviet Union were incarcerating substantial numbers of dissidents in mental asylums aroused widespread concern in the West. As the quantity and reliability of the documentary evidence and victim testimonies steadily increased, the issue of politically directed psychiatry in the Soviet Union quickly became, along with political imprisonment and the refusal of the authorities to allow Soviet Jews to emigrate, a third principal item of human rights contention in Soviet-Western relations. By January 1983, a protracted campaign by Western psychiatric professional bodies and international human rights organizations led to a

---

[23] This article by Robin Munro was first published in the *Columbia Journal of Asian Law*, vol. 14, no. 1 (2000) (actual publication date: January 2001). The initial phase of the writing was done by the author in his former capacity as China researcher and director of the Hong Kong office of Human Rights Watch. The original footnotes have been stylistically amended in the present edition and a small number of documentary source corrections have been made (notably in Section VII.: "Official Statistics on Political Psychiatry").

[24] See "On Khrushchev's Phony Communism and its World Historical Lessons (Ninth Letter to the Soviets)," *Renmin Ribao (People's Daily)*, July 14, 1964. This important article, a fifty-page "Open Letter" sent by the Chinese Communist Party leadership to the Central Committee of the Communist Party of the USSR, signaled the final stages of the Sino-Soviet split. The passage quoted above is said to have been written by Wang Li and Wu Lengxi, but Mao Zedong almost certainly edited and approved the article as a whole.

decision by the Soviet All-Union Society of Psychiatrists and Neuropathologists to withdraw from the World Psychiatric Association in order to avoid almost certain expulsion.[25] It was not readmitted to the body until 1989, after several years of *perestroika* and the preliminary establishment of direct access by Western psychiatric delegations to Soviet forensic-psychiatric institutions and their alleged mentally ill political inmates.[26]

The subject of forensic psychiatry in China has thus far received little academic attention outside of China. A number of very detailed and informative studies of China's general psychiatric and mental healthcare system have been written,[27] but these have rarely addressed the legal or forensic dimension of the topic in significant depth.[28] In particular, very little documentary or other

[25] Some historical context:

> Twelve years ago, during the World Congress of the World Psychiatric Association (WPA) in Honolulu, the Soviet All-Union Society of Psychiatrists and Neuropathologists was condemned by the General Assembly of the WPA for abusing psychiatry for political purposes. Six years later, at the beginning of 1983, it was almost certain that later that year a majority of the WPA General Assembly would vote in favor of either expulsion from the WPA or suspension of membership of the Soviet All-Union Society. Keeping the honor to themselves, the Soviets withdrew from the WPA. (Robert van Voren, ed., *Soviet Psychiatric Abuse in the Gorbachev Era* [Amsterdam: International Association on the Political Use of Psychiatry (IAPUP), 1989], p.10.)

[26] For full and detailed accounts of the political abuse of psychiatry in the former Soviet Union see: Sidney Bloch and Peter Reddaway, *Russia's Political Hospitals: The Abuse of Psychiatry in the Soviet Union* (Victor Gollancz, 1977), and *Soviet Psychiatric Abuse: The Shadow Over World Psychiatry* (Victor Gollancz, 1984); Theresa C. Smith and Thomas A. Olesczuk, *No Asylum: State Psychiatric Repression in the Former USSR* (New York University Press, 1996); and Robert van Voren, ed., *Soviet Psychiatric Abuse* (1989).

[27] See Veronica Pearson, *Mental Health Care in China: State Policies, Professional Services and Family Responsibilities*, (Gaskell, 1995); Michael R. Phillips, "The Transformation of China's Mental Health Services," *The China Journal*, no. 39 (January 1998), pp.1-36; Arthur Kleinman, M.D., *Social Origins of Distress and Disease: Depression, Neurasthenia and Pain in Modern China* (Yale University Press, 1986); and Michael R. Phillips, Veronica Pearson and Ruiwen Wang, eds., *Psychiatric Rehabilitation in China: Models for Change in a Changing Society*, vol. 165, Supplement 24 (August 1994). For a disturbing photo-journalistic portrayal of conditions in ordinary mental hospitals in China in the early 1990s, see Jurgen Kremb, "Wie ein Tier am Pfahl," *Der Spiegel*, no. 32 (August 1992), pp.140-146.

[28] For an important exception, see Veronica Pearson, "Law, Rights, and Psychiatry in the People's Republic of China," *International Journal of Law and Psychiatry*, vol.15 (1992), pp.409-423.

evidence has hitherto come to light suggesting that abusive practices similar to those that occurred in the former Soviet Union might also have existed, or might even still be found, in China. The general assumption has therefore been that the Chinese authorities, despite their poor record in many other areas of human rights concern, have at least never engaged in the political misuse of psychiatry. This article seeks to challenge and correct that assumption.

From the early 1990s onwards, scattered reports from China began to indicate that individual dissidents and other political nonconformists were being subjected to forensic psychiatric appraisal by the police and then committed to special psychiatric hospitals on an involuntary and indefinite basis. One prominent example was that of Wang Wanxing, a middle-aged worker who had first been arrested in the mid-1970s for supporting the then officially denounced policies of Deng Xiaoping. Partially rehabilitated after the death of Mao, Wang resumed his political-activist career in the 1980s and became personally acquainted with the student leaders of the spring 1989 pro-democracy movement in Beijing. In June 1992, he unfurled a banner in Tiananmen Square calling for greater human rights and democracy in China, was immediately arrested, and then sent to an institution for the criminally insane in the outskirts of the capital, where he remained — diagnosed by police psychiatrists as a "paranoid psychotic" — until early 1999. In November of that year, after he announced his intention to hold a press conference with foreign journalists to discuss his ordeal, he was again detained and sent back to the same psychiatric detention facility for an indeterminate period. Wang's case and others like it have been the subject of several statements of concern to the Chinese authorities by relevant bodies of the United Nations.[29]

---

[29] See Nigel S. Rodley, United Nations, Economic and Social Council, *Report of the Special Rapporteur on Torture, Submitted Pursuant to Commission on Human Rights Resolution 1992/32*, (New York: United Nations, January 12, 1995), General E/CN.4/1995/34. The report stated: "The Special Rapporteur also transmitted [to the Chinese government] reports he had received of persons detained in a psychiatric hospital for political reasons, where no medical justification was said to exist for their detention. The cases summarized in the following paragraphs concerned persons detained at An Kang Public Security Bureau Hospital[s]..." The report continued, "Wang [W]anxing was arrested on 3 June 1992 while attempting to unfurl a banner commemorating the June 1989 demonstrations at Tiananmen Square. He was transferred to An Kang in July 1992, where he was allegedly administered medicine that kept him drowsy and weak. Although he was said to have no psychiatric problems, his wife signed documents confirming that he did, after being pressured to do so and being reassured that this would lead to her husband's early release." According to the report, the Chinese government replied as follows: "An Kang hospital's psychological appraisals unit had determined that he was suffering from paranoia, that some of his actions were governed by wishful

Another recent example is that of Xue Jifeng, an unofficial labor-rights activist who in December 1999 was detained by police in Zhengzhou, the capital of Henan Province, for attempting to hold a meeting with other labor activists and independent trades-unionists. He was then committed involuntarily to the Xinxiang Municipal Mental Hospital, where he remained until June 2000. Xue was reportedly force-fed psychiatric drugs and held in a room with mental patients who kept him awake at night and harassed him by day.[30] Moreover, this was his second forced term in a mental hospital for "illegal" labor activities. The first came in November 1998, after he tried to pursue legal action against local Party officials who he alleged had swindled, through a bogus commercial fundraising scheme, thousands of his fellow residents of their life savings. On that occasion, more than 2,000 people staged a public demonstration in Zhengzhou demanding their money back and calling for Xue's release.[31]

Finally, in July 1999, the Chinese government launched a major and continuing campaign of repression against the Falun Gong spiritual movement, a neotraditional sectarian group, several months after the group staged a massive peaceful demonstration outside the Zhongnanhai headquarters of the Chinese leadership. Over the past year or so, numerous reports have appeared indicating that practitioners of Falun Gong were also being forcibly sent to mental hospitals by the police authorities. The overseas Falun Gong support network has so far compiled details of around 100 named individuals who have been dealt with in this manner,[32] while overall estimates suggest the total number may be as high as 600. To date, reports indicate that three Falun Gong practitioners

---

thinking, that he had lost his normal capacity for recognition and was irresponsible. He was continuing to undergo treatment at the hospital."

[30] "Rights Group Says China Sent Labor Activist to Mental Hospital," Associated Press, April 11, 2000.

[31] "AFP Reports 2,000 Protest against Failed Investment Firm," FBIS Daily Report, November 16, 1998. According to the report, "Xue Jifeng was taken from his home last Monday and placed in a psychiatric asylum after accusing the Henan authorities of being responsible for the failure of the Three Stars investment group. The provincial government in May announced the closure of the three-year-old group, which collapsed owing about 10,000 investors more than three billion *yuan* (360 million dollars)..." NB: In the original *Columbia Journal of Asian Law* version of this article, it was wrongly stated that Xue Jifeng was still being detained at the mental hospital "as of December 2000"; according to subsequent information from the monitoring group Human Rights in China, Xue was discharged from the hospital in late June 2000.

[32] This was the figure as of late 2000; by March 2002, the Falun Gong network had reported more than 300 cases involving the psychiatric detention of Falun Gong practitioners.

have died as a direct result of their detention and mistreatment in Chinese mental asylums.

These disturbing cases highlight the need for a comprehensive reexamination of our previous understanding of the role and purposes of forensic psychiatry in China, both historically and contemporaneously. All countries have valid and necessary reasons for detaining certain criminally active members of the mentally ill population (especially psychotic murderers, arsonists, and rapists) in secure psychiatric hospitals.[33] This also holds true in China where there are officially said to be around 10 million mentally ill people in the country, of whom some ten to twenty percent are regarded as posing a "serious danger" to society.[34] Under internationally agreed standards of legal and medical ethics, however, peaceful religious or political dissidents are emphatically not considered as belonging to this highly select category of people.

An extensive study of the officially published legal-psychiatric professional literature in China from the 1950s to the present day, viewed in conjunction with the growing number of independent case accounts of the kinds outlined above, has now produced a substantial amount of documentary evidence to indicate that the Chinese authorities have, in fact, a longstanding record of the misuse of psychiatry for politically repressive purposes, one that resembles in all key respects that of the former Soviet Union, and one, moreover, that may well have exceeded in scope and intensity the by now thoroughly documented abuses that occurred in the latter country prior to 1990. It should be stressed at the outset that the extent to which China's psychiatric profession as a whole is complicit in the legal-psychiatric abuses described in this article remains unclear. It seems likely that these abuses are confined mainly to those working within the sub-specialist domain of forensic psychiatry, a small and still secretive field of which most regular Chinese psychiatrists may have little direct knowledge or experience.

---

[33] According to one source, for example, mental illness was the chief cause of crime in 20.7 percent of all cases of murder, injury, arson, poisoning and explosions committed in a certain area of China in 1982 (see Li Tianfu et. al., *Fanzui Tongjixue (Criminal Statistics)*, [Qunzhong Chubanshe, 1988], p.45). More recent reports indicate that mental illness-related crime remains a serious national problem.

[34] See, e.g., Li Congpei, ed., *Sifa Jingshenbingxue (Forensic Psychiatry)*, (Renmin Weisheng Chubanshe, February 1992), p.381. According to the author, out of three million mentally ill people in six central Chinese provinces, approximately 400,000 posed a direct danger to society.

The present article is an attempt to reconstruct the shadowy history of the political misuse of forensic psychiatry in the People's Republic of China — its antecedents and influences, general nature and overall scope and extent — and also to assess the degree to which it remains a problem in China today. The article comprises the following main themes and sections. The first is an overview of the origins and development of Chinese forensic psychiatry through the country's main historical periods since 1949, with a focus on the 1950s, during which Soviet influences predominated; the Cultural Revolution decade (1966-76), when political psychiatry reached its absurd apogee; the 1980s, when the reform era of Deng Xiaoping seems to have meant, for forensic psychiatry, a partial return to the orthodoxies of the pre-Cultural Revolution period; and the 1990s, which appeared to see a significant decrease in politically-directed psychiatry in China, only to be followed, at the end of the decade, by a substantial resurgence of abusive practices, notably in the case of Falun Gong detainees.

The second is a discussion of the judicial and legislative framework governing the practice of forensic psychiatry in China: the criminal and civil law contexts, legislation on mental health and forensic-psychiatric assessment, the levels of determination of criminal "non-imputability" by reason of insanity that can be made, the kinds of offenders falling within the system's purview, and the extent to which the rights and interests of the latter are (if at all) taken into account and afforded legal protection. Also considered is the question of China's expansive definition of the key legal determinant of involuntary psychiatric committal, namely "social dangerousness." Whereas under international standards, the applicable scope of the "dangerousness" criterion is mainly restricted to situations where mentally ill people pose a direct physical danger either to themselves or to others, in China it is applied also to those, such as certain types of dissidents, whom the government regards as posing a political threat to "social order."

The third is a survey of the professional legal-medical literature from China, including numerous quoted passages illustrating the close and longstanding cooperation between forensic psychiatrists and the security authorities in effecting the simultaneous criminalization and medicalization of certain forms of dissenting activity. The focus here is on official statistics showing the relatively high proportion of so-called "political cases" among those brought for forensic psychiatric examination throughout China, and on passages describing the various diagnostic theories and perspectives that are commonly applied in such cases. Also discussed are the several main categories of political and religious nonconformists that are especially liable to fall prey to these police-dominated diagnostic and judicial procedures: so-called "political maniacs," whistleblowers and exposers of official corruption, persistent complainants and petitioners, and also unconventional religious sectarians of various kinds.

Several more detailed case accounts are presented to complement and concretize this general picture. These afford both an illustrative insight into the kinds of individuals most at risk of being branded as criminally insane on account of their peaceful views and activities, and also an opportunity to evaluate whether or not they may indeed, as claimed by the authorities, have been mentally disordered to any significant degree. While this is clearly a relevant issue, it should be noted that the persons in question were in most cases arrested on criminal charges — but for activities not held to be crimes under international legal standards — prior to being committed for forensic psychiatric evaluation. If truly mentally disturbed, they should not have fallen within the scope of the psychiatric-criminal justice system, but should rather have been given appropriate treatment by the regular mental healthcare system.

Also included below is a first introduction to China's little-known network of special custodial centers for the criminally insane. Although several such institutions have existed in China since at least the 1960s, in 1987 the Chinese government for the first time decided to establish a nationwide system of high-security facilities for "dangerously mentally ill offenders." These, the equivalent of the USSR's Special Psychiatric Hospitals run by the Interior Ministry, were to be uniformly designated as "Ankang" (Peace and Health) institutions, and were to be directly administered and run by the Ministry of Public Security and its subordinate provincial-level departments. Arrested political dissidents and others in similar categories brought for assessment by the State's forensic psychiatrists are often officially treated as ranking among the most "serious and dangerous" of all alleged mentally ill offenders, and are thus prime candidates for compulsory committal in such institutions. To date, twenty Ankang facilities have already been built and brought into service around the country. These highly secretive institutions deserve to become more widely known as perhaps the last unexplored aspect, and possibly the most sinister one, of China's extensive *laogai* system of judicial incarceration.

Perhaps the most striking aspect of all the official documentary sources consulted is the high frequency with which they refer to "cases of a political nature" (*zhengzhixing anjian*) in describing the day-to-day casework of State-appointed forensic psychiatrists in China. Time and again, even in the most cursory accounts of this type of work, specific mention is made of "political cases" as constituting a distinct category among the various types of criminal defendants routinely referred by various law-enforcement authorities for expert "forensic-psychiatric evaluation" (*sifa jingshenbing jianding*) — and even percentage rates for cases of this type are often provided. Indeed, it was from passages of this nature found in the official psychiatric literature almost a decade ago that the evidentiary paper trail for this article first began. In the Soviet case, by contrast, no such official mention or statistics were ever found in the relevant literature.

This study does not claim to be a comprehensive analysis of the political aspects and abuses of Chinese forensic psychiatry. Many important questions remain to be considered elsewhere and by other observers, many of whom will doubtless be better qualified than this writer to comment on matters relating to law and psychiatry. What follows is a preliminary attempt to bring together a significant corpus of new, though sometimes fragmentary, documentary evidence about the theory and practice of Chinese forensic psychiatry since 1949. It is one that amounts, however, to a clear and unmistakable prima facie case showing the longstanding and continuing existence of political psychiatric abuse in China.

II. INTERNATIONAL STANDARDS ON ETHICAL PSYCHIATRY

In evaluating China's past and current practices in the field of forensic psychiatry, it is important to be aware of the more widely applicable standards of law and ethics that have been established by the international community in the general area of mental healthcare and psychiatry in recent decades. The bodies chiefly responsible for defining these standards are the United Nations, the World Psychiatric Association (WPA), and the various psychiatric professional organizations of different countries.[35] The pre-eminent or overarching relevant provisions — namely, that people everywhere enjoy equal rights to freedom of the person, freedom of political and religious belief, freedom of expression, the right to a fair trial and so forth — are comprehensively set forth in the Universal Declaration of Human Rights[36] and

---

[35] Several Western psychiatric associations have formulated national-level ethical guidelines in recent years. One example is the Canadian Medical Association's "Code of Ethics Annotated for Psychiatrists," approved by the board of directors of the Canadian Psychiatric Association in October 1978; see http://www.cma.ca/eng-index.htm. In the area of forensic psychiatry, one of the more noteworthy examples is the "Ethical Guidelines for the Practice of Forensic Psychiatry," adopted by the American Academy of Psychiatry and the Law in May 1987 (and revised in October 1989); see http://www.cc.emory.edu/AAPL/ethics.htm.

[36] According to Article 2 of the Universal Declaration of Human Rights (adopted and proclaimed by General Assembly Resolution 217 A (III) of 10 December 1948), "[N]o distinction shall be made on the basis of the political, jurisdictional or international status of the country or territory to which a person belongs"; in other words, all rights listed in the document apply equally to all citizens of any country. Article 5 states, "No one shall be subjected to torture or to cruel, inhuman or degrading treatment or punishment"; Article 9 adds, "No one shall be subjected to arbitrary arrest, detention or exile"; and Article 10 continues, "Everyone is entitled in full equality to a fair and public hearing by an independent and impartial tribunal, in the determination of his rights and obligations and of any criminal charge against him."

On more specific related matters, the Declaration states, in Article 18, "Everyone has the right to freedom of thought, conscience and religion; [including the right...] to manifest his religion or belief in teaching practice, worship and observance"; in Article 19, "Everyone has the right to freedom of opinion and expression..."; and in Article 23 (4), "Everyone has the right to form and to join trades unions for the protection of his interest."

Finally, addressing the general question of states of emergency and national security-related measures, Article 29 specifies: "In the exercise of his rights and freedoms, everyone shall be subject only to such limitations as are determined by law solely for the purpose of securing due recognition and respect for the rights and freedoms of others and of meeting the just requirements of morality, public order and the general welfare in a democratic society."

the International Covenant on Civil and Political Rights (ICCPR).[37]

In the early 1980s, in response to growing international concern over the political misuse of psychiatry in the Soviet Union, its satellite states and a small number of other countries (notably, South Africa under *apartheid*),[38] the United Nations undertook a major investigative review of mental healthcare provision around the world. In particular, the world body focused on the rules, procedures and practices pursued by various countries in the area of involuntary psychiatric committal and treatment. In 1983, Special Rapporteur Daes presented the results

---

[37] The relevant rights as set forth in the Universal Declaration are enlarged and elaborated upon in the International Covenant on Civil and Political Rights (ICCPR) (adopted Dec. 16, 1966, G.A. Res. 2200A [XXI], entered into force March 23, 1976, signed by China in October 1998, not yet ratified) in the following provisions: Article 2 (non-discrimination on the basis of political and religious opinion, ethnicity or similar grounds), Article 4 (exclusion of the right to freedom of thought, conscience and religion from the scope of rights that States Parties may derogate from in times of national emergency), Article 7 (freedom from torture), Article 9 (ban on arbitrary arrest or detention), Article 12 (no restriction allowed on key rights except as necessary to protect national security, public order, public health or morals or the rights and freedoms of others), Article 14 (right to a fair and impartial trial), Article 18 (freedom of thought, conscience and religion), Article 19 (freedom of expression and the right to hold opinions without interference), Article 21 (right of peaceful assembly), Article 22 (freedom of association, including the right to form and join trades unions), and Article 26 (equality before the law and prohibition of discrimination on grounds such as race, color, sex, and political or other opinion).

[38] In a major report of 1986 submitted to the U.N.'s Sub-Commission on Prevention of Discrimination and Protection of Minorities, for example, the Sub-Commission's Special Rapporteur stated:

> Between 8,000 and 9,000 [black] Africans suffering from mental disorders are detained against their will in privately owned institutions in the Republic of South Africa... There is not a single black psychiatrist in South Africa and vital decisions about thousands of African mental patients are made by part-time physicians who do not even speak the language of the patients... Recent legislative measures of the Government concerning the "rehabilitation" of African pass [law] offenders equate in a dangerous way the non-observance of the *apartheid* laws with mental disorder... These conditions and policies, being a direct effect of *apartheid* in the health field, are inimical to the letter and spirit of the Constitution of the World Health Organization... (Erica-Irene A. Daes, Special Rapporteur of the U.N. Sub-Commission on Prevention of Discrimination and Protection of Minorities, *Principles, Guidelines and Guarantees for the Protection of Persons Detained on Grounds of Mental Ill-Health or Suffering from Mental Disorder* [New York: United Nations Publications, 1986] E/CN.4/Sub.2/1983/17/Rev.1, p.8.)

of the investigative review in a report to the U.N., figuring the following passage prominently in its conclusions:

> [W]e are painfully aware that:
> Psychiatry in some States of the international community is often used to subvert the political and legal guarantees of the freedom of the individual and to violate seriously his human and legal rights.
> In some States, psychiatric hospitalization treatment is forced on the individual who does not support the existing political regime of the State in which he lives.

On the basis of these findings, the Special Rapporteur recommended that the U.N. Commission on Human Rights should, among other things, urge all member States "[To] prohibit *expressis verbis* psychological and psychiatric abuses, in particular for political or other non-medical grounds."[39] After several years of discussion and drafting work within the U.N., this initiative bore legislative fruit in December 1991, when the world body's General Assembly adopted a wide-ranging set of provisions entitled "Principles for the Protection of Persons with Mental Illness and for the Improvement of Mental Health Care." According to Principle 4 of this important U.N. document,

- A determination that a person has a mental illness shall be made in accordance with internationally accepted medical standards.
- A determination of mental illness shall never be made on the basis of political, economic or social status, or membership in a cultural, racial or religious group, or for any other reason not directly relevant to mental health status.
- Family or professional conflict, or non-conformity with moral, social, cultural or political values or religious beliefs prevailing in a person's community, shall never be a determining factor in the diagnosis of mental illness.
- A background of past treatment or hospitalization of a patient shall not of itself justify any present or future determination of mental illness.
- No person or authority shall classify a person as having, or otherwise indicate that a person has, a mental illness except for purposes directly relating to mental illness or the consequences of mental illness.

---

[39] Ibid., p.30.

Among other important general provisions, the Principles state: "Every patient shall have the right to be treated in the least restrictive environment and with the least restrictive or intrusive treatment appropriate to the patient's health needs and the need to protect the physical safety of others" (Principle 9). "Medication shall meet the best health needs of the patient, shall be given to a patient only for therapeutic or diagnostic purposes and shall never be administered as a punishment or for the convenience of others" (Principle 10). "Physical restraint or involuntary seclusion of a patient shall not be employed except in accordance with the officially approved procedures of the mental health facility and only when it is the only means available to prevent immediate or imminent harm to the patient or others" (Principle 11.11). "Psychosurgery and other intrusive and irreversible treatments for mental illness shall never be carried out on a patient who is an involuntary patient in a mental health facility..." (Principle 11.14). "In the cases specified [where involuntary committal or treatment is involved] the patient or his or her personal representative, or any interested person, shall have the right to appeal to a judicial or other independent authority concerning any treatment given to him or her" (Principle 11.16). And according to Principle 13, all mental patients shall have "the right to full respect for his or her...freedom of communication...and freedom of religion or belief."

Principle 20 deals specifically with the rights of mentally ill criminal offenders and reads as follows:

- The present Principle applies to persons serving sentences of imprisonment for criminal offenses, or who are otherwise detained in the course of criminal proceedings or investigations against them, and who are determined to have a mental illness or who it is believed may have such an illness.
- All such persons should receive the best available mental health care as provided in Principle 1 above. The present Principles shall apply to them to the fullest extent possible, with only such limited modifications and exceptions as are necessary in the circumstances. No such modifications and exceptions shall prejudice the persons' rights under the instruments noted in paragraph 5 of Principle 1, above.[40]

---

[40] Paragraph 5 of Principle 1 reads: "Every person with a mental illness shall have the right to exercise all civil, political, economic, social and cultural rights as recognized in the Universal Declaration of Human Rights, the International Covenant on Economic, Social and Cultural Rights, the International Covenant on Civil and Political Rights and in other relevant instruments, such as the Declaration on the Rights of Disabled Persons

- Domestic law may authorize a court or other competent authority, acting on the basis of competent and independent medical advice, to order that such persons be admitted to a mental health facility.
- Treatment of persons determined to have a mental illness shall in all circumstances be consistent with Principle 11 above.[41]

Thus, the U.N. General Assembly ruled that no derogation from or restriction of fundamental civil and political liberties was to be permitted, or otherwise viewed as justifiable, in the case of detained criminal offenders who were ascertained by governmental authorities as being mentally ill.

Within the international psychiatric community, increasing reports in the 1970s and thereafter concerning the political abuse of psychiatry in the former Soviet Union and elsewhere provided a powerful impetus to efforts by concerned professionals to establish clear ethical codes aimed at eliminating political and other forms of unwarranted outside interference from the practice of psychiatry in all countries. The first major outcome of these efforts was the "Declaration of Hawaii," passed by the General Assembly of the World Psychiatric Association in July 1977 and updated at its July 1983 world congress. According to the preamble of the Declaration,

> It is the view of the World Psychiatric Association that due to conflicting loyalties and expectations of both physicians and patients in contemporary society and the delicate nature of the therapist-patient relationship, high ethical standards are especially important for those involved in the science and practice of psychiatry as a medical specialty. These guidelines have been delineated in order to promote close adherence to those standards and to prevent misuse of psychiatric concepts, knowledge and technology.

---

and the Body of Principles for the Protection of All Persons under Any Form of Detention or Imprisonment."

[41] U.N. General Assembly, report of the Third Committee, *Principles for the Protection of Persons with Mental Illness and for the Improvement of Mental Health Care* (New York: United Nations, December 17, 1991), A/46/721. For a wider discussion of the ethical aspects of compulsory psychiatric hospitalization, see Robert Miller, "The Ethics of Involuntary Commitment to Mental Health Treatment," in Sidney Bloch and Paul Chodoff, eds., *Psychiatric Ethics* (Oxford University Press, 1991) pp.265-289.

The WPA statement continued,

> If and when a relationship is established for purposes other
> than therapeutic, such as in forensic psychiatry, its nature must
> be thoroughly explained to the person concerned... As soon as
> the conditions for compulsory treatment no longer apply, the
> psychiatrist should release the patient from the compulsory
> nature of the treatment and if further therapy is necessary
> should obtain voluntary consent... The psychiatrist must on no
> account utilize the tools of his profession once the absence of
> psychiatric illness has been established. If a patient or some
> third party demands actions contrary to scientific knowledge
> or ethical principles the psychiatrist must refuse to cooperate...
> The psychiatrist should stop all therapeutic, teaching or
> research programs that may evolve contrary to the principles
> of this Declaration.[42]

At its world conference in Athens in October 1989, moreover, the WPA
adopted a further resolution stating, among other things: "A diagnosis that a
person is mentally ill shall be determined in accordance with the internationally
accepted medical standards.... Difficulty in adapting to moral, social, political,
or other values, in itself should not be considered a mental illness."[43] In addition,
the Athens resolution affirmed a number of key subsidiary protections for the
rights of the mentally ill. For example: "The final decision to admit or detain a
patient in a mental health facility as an involuntary patient shall be taken only by
a court or a competent independent body prescribed by law, and only after an
appropriate and proper hearing... They have the right of appeal and to be heard
personally by the court or competent body." Also, "Patients who are deprived of
their liberty shall have the right to a qualified guardian or counsel to protect their

---

[42] Declaration of Hawaii, 1983, as included in Appendix II of Bloch and Reddaway,
Soviet Psychiatric Abuse: The Shadow Over World Psychiatry, pp.237-239.

[43] The World Federation for Mental Health (WFMH) adopted the same principle in its
January 1989 "Declaration of Human Rights and Mental Health." According to the
document's preamble, "Whereas a diagnosis of mental illness by a mental health
practitioner shall be in accordance with accepted medical, psychological, scientific and
ethical standards...and whereas persons have, nonetheless, been at times and continue to
be inappropriately labeled, diagnosed and treated as mentally ill...difficulty in adapting
to moral, social, political or other values in itself shall not be considered a mental illness"
(from a pamphlet issued by the WFMH, on file with author).

interests."[44] In August 1996, the WPA's General Assembly reiterated and updated these various principles in its Declaration of Madrid.[45] As noted above, China is a full member of the WPA.

Taken together, the UN's 1991 Principles and the WPA's Declarations of Hawaii and Madrid provide the core set of international standards upon which the ethical and legal practices of psychiatrists around the world should properly be evaluated. By detaining large numbers of non-violent political and religious dissenters and subjecting them to forensic psychiatric assessment and compulsory hospitalization, China's medico-legal establishment is acting in violation of almost all of these international legal and ethical standards.

---

[44] "WPA Statements and Viewpoints on the Rights and Legal Safeguards of the Mentally Ill," adopted by the WPA General Assembly in Athens, October 17, 1989; in Geneva Initiative on Psychiatry, *Human Rights and Professional Responsibilities of Physicians in Documents of International Organizations* (Amsterdam and Sofia, 1998), pp.70-71.

[45] Declaration of Madrid, 1996, as cited in *Mental Health Reforms* (Journal of the Geneva Initiative on Psychiatry), no.1, pp.8-9 (1997). Among new provisions included in the Madrid Declaration were that "psychiatrists should devise therapeutic interventions that are least restrictive to the freedom of the patient," and that "no treatment should be provided against the patient's will unless withholding the treatment would endanger the life of the patient and/or those who surround him or her."

III. HISTORICAL OVERVIEW

Law and Psychiatry Prior to 1949

Chinese historical records from the past two millennia contain occasional references to cases of insane persons who committed violent crimes but were pardoned or treated leniently by the courts on account of their mental disorders; also recorded are the cases of several famous individuals who successfully avoided punishment by feigning insanity. Over the last few hundred years of the imperial era, however, more systematic legal norms were gradually applied in this area of the criminal justice system. According to one scholarly account,

> The Ch'ing government came to grips with the problem of criminal insanity soon after the consolidation of its rule in the late seventeenth century. It initially relied on the voluntary efforts of the families and neighbors of insane persons to keep them under control, but this soon gave way to the more interventionist measure of registration and confinement, designed to isolate the insane from the rest of society. Mandatory confinement of all insane persons was soon followed by the introduction of prison sentences for insane killers.[46]

Where family members were ordered to take charge of the care and custody of a mentally ill person, they assumed collective legal responsibility for their ward's good conduct and could be punished by up to forty blows with a bamboo stave if he or she subsequently committed an offense.[47] Moreover, according to a contemporary Western observer, "Lunatics are in general required to be manacled, and the relatives must not remove the manacles without proper authority."[48] The death penalty for murder, normally mandatory in such cases, was not applied in cases where the offender was shown to be

---

[46] Vivien W. Ng, "Ch'ing Law Concerning the Insane: An Historical Survey," *Ch'ing Shi Wen-t'i* (*Problems in Ch'ing History*), vol. 4, no.4 (December 1980), p.84.

[47] Technically, the maximum number of blows with a heavy bamboo stave prescribed by law was one hundred; in practice, however, this would often have been fatal, so the lesser number was used as a maximum instead. See Derk Bodde & Clarence Morris, *Law in Imperial China* (University of Pennsylvania Press, 1967), p.77.

[48] Ernest Alabaster, *Notes and Commentaries on Chinese Criminal Law* (Luzac & Co., 1899), p.93. See also Andrew H. Woods, M.D., "A Memorandum to Chinese Medical Students on the Medico-Legal Aspects of Insanity," *Journal of the National Medical Association of China*, vol. 9 (September 1923), pp.203-212.

insane at the time of the crime, even when the victim was one of the offender's own parents. An exception to this rule of clemency was made, however, if the victim was one of the grandparents.[49] The death penalty was applied also in the case of multiple homicides by the insane.

After the founding of the Republic in 1911, a new criminal law was passed stipulating that punishment was to be waived or reduced in the case of crimes committed by the mentally ill. China's first specialized mental hospital was established in Guangzhou in 1898, with others following in Beijing (1906), Suzhou (1929), Shanghai (1935) and Nanjing (1947). In 1922, the country's first teaching center for psychiatry was established at the Xiehe Hospital in Beijing; and in 1932, the Nationalist government established an Institute of Forensic Medicine, headed by Lin Ji, who is today renowned as the father of the discipline in China. Also in the early Republican era, a new and more specialized type of institution known as the "psychopathic hospital" gradually began to appear in major Chinese cities. The earliest such institution was apparently located in Guangzhou (Canton), where opium addiction, syphilis, vagabondage and concubinage were among the more common social causes of crime-related mental illness. According to a contemporary Western account,

> The only separate psychopathic hospital in China up to 1933
> was a mission hospital in Canton, the John G. Kerr Hospital
> for the Insane. In 1924 this institution had 726 patients, half of
> whom were men... There are special psychopathic wards in a
> few general hospitals, such as in Soochow, Peiping[50] and
> Shanghai but these are small. China urgently needs modern
> special hospitals for mental disease in the large centers. In
> 1930 the [KMT] Ministry of Justice announced its intention to
> erect special reformatories and "lunatic asylums" in various
> large cities. There is a dearth of trained psychiatrists in
> China.[51]

The equivalent institution in the Chinese capital, the Peiping Municipal Psychopathic Hospital, was by 1935 responsible for the custody and care of

---

[49] "And the sentence (slicing to pieces) is [in such cases] to be carried out in all its horror, even though the lunatic be already dead" (Alabaster, *Notes and Commentaries*, p. 96).

[50] The name used for Beijing during much of the Republican era.

[51] H.D. Lamson, *Social Pathology in China*, (Shanghai: The Commercial Press, 1935), p.434.

around 250 criminally insane and other mentally disordered persons of various types. Of these, around a third had been referred to the hospital by "families, institutions or relatives," while as many as two thirds had been directly placed there by the police authorities.[52] The average length of stay for inmates was between one month and eighteen months, and hospitalization (especially for the "police cases") was essentially compulsory,[53] although there seems to have been no formal legislation in this area at the time.

The psychopathic hospitals differed in two important respects from the earlier forms of compulsory custody for the mentally ill practiced during the pre-Republican period. First, their main purpose was to provide medical care and treatment, whereas the previous legal measures had simply been a prolonged form of preventive detention. Second, however, the scope of admissions was now considerably broader, with the types of offending behavior ranging from "killing mother with an axe," "attacking parents," "attempted suicides," "lying on the street and scolding people" and "appearing naked in public" at one end of the spectrum, all the way through to "ideas of grandeur," "burning of incense," and "restless patients with reports of jumping around, singing, laughing, [and] clapping hands" at the other.[54] Significantly, contemporary accounts give no indication that expressions of political deviance or heterodox thinking, whether as a symptomatic manifestation of mental pathology or otherwise, were seen or used by the authorities as grounds for imposing psychiatric incarceration at this time.

If anything, the law tilted more towards a lackadaisical approach in its construal of the "dangerousness" criterion, sometimes even in the most violent of cases. For example,

> The police will loosen the control of any mental patient if his family is willing to bear the responsibility. One of the best examples of this kind is found in case No. 513, in which the patient chopped up more than ten people fatally with a knife during one of his attacks, but was allowed by the police to be discharged against the advice of the hospital because the patient's wife repeatedly petitioned the Bureau [of Public

---

[52] Francis L.K. Hsu, "A Brief Report on the Police Co-operation in Connection with Mental Cases in Peiping," in R. Lyman et al., ed., *Social and Psychological Studies in Neuro-Psychiatry* (Beijing: Henri Vetch, 1939), pp.202-230.

[53] "The police considers it a custodial place" (Ibid, p.225).

[54] Ibid., pp.210-211.

Security] that she would take all possible care to guard against
the recurrence of a similar incident.[55]

It should be noted in passing that, in the 1980s and 1990s, it remained a
common complaint within the Chinese psychiatric profession that once a
determination of "absence of legal responsibility" on the grounds of mental
illness had been made, even the most violent of offenders could still, in many
cases, be released straight back into society.[56] While the reasons for this
hazardous practice stem mainly from the country's lack of secure psychiatric
facilities, it contrasts sharply, nonetheless, with the apparent frequency with
which those involved in "cases of a political nature" are officially deemed to be
in need of custodial care.

The Early Years of the People's Republic
By 1949, after several decades of virtually continuous warfare and national
revolution, there were no more than fifty or sixty qualified psychiatrists to be
found in the whole of China.[57] As the Communist Party began rebuilding the
country, it turned primarily to the Soviet Union for scientific and technical
assistance throughout the 1950s. While many of the earlier trained psychiatrists,
some of whom had studied in the West, played a key role in expanding the
professional infrastructure during these early years, they increasingly became a
target of official suspicion for their alleged "bourgeois ideology." As one
psychiatric journal succinctly put the matter: "With the arrival of advanced
Soviet medical science, China's psychiatric workers were liberated from the
ideological influence of the reactionary academic doctrines of Europe and

---

[55] Ibid., p.222.

[56] See, e.g., Zhang Jun, *Xingshi Cuo'An Yanjiu* (*Research on Miscarriages of Criminal Justice*), (Beijing: Qunzhong Chubanshe, 1990), pp.110-111.

[57] See Shen Yucun, ed., *Jingshenbingxue (Psychiatry) 3rd Edition* (Beijing: People's Health Publishing House, May 1997), p.16. Other official sources give a figure of as low as thirty psychiatrists for the whole country. Sixty psychiatrists for the population of China at that time works out at approximately one per eight million inhabitants. The figure for general physicians was approximately 670 for every one million inhabitants (see "Fifty Years of Progress in China's Human Rights," Xinhua News Agency, February 17, 2000, p.1). There are currently said to be around 12,000 psychiatrists in China (see *Psychiatric News*, June 16, 2000, available at http://www.psych.org/pnews/00-06-16/china.html). And according to an official Chinese news source, there are currently altogether 575 hospitals and 77,000 doctors and nurses dealing with mental diseases in China (see "Nation's Mentally Ill Need More Care," *China Daily*, November 27, 2000; available at http://www.chinadaily.com.cn/cndydb/2000/11/d2-1ment.b27.html).

America."[58] The new generation of psychiatric professionals that emerged in China after 1949 was thus overwhelmingly influenced by Soviet psychiatric theory and doctrine. And in particular, according to one of China's leading authorities on the subject, "Soviet forensic psychiatry exerted a very great influence after it was first introduced into China."[59] Within a few years, forensic-psychiatric assessment centers organized along Soviet lines had been set up in the cities of Nanjing, Beijing, Shanghai, Changsha and Chengdu;[60] clinical practice in the area of forensic psychiatry developed steadily thereafter. While psychiatry in general received relatively little support from the authorities, legal assessment work appears to have been given (perhaps unsurprisingly, considering the government's clear emphasis at this time on national and public security-related matters) significant priority.

It was during this same period that the Soviet psychiatric establishment began to apply, especially in the field of forensic assessment, the now widely deplored range of unorthodox clinical theories whereby particular forms of political and religious dissent were seen as being attributable to certain specific (though in other contexts, oddly rare) varieties of "dangerous" mental illness. The most frequently used diagnosis of this type was "sluggish schizophrenia," a diagnostic concept that was first formulated and used briefly by American psychiatrists during the 1930s, and then later adopted and radically developed by Academician Andrei Snezhnevsky, the leading figure in Soviet psychiatry from the 1940s until his death in 1987. Under the directorship of Georgi Morozov, a key student and follower of Snezhnevsky who applied the latter's doctrine of "sluggish schizophrenia" with increasing enthusiasm to cases of alleged ideological deviance, the notorious Serbski Institute for Forensic Psychiatry in Moscow served, from 1953 until the late 1980s, as the main theoretical and practical stronghold for the political abuse of psychiatry in the USSR.[61]

---

[58] See Li Xintian, "One Decade of the Clinical Application of Artificial Hibernation Therapy in China," *Zhonghua Shenjing Jinshenke Zazhi (Chinese Journal of Nervous and Mental Diseases)*, No. 6 (1959), p.351.

[59] See Jia Yicheng, ed., *Shiyong Sifa Jingshenbingxue (Applied Forensic Psychiatry)*, (Anhui Renmin Chubanshe, September 1988), p.10.

[60] See the Internet site of the Beijing Institute of Forensic Medicine and Science (*Beijing Shi Fating Kexue Jishu Jianding Yanjiusuo*) at http://www.fmedsci.com/sfjs/sfjs6.htm.

[61] Underlying the strange complicity between law and psychiatry in the Soviet Union was the official view that, since socialist society was inherently superior to capitalist countries and thus the former social sources and causes of crime had mostly been eradicated, the continued occurrence of criminal or dissenting acts must be due to flaws in the offender's mental state. As Nikita Khrushchev explained: "A crime is a deviation from the generally recognized standards of behavior [and is] frequently caused by mental disorder. Can there

The key features of "sluggish schizophrenia," so called because of its slow rate of progression, which more often than not gave outsiders the impression that the reform-minded "sufferer" was mentally quite normal, were described as follows by Sidney Bloch, a Western psychiatrist and co-author of one of the major studies on Soviet psychiatric abuse:

> Characteristically, patients given this diagnosis are able to function almost normally in the social sense. The symptoms may resemble those of a neurosis or take a paranoid quality. The patient with paranoid symptoms retains some insight into his condition, but overvalues his own importance and may exhibit grandiose ideas of reforming society... The concept of sluggish schizophrenia [thus] facilitated the application of a label of disease of the most serious kind to people whom psychiatrists in the West would regard as either normal, mildly eccentric, or at worse neurotic. In other words, it does not require much to be labeled as mad by the Snezhnevsky-trained psychiatrist.

> Professor Georgi Morozov...states: "Schizophrenia is a disease in which patients are with rare exceptions deemed not responsible." Yet he concedes that: "Forensic psychiatrists often experience difficulties when...symptoms are mild and the presence or absence of schizophrenia must be established." The diagnosis may then be made on a history of psychiatric symptoms in the past, that is long before the offense was committed, and, also possibly in the *absence of symptoms* at the time of the offense. Thus, the defendant may appear normal when under psychiatric examination, but according to the Snezhnevsky school, still harbor the disease.[62]

---

be diseases, nervous disorders among certain people in Communist society? Evidently yes. If that is so, then there will also be offenses which are characteristic of people with abnormal minds.... To those who might start calling for opposition to Communism on this basis, we can say that...clearly the mental state of such people is not normal" (*Pravda*, May 24, 1959).

[62] Sidney Bloch, "Soviet Psychiatry and Snezhnevskyism," in Robert van Voren, ed., *Soviet Psychiatric Abuse in the Gorbachev Era*, p.56.

Another catch-all diagnosis that was commonly applied to people detained for particularly "puzzling" or "flagrant" acts of ideological dissent in the Soviet Union from the 1950s onwards was "paranoid psychosis." A wide repertoire of nonconformist behaviors was, however, shared between both sets of sufferers. These included: "reformist delusions," "litigation mania," "overvalued (or excessive) religiosity," "serious illegal acts [such as] the writing of complaints," "slander and dissemination of false information," "persistent ideas of reform that tend to be convincing to others and tend to cause recurrent illegal actions" and even "an interest in poorly-understood and bizarre foreign fashions and trends in art, literature and philosophy, and discussion of such interests."[63] The State's medico-legal punishment for such activities, moreover, was severe. According to a report on the authorities' handling of nineteen such cases:

> Their pattern of adaptation changes to such a degree that their life undergoes a fundamental change; they dedicate their activities entirely to the struggle for their idea, which they often characterize as a "struggle for justice"... [However,] environmental change, the strict regime of a psychiatric ward, the impossibility of a continuation of their pathological litigious activity, sedative and neuroleptic medication, all served to normalize their behavior rather quickly.[64]

The standard Soviet textbooks on forensic psychiatry were required reading for Chinese legal psychiatrists from the mid-1950s onwards, and full Chinese translations of Morozov's works were widely available in China from at least the early 1960s and possibly earlier. Even in the 1990s, favorable references to the Soviet school of forensic psychiatry were quite commonly found among the pages of the Chinese professional literature. Several recently published textbooks, moreover, still contain the full or partial texts of the main Soviet-era laws and regulations on the compulsory hospitalization of mentally ill offenders.[65] In classifying the schizophrenic conditions, the Russian term

---

[63] This list of symptoms is taken from a series of translations from official Soviet forensic psychiatric reports that appear in Semyon Gluzman, *On Soviet Totalitarian Psychiatry* (International Association on the Political Use of Psychiatry [IAPUP] Amsterdam, 1989), pp.39-44.

[64] L.N. Diamant, "Issues in Clinical Evaluations and Compulsory Treatment of Psychopathic Personalities with Paranoid Delusions and Overvalued Ideas," cited in Gluzman, *On Soviet Totalitarian Psychiatry*, p.40.

[65] For example, the now discredited Soviet laws on forensic psychiatric hospitalization are extensively quoted in two Chinese textbooks published in 1992 (when the Soviet

vyalotekushchaya can be rendered in English as either "sluggish" or (more broadly) as "latent"; the Chinese medical lexicon lists latent or sluggish schizophrenia as *qianyinxing jingshenfenliezheng*.[66] As late as 1994, the condition was still listed as being one of several officially acknowledged "borderline states,"[67] but from the 1980s onwards, it rarely appears in the relevant literature.[68] In the earliest known examples of political-style psychiatric diagnosis in China, which date from the early 1960s, the less specific term "schizophrenia," in either an undifferentiated or a "paranoid" form, appears to have been the most prevalent label used.

In China, as in the former Soviet Union, the diagnosis of schizophrenia was and continues to be made in a far higher proportion of mental illness cases than in most other countries. Moreover, where diagnosed schizophrenics commit crimes and are brought for forensic psychiatric assessment in China, a finding of "absence of legal responsibility" — leading to the high likelihood of compulsory forensic hospitalization — is almost invariably made. For example, among 386 cases of schizophrenic offenders forensically assessed in the Beijing and Tianjin areas between 1978 and 1987, no fewer than 97.5 percent of the examinees were

---

Union was finally collapsing). See Li Congpei, ed., *Sifa Jingshenbingxue*, pp.404-406. See also Chen Weidong et al., "Chapter 9: Litigation Procedures for the Adoption of Coercive Medical Measures," in *Xingshi Tebie Chengxu de Shijian yu Tantao (Practice and Explorations in Special Criminal Procedure)* (People's Court Publishing House, 1992), pp.467-505. See also Shen Zheng, ed., *Falü Jingshenbingxue (Legal Psychiatry)* (China Politics and Law University Press, 1989), pp.64-68.

[66] The Chinese term *"qianyinxing jingshenfenliezheng"* was specifically used, for example, by the leading forensic psychiatrists Jia Yicheng and Ji Shumao in a brief account of criticisms made against Soviet political psychiatry at an international academic conference in 1977 (see Jia Yicheng, ed., *Shiyong Sifa Jingshenbingxue*, p.15). Note that the Chinese term for "sluggish schizophrenia" is not to be confused with that used for "chronic schizophrenia": *"manxing jingshenfenliezheng."*

[67] See Zhai Jian'an, ed., *Shiyong Fayixue Cidian (A Dictionary of Applied Forensic Science)*, (People's Health Publishing House, September 1994), p.18.

[68] Where "sluggish schizophrenia" is mentioned in Chinese sources, it is usually accompanied by cautionary remarks about the need to avoid "over-diagnosing" the condition. The principal objection, however, seems not to stem from any concerns about the possible use of political psychiatry, but is rather that the diagnosis of this "borderline condition" in the case of criminal offenders, and a resultant finding of non-imputability, can lead to their escaping punishment for serious crimes. One author, for example, recounts the case of a rapist who was diagnosed as having "sluggish schizophrenia" and was then promptly released by the police, to the consternation of the victim's family; a fresh forensic appraisal was arranged and the man was eventually ruled to bear "partial legal responsibility" for his crime (Jia Yicheng, *Shiyong Sifa Jingshenbingxue*, pp.196-198).

found to be "not legally responsible" for their actions.[69] Furthermore, other studies indicate that "cases of a political nature" have accounted for a very high proportion of the targets of assessment. In a study of 181 cases of schizophrenic offenders forensically examined at the Harbin No.1 Special Hospital between 1976 and 1980, political cases involving "reactionary speeches," "sticking up posters with absurd content" and "shouting reactionary slogans" amounted to 59 in number, or 33.3 percent of the total.[70] Another authoritative account from the same period, moreover, put the figure for the country as a whole at an overwhelmingly high level: "In [psychiatrically appraised criminal] cases involving political speech and expression, schizophrenia sufferers accounted for 91 percent of the total, and 70 percent of these were chronic schizophrenics who had been living at large in society."[71] The shadow of Soviet-era political psychiatry looms conspicuously in all these reports.

From the late 1970s and early 1980s onwards in China, the diagnosis of choice in political cases appears to have shifted towards "paranoid psychosis" and its various sub-categories (e.g., "litigious mania"), although schizophrenia continued also to be diagnosed. As we shall see, while the medical connotations are substantially different, the diagnosis of "paranoid psychosis" shares many of the characteristic features of vagueness, non-specificity and "apparent normality" found in the case of Soviet-style "sluggish schizophrenia."[72]

---

[69] Li Congpei, et al., "An Analysis of Forensic Psychiatric Evaluations in Cases of Schizophrenia," *Chinese Journal of Nervous and Mental Diseases*, vol. 20, no.3 (1987), pp.135-138. Incidentally, one of the scholarly sources referred to in this article is a book by Georgi Morozov.

[70] Wu Xinchen, "An Exploration of the Hallmarks of Criminal Behavior Among Schizophrenics," *Chinese Journal of Nervous and Mental Diseases*, vol.16, no.6 (1983), pp.338-339.

[71] Luo Dahua, ed., *Fanzui Xinlixue (Psychology of Crime)*, (Qunzhong Chubanshe [volume marked "for internal distribution only"], 1984), p.216. The Chinese phrase "living at large in society" (*sanju zai shehuishang*) is a somewhat pejorative term generally used in respect of "socially undesirable elements" whom the authorities feel should be placed under some form of supervision or restriction; in this case, it probably signifies that the alleged schizophrenics had not previously been institutionalized in any way.

[72] As two expert observers of the Soviet psychiatric scene later remarked, a diagnostic shift in a broadly similar direction also occurred in the Soviet Union around the same period. According to one of the experts, Richard J. Bonnie, a legal academic who participated in a 1989 visit to the USSR by an American psychiatric delegation that examined a number of psychiatrically-detained Soviet dissidents,

> In the mid-1980s, Soviet psychiatric officials began to acknowledge that a pattern of "hyperdiagnosis" had resulted in inappropriate psychiatric labeling and unnecessary hospitalization in the USSR. It

A brief outline of the therapeutic regime that came into being in the Chinese psychiatric field in the 1950s may also be useful. In light of the intense controversy that exists in the West over several of these therapies, it is important to bear in mind that the therapeutic resources available to psychiatrists throughout the world at that time were highly limited in both range and effectiveness, especially with respect to the major psychiatric diseases such as schizophrenia. Until the early part of the twentieth century, psychiatrists everywhere were largely helpless to relieve the catastrophic symptoms of these illnesses, and sufferers were for the most part simply warehoused in primitive insane asylums. During the inter-War period, however, several new treatments marked a major turning point in psychiatric clinical practice. One was insulin coma therapy, discovered in 1927 by Manfred Sakel, a Polish neurophysiologist and psychiatrist;[73] another was electroconvulsive shock therapy (ECT), discovered by the neurologists Ugo Cerletti and Lucio Bini in Rome in 1937; a

---

was therefore noteworthy that Soviet psychiatrists who interviewed the twenty-seven patients concurrently with the U.S. team in 1989 found no current evidence of schizophrenia in the cases of fourteen patients who were thought to be without mental disorder by the U.S. psychiatrists. However, it is also noteworthy that the Soviet psychiatrists nonetheless still retained *some* psychiatric diagnosis for most of these patients. In this respect, the U.S. delegation found continuing evidence of "hyperdiagnosis," particularly in the tendency to characterize these patients as having "psychopathy," a term that seems to be roughly equivalent to the general concept of personality disorder. Specific examples of "psychopathic" symptoms identified in the interviews by Soviet psychiatrists included "unitary activity," which related to a high level of commitment to a single cause, such as political reform, and "failure to adapt to society," which was used to describe a dissident patient who was "unable to live in society without being subject to arrest for his behavior." One of the Soviet psychiatrists was asked whether a patient who had been sent to a special hospital for distributing anti-Soviet leaflets presented a danger to society. "Of course not," he responded, "everything the patient distributed can be read in the newspapers now." As this observation implies, what had changed was the meaning of a socially dangerous act, not the meaning of mental disorder. (Richard J. Bonnie and Svetlana V. Polubinskaya, "Unraveling Soviet Psychiatry," *The Journal of Contemporary Legal Issues*, no.10 (1999), pp.285-286.)

[73] In the course of treating diabetics, "Sakel discovered accidentally, by causing convulsions with an overdose of insulin, that the treatment was efficient with patients afflicted with psychosis, particularly schizophrenia" (Renato M.E. Sabbatini, "The History of Shock Therapy in Psychiatry," *Brain and Mind*, no. 4 (Dec. 1997-March 1998) (electronic magazine on neuroscience, found at http://www.epub.org.br/cm/history_i.htm).

third was the psychosurgical technique of prefrontal lobotomy, discovered in 1936 by Egas Moniz, a Portuguese neuropsychiatrist. The history of psychiatry is replete with major instances and patterns of the abuse of all these forms of treatment, especially in America and Europe in the 1940s and 1950s.[74] With the next important breakthrough in the treatment of mental illness — the synthesis and widespread dissemination from the early 1950s onwards of major antipsychotic medications such as chlorpromazine — the use of these earlier therapies greatly declined in most countries.

It is clear from the Chinese psychiatric literature of the late 1950s and early 1960s that ECT and insulin coma therapy were in widespread clinical use in China (as in the U.S. and other Western countries) by that time, and that the theory and practice of these techniques had been learned directly from the Soviets.[75] Viewed in historical context, and when used for genuine therapeutic

---

[74] The best overview of the extensive misuse of somatic therapies in the West is Elliot S. Valenstein, *Great and Desperate Cures: The Rise and Decline of Psychosurgery and Other Radical Treatments* (Basic Books, February 1986). Tens of thousands of lobotomies were performed in the United States from 1936 until around 1952. The most egregious practitioner was the American neurologist Walter Freeman, who invented a technique known as "ice-pick lobotomy," which took no more than a few minutes to perform. According to one account, "This procedure was so ghastly, however, that even seasoned and veteran neurosurgeons and psychiatrists could not stand the sight of it, and sometimes fainted at the 'production line' of lobotomies assembled by Freeman." Moreover, "[Lobotomies were] widely abused as a method to control undesirable behavior, instead of being a last-resort therapeutic procedure for desperate cases...Families trying to get rid of difficult relatives would submit them to lobotomy. Rebels and political opponents were treated as mentally deranged by authorities and operated [upon]" (Sabbatini, *The History of Shock Therapy*). The use of psychosurgery did not really end in the U.S. until the 1970s (partly as a result of the influence of the film "One Flew Over the Cuckoo's Nest"), and since then there have continued to be voices (so far, mainly in the wilderness) seeking to bring it back. Finally, according to a leading authority on medical ethics, "ECT stands practically alone among the medical/surgical interventions in that its misuse was not so much an overzealous effort to cure patients but to control them so as to benefit hospital staff." (David J. Rothman, Director of the Center for the Study of Society and Medicine at the Columbia College of Physicians and Surgeons, New York; personal communication to the author, July 11, 2002,)

[75] For example, while acknowledging insulin coma treatment to be a "radical therapy with very severe side effects," one study reported that at the Nanjing Mental Hospital in 1958 (the peak year of Mao's "Great Leap Forward," when the entire nation was being urged to make "greater, faster, better and more economical" strides towards Communism), doctors had begun applying the therapy to some 500 patients "on a continual daily basis...omitting the [previous] weekly rest day" (Tao Guotai et al., "Clinical Observations on 2,663 Cases of Insulin Shock Treatment," *Chinese Journal of Nervous and Mental Diseases*, no.1,1960, pp.19-24; Bao Zhongcheng et al., "Clinical Observations on 400 Cases of Electro-shock Therapy," *Chinese Journal of Nervous and Mental Diseases*, no.1, 1960, pp.28-30; and Wang Jingxiang, "China's Achievements Over the Past Decade in Insulin Shock Therapy Work," *Chinese Journal of Nervous and*

purposes, neither therapy would appear to be particularly controversial. According to reports from former victims of political psychiatric abuse in China, however, both insulin coma treatment and ECT (without concomitant use of sedatives or muscle relaxants) were often used by psychiatric staff from the 1960s onwards as methods of punishment rather than of treatment. ECT remains in widespread use in Chinese mental hospitals today.

Regarding the use of psychosurgery, an official source states that Chinese neurosurgeons carried out numerous cases of human prefrontal lobotomy between 1949 and 1955 at hospitals in Tianjin, Nanjing, Shanghai, Beijing and Xian, but that the practice was discontinued for many years thereafter.[76] This was due to the fact that psychosurgery was banned from the mid-1950s onwards in the Soviet Union, where it was seen as contravening the "conditioned reflex" orthodoxies of the Pavlov school. The same source adds, however, that in 1986 a number of Chinese hospitals began to perform such operations once again, reportedly of a kind involving less drastic surgical intervention than had been required in the earlier series of operations.[77] Other studies indicate a further rise in the use of psychosurgery in China in recent years.[78] As one Western scholar writes,

> Psychosurgery is also reemerging. During a visit to Guangzhou in 1988 I was told that one hospital had provided 20 patients to undergo this kind of surgery in the previous two

---

Mental Diseases, no.6, 1959, pp.349-351.) Another form of treatment that was apparently widely used in Chinese mental hospitals at this time was "artificial hibernation therapy" (*dongmian liaofa*), a prolonged state of deep sleep induced by means of either chlorpromazine hydrochloride or wintermin (*dongmian ling*); a less radical version of this treatment was known simply as "sleep therapy" (*shuimian liaofa*).

[76] Shen Zheng, *Falü Jingshenbingxue*, pp.1016-1017; and Zhu Qihua et al., eds., *Tianjin Quanshu (An Encyclopedia of Tianjin)* (Tianjin People's Publishing House, December 1991), p.630.

[77] Technical advances in recent decades have led to the widespread use internationally of less invasive forms of psychosurgery than those generally used before. Known as "stereotactic" techniques, these allow more precise and less damaging surgical interventions (for example, leucotomy and cingulotomy) to be carried out in place of the former "broad spectrum" lobotomy procedure.

[78] See, e.g., "Observations on the Effectiveness of Stereotactic Brain Surgery in Cases of Schizophrenia with Aggressive Behavior," *Chinese Journal of Nervous and Mental Diseases*, vol. 18, no. 3 (1992), pp.153-155; and "A Follow-up Review of Stereotactic Brain Surgery in Cases of Chronic Schizophrenia," *Zhonghua Shenjing Waike Zazhi (Chinese Journal of Neurosurgery)*, vol. 8, no. 4 (1992), pp.263-265.

years. In a visit to a hospital in Beijing in 1989, I discovered that doctors in Beijing and Tientsin [Tianjin] were collaborating on a psychosurgery project. It was clear from reading some of the files of the patients, who had had psychosurgery in Guangzhou, that selection and monitoring before or after the operation, as well as the procedure itself, gave great cause for concern.[79]

Most worryingly, according to a reliable eyewitness report, the Ankang forensic-psychiatric facility in the city of Tianjin had by 1987 established a large and technically advanced unit for carrying out psychosurgical operations; the director of the institute at the time was a neurosurgeon, and dozens of lobotomies and similar brain operations were reportedly being performed on inmates there each year.[80]

Three general varieties of ethically suspect or abusive psychiatry will be singled out for attention in the following discussion. The first involves a phenomenon known within the psychiatric profession as "hypo-diagnosis," or the under-diagnosing of mental illness. In China, within the legal or forensic domain, this was most often seen in the cases of people who apparently were suffering from some form of mental illness, but whose symptoms included

---

[79] Veronica Pearson, "Law, Rights and Psychiatry in the People's Republic of Psychiatry," p. 420. Pearson continues by saying, "Other matters for concern are the lack of consent to treatment, (particularly hazardous and irreversible practices), the custodial nature of most settings, the lack of any effective protection against compulsory detention, the summary removal of civil status, and the lack of an appeal mechanism." It should be noted, however, that she then states: "Reading through hundreds of case files, I have found no evidence that sane people are being detained for political offenses. When the direct question has been put as to why this does not happen in China, the consensus is that there is no need. There are other ways of dealing with dissidents that do not require the inappropriate utilization of a scarce and expensive hospital bed." Pearson continues, "There are undoubtedly people in psychiatric hospitals whose breakdowns have been precipitated by political events, or persecution for political reasons, but that is a different matter." Although a correct and reasonable observation in itself, the latter point by no means exhausts the wide repertoire and typology of "cases of a political nature" found in China since 1949. In particular, it misses the core question of why, in China, such people are commonly dealt with on the forensic (criminal) psychiatric track, rather than under normal mental healthcare procedures. The more sinister variations on this theme are discussed in detail below.

[80] The source is a doctor who wishes to remain anonymous; however, official confirmation that a lobotomy unit had been established at the Tianjin facility appeared in "*Gong'an Xitong Jingshenbing Guan-Zhi Gongzuo Chengxiao Xianzhu* (Public Security System's Work of Custody and Treatment of the Mentally Ill Achieves Conspicuous Results)," *Renmin Gong'an Bao (People's Public Security News)*, May 18, 1990, p.1.

random or disconnected "political ravings" of a kind that the police viewed as being reactionary or "anti-government." Owing to the extreme sensitivity of political discourse in post-1949 China, forensic psychiatrists came under strong implicit pressure from the authorities to interpret such utterances in a literal, or face-value, sense; the "offenders" would then be found "legally responsible" for their acts or statements, and duly sentenced as political enemies of the State. This represents one important instance (or medico-legal trope) of the "totalitarian" distortions of psychiatry found first in the Soviet Union and later, especially during the Cultural Revolution, in China.

The second relevant category is that of "hyperdiagnosis," or the excessively broad clinical determination of mental illness. Within the legal domain in China, this has been reflected in a tendency on the part of forensic psychiatrists to diagnose as severely mentally ill, and therefore legally non-imputable for their alleged offenses, certain types of dissident or nonconformist detainees who were perceived by the police as displaying a puzzling "absence of instinct for self-preservation" when staging peaceful political protests, expressing officially banned views, pursuing legal complaints against corrupt or repressive officialdom, etc. This particular ethical distortion, which was perhaps the main hallmark of Soviet-era "totalitarian-style" psychiatry, is the one that has been most conspicuously in evidence, or readily apparent, in China for the past two decades and more.

A third category of politically motivated ethical abuse within the field of Chinese legal psychiatry can be summed up under the heading of severe medical neglect. In certain respects, the problem of hypo-diagnosis can be seen as one major sub-form of the latter, since it resulted in numerous mentally ill individuals being sent to prison as political "counter-revolutionaries" and then denied all medical or psychiatric care for many years in an environment bound only to worsen their mental condition. But there was also a much broader aspect to the phenomenon, reflected both in the absence of medical-care provision for mentally ill prisoners in general, and, more specifically, in the deliberate withholding of such care from political offenders whom the authorities had already clearly diagnosed as being mentally ill.[81]

---

[81] The nature and significance of such medical neglect appears to have been different during the two main historical periods since 1949. Prior to 1978, it seems mainly to have resulted from a policy of deliberate official discrimination against mentally ill political offenders, who were seen as being too "heinous" in their crimes to merit any humanitarian attention, let alone proper psychiatric care; at that time, somewhat ironically, the fact that China's mental healthcare resources were much scarcer and even less well-developed than they nowadays are seems to have been a factor of secondary importance in the absence or denial of psychiatric care. In the post-Cultural Revolution

One of the best-documented examples of the latter form of abuse arose in the late 1950s and concerned a prominent Chinese writer named Lu Ling. From 1952 to 1955, a group of leading figures on the Chinese literary scene, including Lu Ling and led by the famous writer Hu Feng, came under increasing attack from the Party's cultural commissars for their alleged repudiation of Mao's doctrine that arts and literature should follow the path of "socialist realism" and serve the interests of the workers and peasants, and for their stubborn adherence to such "bourgeois notions" as the literary genre of "subjective inner realism." In July 1954, both Hu and Lu issued long written rebuttals of the charges against them, and the following year, the Party launched its first major political crackdown against China's intellectual establishment since 1949. Hu Feng was sent to jail for more than twenty years and many of his associates received lesser prison terms.

Lu was married, with three daughters, and was thirty-three years old at the time of his initial arrest in June 1955. During his first few years in detention, his refusal to admit any serious wrongdoing led to ever-harsher treatment at the hands of the authorities, and he eventually began to show clear signs of mental disturbance. In June 1959, after four years of solitary confinement without formal charge, during which he had been forced by his inquisitors to write endless screeds of self-denunciatory material, he finally exploded and wrote a second major rebuttal of all the charges against him. For this "odious act of resistance," he was transferred to China's primary detention facility for high-ranking political criminals, the secretive and much-feared Qincheng Prison, located just north of Beijing. For further resisting "ideological reform" and for moaning or shouting incoherently, he was often left bound and handcuffed by his jailers, although still held in solitary confinement. Finally, in early 1961, his sanity deteriorated to the point where the authorities decided to transfer him for secure custody and treatment to the capital's Anding psychiatric hospital. After three years of intensive medication, he was deemed ready for release and

---

period, by contrast, there is little evidence to suggest that psychiatric care has continued to be withheld from mentally ill prisoners on solely political grounds, and it is instead the persistent scarcity of such resources more generally that mainly explains the continuing problem of widespread medical neglect within the country's prison system. However, for the apparently small minority of psychiatrically incarcerated offenders in the post-1978 era who may, in fact, have been mentally ill at the time of committing their "political crimes," forced psychiatric custody also represents an abusive type of treatment that might best be described as a politically-motivated form of medical neglect. In such cases, the authorities' fallacious ascription of a criminal nature and purpose to the acts of mentally disordered speech or behavior in question means that the sufferer, whilst being denied access to proper and appropriate forms of medical care, is also placed in a coercive judicial setting that can only exacerbate his or her mental condition, especially if the underlying illness is of a paranoid nature.

allowed to return home on conditions of medical bail. For a year, he sat quietly at home, in an apparently catatonic state of post-traumatic stress, then in 1965 he began writing a long series of "petition letters" to the authorities seeking redress for his treatment at their hands. According to a recently published account of Lu's case, these writings were largely incoherent:

> Oh, but what letters they were! Some were left unaddressed, others had no recipient's name written on them; most of them were incomprehensible, or filled with random abuse as if written by a small child; some were even marked for the attention of "Queen Elizabeth" and suchlike, bringing to mind the various mad characters of Chekhov's plays. They were filled with a cold and remote sense of despair...[82]

The security authorities, however, interpreted these sad scribblings differently, and in November 1965 Lu was rearrested and sent back to Qincheng Prison on charges of engaging in "active counterrevolutionary activities." He was to remain there, in continuous solitary confinement and reduced to spending most of his waking hours muttering incoherently at the cell wall, until June 1974, by which time he had lost all semblance of sanity. In 1979, after several years spent sweeping the streets of the capital "under supervision by the masses," he received an official letter of rehabilitation from the Beijing Intermediate People's Court:

> This Court has carried out a review and determined the following. On the question of Lu Ling's participation in the Hu Feng [Anti-Party] Clique, the Ministry of Public Security reached a conclusion on the matter in 1969 and thus no further action will be taken. As regards the more than thirty counterrevolutionary letters that Lu Ling wrote and mailed out between July and November 1964: since these actions resulted from the fact that he was afflicted by mental illness at the time, he should not be held criminally responsible for them.[83]

---

[82] Zhu Hengqing, *Lu Ling: Wei Wancheng de Tiancai (Lu Ling: A Talent Unfulfilled)*, (Shandong Wenyi Chubanshe, April 1997), pp.112-113. This book provides the most detailed account to date of all aspects of Lu Ling's case.

[83] Ibid., p.113.

Some months later, Lu received a second letter from the court, stating: "Regardless of whether [you were] sane or insane, the expression of 'politically hostile'[84] language should never be seen as grounds for bringing charges of counterrevolution." This statement probably marked the high point of official efforts to reform China's highly repressive laws on political dissent; as we shall see, however, it proved to be little more than an ephemeral blip on the country's law enforcement horizon.[85]

For several decades in China, therefore, two distinct but closely related forms of political abuse have coexisted within the broad domain of Chinese law and psychiatry: on the one hand, an official reluctance to extend appropriate medical care to mentally ill prisoners convicted of political offenses, on the implicit grounds that the heinous nature of their offenses rendered them ineligible for even the most basic humanitarian consideration; and on the other, a parallel and rather more sophisticated tendency, inherited from the Soviet psychiatric tradition, according to which the uninhibited expression of ideologically unorthodox views was seen, in certain cases, as indicative of

---

[84] The Chinese term used was *gongji*: technically, this means simply "hostile" or "attacking," but when used in Chinese legal discourse (especially in the phrase "*e'du gongji*" — "viciously attacking") in connection with proscribed acts of speech or writing, it invariably means "politically hostile."

[85] The same sentiment as that expressed in the court decision on Lu Ling's case appeared in March 1979 in one of the country's main daily newspapers: "In order genuinely to protect the democratic rights of the Chinese people, the following must be clearly and unequivocally written into the Constitution and the law: 'Speech shall not be taken as a grounds for the crime of counterrevolution. Whoever determines the crime of counterrevolution on the basis of a person's acts of expression shall himself be guilty of a criminal offense'" (*Guangming Ribao*, March 10, 1979). (For the full background story on the publication of this remarkable article, see Xu Bing and Min Sheng, "Reminiscences on the Article '*Speech is No Crime* and *Making Speech a Crime*'," in Guo Daohui et al., eds., *Zhongguo Dangdai Faxue Zhengming Shilu [A Record of the Contention on the Science of Law in Contemporary China]*, [Hunan Renmin Chubanshe, 1998], pp.183-189.) Ten years later, however, this bold opinion was roundly dismissed in the following terms in a textbook on criminal law: "Viewpoints such as this run contrary to the stipulations of China's Criminal Law and are therefore wrong" (Gan Yupei, ed., *Xingfaxue Zhuanlun [Essays on Criminal Law]* [Beijing University Publishing House (volume marked: "for internal use only"), November 1989], p.512).

The *locus classicus* post-Cultural Revolution document on why "hostile speech or statements" (especially those directed against State and Party leaders) were still to be dealt with as a criminal offense is the CPC's Central Political-Legal Commissions' *Opinion on the Question of Whether Viciously Attacking or Slandering Central Leading Comrades Constitutes a Crime*, December 17, 1981; a full translation (by Donald C. Clarke) can be found on the Internet at http://faculty.washington.edu/dclarke/public/clpc-opinion.htm.

"mental pathology" in an ostensibly legal and medical sense. Indeed, where the politically sensitive field of forensic psychiatry is concerned, there appears to have been little, since 1949, in the way of a stable middle-ground between these seemingly divergent tendencies, both of which were equally disreputable from the point of view of international standards. With the onset of the Cultural Revolution, however, the distinction in China between "political crime" and "political insanity" was lost entirely.

The Cultural Revolution

> *Political cases: These are very seldom mentioned in the literature of other countries. According to a survey done by this author of forensic psychiatric appraisal cases carried out at the Shanghai Municipal Mental Health Center over the period 1970-71, however, political cases accounted for 72.9 percent of the total. This had to do with the particular historical circumstances of that time.*
> — Zheng Zhanpei, 1988[86]

On the afternoon of January 7, 1967, as China sank ever deeper into the social and political turmoil of the Cultural Revolution, a bizarre conversation took place at the Anding Hospital, Beijing's foremost psychiatric institution, between a group of Red Guard activists and two of Chairman Mao's closest colleagues in the new ultra-leftist Party leadership, Qi Benyu and Wang Li. The topic of discussion was a group of mental patients who had earlier been detained for treatment at the hospital after making "reactionary statements" about President Liu Shaoqi, Mao's erstwhile senior colleague but now principal adversary in the Party leadership, and whom the Red Guards had recently "liberated" from their confinement. The conversation went, in part, as follows:

> *Qi Benyu:* You Red Guards are the pioneers of rebellion in
> China's mental asylums, you are rebels against Revisionism;

---

[86] Shen Zheng, ed., *Falü Jingshenbingxue*, p.314. According to an official biography of Zheng Zhanpei published in 1999, "He has worked at the Shanghai Municipal Institute for the Prevention and Treatment of Mental Illnesses (now called the Shanghai Municipal Mental Health Center) from 1960 up to the present" (Xie Bin, "*Sifa Jingshenbingxuejia Zheng Zhanpei Jiaoshou,*" in *Falü Yu Yixue Zazhi* [*Journal of Law and Medicine*], vol. 6, no. 3 [1999], p.99). Among many other posts Zheng now holds, he is concurrently Chairman of the Shanghai Municipal Experts Committee for Psychiatric Judicial Appraisals and Adviser to the Shanghai Municipal Bureau of Reform Through Labor.

in the future, the Soviet Union will need to carry out a cultural revolution and do the same kind of thing!

Red Guard: I request permission...to conduct similar revolutionary liaison activities in mental asylums throughout the country.

Wang Li: Our purpose in coming here today is to support you.

Qi Benyu (to a recently discharged mental patient): Are you mad?

Wang Fuxian: No...I just had different views and opinions from other people; I was in the minority. When I rebelled against the authority of my local Party Secretary, they said I was mentally ill.

Qi Benyu: How does that make you mentally ill? They're the ones who are mad! ... If the revisionists ever came to power, they'd have Wang Li and me declared "mentally ill" too![87]

This obscure incident from over thirty years ago provides a rare glimpse into the elusive history of political psychiatry in China. The central figure in the Anding Hospital incident was one Chen Lining, a Party member who had incurred the wrath of Mao's political opponents in the early 1960s by writing articles and wall-posters criticizing the "revisionist" policies of President Liu Shaoqi. As a result, between 1962 and 1966, Chen was incarcerated seven times in mental hospitals and placed under secret arrest by the security police. By January 1967, however, the political tables had been turned. Liu was being attacked nationwide as China's "No.1 Capitalist Roader," and Chen was duly released from the mental asylum and proclaimed by Red Guards to be the "Madman of the New Era" (*xin shidai de kuangren*). In a speech given at the Chinese Academy of Sciences two months later, Chen described a part of his ordeal in forensic-psychiatric detention as follows:

> During my political persecution at the Hunan Provincial Mental Hospital, I was subjected to numerous bouts of drug

---

[87] Transcript taken from "Red Guard Publications: Part III — Special Issues," vol. 16, Center for Chinese Research Materials, Association of Research Libraries, Washington D.C. (1975), pp.5186-5187 (conversation edited here for purposes of conciseness). Grateful acknowledgement is due to Lalagy Pulvertaft for providing source materials on the Anding Hospital incident and also (as discussed below) the cases of Chen Lining and the wife of Lu Dingyi.

interrogation,[88] given electro-convulsive therapy more than 40 times and insulin-coma shock therapy altogether 29 times, and was fed large quantities of chlorpromazine. They treated me like an experimental object and it was all a disguised form of physical torture. It was extremely painful, and by the end, I was left trembling and sweating all over and my memory had started to go.

The details of Chen's medical record from that time are highly revealing. According to an entry made by a psychiatrist in December 1963: "The patient's mental illness has recurred; his counterrevolutionary statements are none other than a pathological mental symptom of his longstanding reactionary views. Diagnosis: schizophrenia." The following year, a psychiatrist at Anding Hospital added a further entry: "Patient's mental condition: thinking clear and alert, interacts well with others, answers questions appropriately... But lacks self-knowledge and is unclear as to why he was placed under criminal investigation in the first place. Initial diagnosis: schizophrenia (paranoid type.)"[89]

A number of key pointers to the history of psychiatric abuse in China can be discerned from the above account. First, as the quotation from People's Daily cited at the start of this article showed, the Chinese leadership was aware of the main facts about Soviet political psychiatry by at least the early 1960s. Second, it transpires that very similar abuses were also to be found in Chinese forensic psychiatry by around the same period. Finally, it appears that a significant campaign, albeit a highly politicized and ultimately destructive one, of public exposure of such practices took place in China well before the existence of

---

[88] *Mazui fenxi* is a practice whereby patients were drugged and questioned in an attempt to find out if they were feigning symptoms of mental illness. Most Chinese psychiatrists now regard this practice as "inhumane and contrary to human rights," but Li Congpei — the eminence *grise* of Chinese forensic psychiatry — was still advocating its use as of 1990 (Li Congpei, ed., *Sifa Jingshenbingxue*, pp.73-74).

[89] See "Red Guard Publications: Part III – Special Issues." Less than a year later, however, when Chen Lining was found to have also said "crazy" things about Chairman Mao, the Red Guards swiftly repudiated him as a political role model and once again branded him a "heinous counterrevolutionary element." A detailed account of this dramatic reversal in Chen's political fortunes (and also in those of his erstwhile patron, Qi Benyu) can be found in "*Cong Chen Lining Anjian Kan Bianse Long Qi Benyu zhi Liu de Fan'geming Zuilian (The Case of Chen Lining Shows Us the Counterrevolutionary Features of the Chameleon-like Qi Benyu and His Ilk)*," published in the Red Guard journal *Xin Bei-Da — Changcheng* (New Beijing University — Great Wall, March 20, 1968), pp.1-4. It is not known what eventually became of Chen.

Soviet political-psychiatric abuse was even known about in the West or had become a focus of Soviet dissident concern.

As the Cultural Revolution unfolded, however, the distinction between political crime and mental illness — one that had apparently been tenuous even at the best of times — was effectively abandoned in Chinese public life. For a decade and more, until roughly 1978, both legal and medical specificity were discarded outright in favor of an essentially pre-modern concept whereby, much as in Europe during the middle ages, the political or religious dissenter was viewed as being possessed by a deeply wicked, or "counterrevolutionary," form of madness; for their part, the genuinely mentally ill were all too often condemned and punished as dangerous political subversives.

As a direct consequence of Qi Benyu's "important directives" at the Anding Hospital meeting of January 1967, a sinister campaign of persecution — later dubbed the "tide of reversing psychiatric verdicts" (*jingshenbing fan'an feng*) — was launched and carried out by Red Guards around the country. A certain number of mental patients were, as in Wang Fuxian's case, released after being found to have the requisite "revolutionary thinking," while others, mostly senior cadres or their relatives, were accused by the ultra-leftists of having been diagnosed as mentally ill and admitted to the hospital solely as a means of protecting them from the political purges then underway. In many more cases, however, genuinely mentally ill people, especially those whose symptoms had included pseudo-political "ravings" against Mao, were dragged out of mental asylums and brutally coerced into "confessing" that they had been sane all along. These unfortunate individuals were then officially reclassified as counterrevolutionaries and either jailed or summarily executed. As Guan Xin, an official of the Zhejiang High People's Court, explained in a restricted-circulation official report of 1981:

> In the course of reviewing trumped-up cases and miscarriages of justice [*yuan jia cuo an*] from that period, numerous cases have been discovered of people who were obviously mentally ill but who were wrongfully imprisoned or even executed as "political lunatics."

> During the ten years of the Cultural Revolution, owing to interference and sabotage from the ultra-leftist line, the issue of the forensic-scientific evaluation of mental illness was for the most part consigned to the rubbish heap. Mentally ill people were convicted of crimes on the basis of their strange utterances and wild language, thereby creating the notion of

the so-called "political lunatic" [*zhengzhi fengzi*] — a
hodgepodge of the two unrelated terms "politics" (signifying
class struggle) and "lunatic" (a state of biological pathology.)[90]

Similarly, Yang Desen, one of China's leading forensic psychiatrists, noted
in 1985: "During the ten years of chaos, a minority of mentally ill people were
wrongfully executed or imprisoned as 'counterrevolutionaries.'"[91] One example
serves to convey the extent of the medico-legal confusion that prevailed during
those years and of the judicial absurdities that resulted. According to Shen
Zheng, another leading authority on forensic psychiatry, during the period 1960-
76, even among an unspecified number of mentally retarded people who were
submitted for forensic-psychiatric evaluation for alleged criminal offenses, "the
main subgroup (31.2 percent) consisted of political cases."[92]

The profound crisis into which China's entire psychiatric profession was
thrown during the Cultural Revolution led to the effective dismantling of mental
healthcare institutions across the country. Also, numerous Chinese psychiatric

---

[90] Guan Xin, "How to Discern Mental Illness and Ascertain Legal Capacity," *"Renmin
Sifa" Xuanbianben 1981 Nian (A Compilation of Articles from "People's Judiciary"
1981)* (volume marked "for internal use only"), (Law Publishing House, 1983), p.590. As
Guan concludes from this grotesque record: "Professional experience has clearly shown
us that in order to avoid the wrongful conviction and execution of the mentally ill, it is
vital that we should disseminate basic knowledge about forensic psychiatry with a view
to correctly identifying the mentally ill and ascertaining the question of their [legal]
responsibility."

[91] Yang Desen, "On the Legal Responsibility of Mentally Ill Persons for Their Illegal
Conduct," *Chinese Journal of Nervous and Mental Diseases*, vol. 11, no. 5 (1985),
pp.310–312. Yang Desen (also known as Young Derson) is head of the psychiatry
department at Hunan Medical College. As the American psychiatrist and anthropologist
Arthur Kleinman observed in his landmark 1986 study of Chinese psychiatry, *Social
Origins of Distress and Disease: Depression, Neurasthenia and Pain in Modern China*,
p.9, Yang was himself the target of political attacks during the Cultural Revolution:
"During these years, Dr. Young, Professor Ling's [i.e., Ling Ming-yu, then head of the
HMC psychiatry department] former student and successor, received equally harsh
treatment from the Red Guards because of his defense of the core psychiatric position
that mental illness is an illness, and not wrong political thinking as the Maoists held."

[92] Shen Zheng, *Falü Jingshenbingxue*, p.217. Even in the late 1990s, mentally impaired
or disabled people were still being arrested on political charges and then subjected to
forensic psychiatric assessment. For example, a study published in April 2000 examining
the question of crimes committed by epileptics noted that the sample group included one
person detained for making "anti-social speeches" (Wei Qingping et al., *"Dianxian
Huanzhe Weifa de Sifa Jingshen Yixue Jianding Fenxi* [An Analysis of Expert Psychiatric
Testimony on Epileptic Patients' Illegal Actions]," *Chinese Journal of Nervous and
Mental Diseases*, vol. 26, no.2 [2000], pp.65-67).

professionals, possibly a majority, were labeled as "bourgeois academic authorities" and either purged outright from their positions or sent down to the countryside, often for many years, to perform manual labor and "learn from the peasants." Medicine in general, and psychiatry in particular, had long been a low-status profession in China, but during these years psychiatrists ranked close to the very foot of the social and political ladder. Virtually the entire intellectual domain of psychiatry and human psychology was officially repudiated, to be subsumed under a crude Maoist universalism whereby "correct political ideology" served not only as the key to social survival, but was moreover equated with mental health in general — and vice versa. Thus, in what little remained at that time of the country's mental healthcare institutions, official wall slogans proclaimed to mental patients: "Without a correct political standpoint, one has no soul."[93] Under this reductionist doctrine, psychiatry and psychiatrists became superfluous, and therapy for the mentally ill consisted largely, until the late 1970s, of group "study sessions" on the works of Mao.[94]

The extreme political pressures of this era inevitably led to pervasive ethical corruption within the field of psychiatry and forensic medicine in general. As one writer put the matter, "In the past, owing to the influence of the extreme 'leftist' line, [forensic psychiatrists] overemphasized 'putting class

---

[93] *"Meiyou zhengque de zhengzhi guandian, jiu dengyu meiyou linghun."* This quotation from Chairman Mao appears in his 1957 article "On the Correct Handling of Contradictions Among the People," in *Selected Works of Mao Tse-tung, Vol. 5* (Beijing, 1977), pp.384-421; the official translation of the quoted sentence differs slightly from that given above.

[94] Given the virtual collapse of the country's mental healthcare system at that time, it is surprising to learn that in the legal or forensic area of psychiatric work, things apparently continued much as they had before the Cultural Revolution. As can be seen from the passages cited above, large numbers of "dangerously mentally ill offenders" apparently continued to be arrested, brought before panels of forensic-psychiatric assessors and then dispatched to secure mental hospitals around the country during the Cultural Revolution. But Communist dictatorships sometimes behave in very strange ways. Pol Pot, for example, in planning his new, improved version of Stalinism and Maoism, made provision for a mental hospital in his Democratic Kampuchea utopia. Construction of this facility for the treatment of insanity was planned in 1976, before his Communist Party had reached the conclusion that everything that was going wrong with the revolutionary society it was trying to build was the result of CIA-KGB-KMT-Vietnamese plots. This paranoid delusion on the part of Pol Pot and other Party leaders led them to decide to apply mass execution, rather than psychiatry, to solve social and political problems, and the hospital was never built. For the plans, see David A.T. Chandler, ed., "The Party's Four-Year Plan to Build Socialism in All Fields, 1977-1980," *Pol Pot Plans the Future, Yale University Southeast Asian Studies Monograph No.33* (New Haven: 1988), p.109. With thanks to Dr. Stephen R. Heder, Lecturer in Politics at the School of Oriental and African Studies, London, for this information.

struggle to the fore' and 'making vocational work serve politics,' to the extent that issues of an academic or technical nature were sometimes turned into a question of one's basic political standpoint."[95] According to another official account,

> During those years when class struggle was at the forefront of everything, some [forensic doctors] paid no attention to the principle of seeking truth through facts, and instead took the slogans 'Always be highly conscious of the class struggle' and 'Maintain the highest level of revolutionary vigilance" as their basic guiding ideology for performing forensic evaluations... Some forensic doctors who insisted on upholding the truth were taken in for interrogation, thrown into jail and branded as counterrevolutionaries... Others, however, submitted to political pressure and went against their own consciences, making wrongful forensic evaluations... Still others went so far as to use their scientific knowledge to turn truth and lies upside down, saying black was white, and acting entirely in the service of particular individuals or groups.[96]

In the winter of 1978, a young man named Wei Jingsheng, who was to become China's best-known dissident and who later spent seventeen years in prison for advocating greater human rights and democracy, wrote an article in China's *samizdat* pro-democracy press describing conditions at Qincheng Prison during the Cultural Revolution. His account was probably the first to reveal that psychiatric techniques were being misused in China for purposes of political repression:

> The most common form of torture is simple beating. The prisoner is summoned and surrounded by a group of men who slug and kick until he is bruised, bloody, and completely breathless. Even more common is for prisoners to be so heavily drugged that they become mentally unstable. The

---

[95] Jia Yicheng et al., "On Several Basic Concepts in Forensic Psychiatry," *Chinese Journal of Nervous and Mental Diseases*, vol. 9, no. 2 (1983), p.119.

[96] Zhao Haibo, "On the Fundamental Principles and Methods of Forensic Medical Investigation," in Cui Jian'an, ed., *Zhongguo Fayi Shijian (China's Forensic Medical Practice)*, (Police Officers' Educational Press, August 1993), pp.47-48.

justification for administering these drugs is to cure "mental illness." Sometimes people are sent to the hospital for further "treatment." One person who had received the treatment recalls that after taking the medication he had talked to himself constantly for days on end. Naturally, such monologues were recorded for use during the next interrogation. Among the hospitals that participate in such practices are the Fuxing Hospital, Hospital 301, and Anding Hospital.[97]

Subsequent testimonies from high-ranking government officials who had been incarcerated at Qincheng Prison authoritatively confirmed Wei's general account. According to one former inmate, for example: "Especially inhuman was the practice of...force-feeding you a kind of drug that induced hallucinations."[98] The most vivid and detailed account is that of Mu Xin, a former editor of the *Guangming Daily*, who was arrested in 1968 and held for several years at Qincheng Prison on trumped-up charges of conducting an "anti-Party conspiracy." In his memoir of this period, Mu wrote,

> In the nearly four years from the moment I was thrown into Qincheng Prison to the downfall of Lin Biao, they continuously gave me stimulants. This would happen at least ten to fifteen days every month... They did this with the intention of destroying my brains, not just to impair my memory but also to make me unable to write anything anymore... Even after I returned to my home, having suffered several years of this continuing drugging and poisoning, my brain was severely damaged and traumatized.[99]

---

[97] Wei Jingsheng, "A Twentieth-Century Bastille," in James D. Seymour, ed., *The Fifth Modernization: China's Human Rights Movement*, (New York: Human Rights Publishing Group, 1980), p.217. Wei's article originally appeared in the March 1979 issue of *Tansuo (Explorations)*, a dissident journal founded and edited by Wei the previous winter.

[98] Wang Li, "Wang Li's Testament," *Chinese Studies in Philosophy*, vol. 26, nos. 1-2 (Fall-Winter 1994-95), p.5.

[99] Mu Xin, "Inmate No. 6813 in Qincheng Prison," *Mao's Great Inquisition: The Central Case Examination Group, 1966-1979; Chinese Law and Government*, vol. 29, no. 3 (May-June 1996), pp.74-75. The bizarre lengths that prison guards at Qincheng went to in order to manipulate and control the inmates was related by Mu as follows:

> Before they delivered the newspaper that carried the news of the death of Mr. Dong [Biwu] [one of the founders of the People's

As mentioned earlier, many mental patients, especially senior cadres or their relatives, were accused during the Cultural Revolution of having feigned their illnesses as a means of avoiding punishment for their political opposition toward Mao. One such case involved a woman named Yan Weibing, wife of the then Minister of Propaganda, Lu Dingyi, who was one of the first senior victims of the Cultural Revolution purges. This little-known case bears more than a passing resemblance to the infamous "doctors' plot" concocted in the Soviet Union shortly before Stalin's death.[100] It claimed numerous senior political

---

Republic, who had fallen from official grace during the Cultural Revolution], they surreptitiously gave me a drug that suppresses tears (in fact, many of the female "prisoners" were given this drug before they met with their children who came to meet them in prison). This drug makes it impossible, somehow, for a person to shed tears, no matter how badly he or she might feel. On the other hand, before they delivered the newspaper that carried the news of [the death of] Chiang Kai-shek, they deliberately doped me with some drug that had the opposite effect of the first one. In spite of all this, however, it was most certainly unlikely that I would feel the slightest bit of "grief" at the death of a public enemy of the people like Chiang Kai-shek, and I most certainly would not be able to bring myself to shed tears on his account. Those people were able, in fact, to sense this, and so they ordered the "guard" to pour some liquid sulfuric acid — which attacks one's eyes severely and makes one's eyes all runny — on the ground right outside the door of my cell, and then they tried to fan the fumes into my room in an effort to force me to shed tears, thus allowing them to make a report on my "counterrevolutionary sentiments." (Ibid., pp.92-93.)

[100] The *Encyclopedia Britannica* provides the following summary of this incident:

Doctors' Plot: (1953), alleged conspiracy of prominent Soviet medical specialists to murder leading government and party officials; the prevailing opinion of many scholars outside the Soviet Union is that Joseph Stalin intended to use the resulting doctors' trial to launch a massive party purge. On Jan. 13, 1953, the newspapers Pravda and Izvestiya announced that nine doctors, who had attended major Soviet leaders, had been arrested. They were charged with poisoning Andrey A. Zhdanov, Central Committee secretary, who had died in 1948, and Alexander S. Shcherbakov (d. 1945), who had been head of the Main Political Administration of the Soviet army, and with attempting to murder several marshals of the Soviet army. The doctors, at least six of whom were Jewish, also were accused of being in the employ of U.S. and British intelligence services, as well as of serving the interests of international Jewry. The Soviet press reported that all of the doctors had confessed their guilt. The trial and the rumored purge that was to follow did not occur because the death of Stalin (March 5, 1953) intervened. In April Pravda announced that a reexamination of the case showed the charges against the doctors to

casualties and delivered a traumatic blow to China's psychiatric profession in general. According to an account of the case compiled by Red Guards in June 1968,

> The active counterrevolutionary element Yan Weibing, wife of the counterrevolutionary revisionist clique leader Lu Dingyi, over the six-year period from March 1960 to January 1966 wrote dozens of anonymous counterrevolutionary letters that insanely attacked Deputy Commander Lin Biao, the close comrade-in-arms of our most dearly beloved leader Chairman Mao, and members of his family; she insanely opposed Comrade Lin Biao, and is [thus] an active counterrevolutionary element who has committed towering and heinous crimes.[101]

---

be false and their confessions to have been obtained by torture. The doctors (except for two who had died during the course of the investigation) were exonerated. In 1954 an official in the Ministry of State Security and some police officers were executed for their participation in fabricating the cases against the doctors. In his secret speech at the 20th Party Congress (February 1956), Nikita S. Khrushchev asserted that Stalin had personally ordered that the cases be developed and confessions elicited, the "doctors' plot" then to signal the beginning of a new purge. Khrushchev revealed that Stalin had intended to include members of the Politburo in the list of victims of the planned purge. (See http://www.britannica.com/seo/d/doctors-plot/.)

[101] Documentation Group of the Revolutionary Committee of Beijing College of Politics and Law and Documentation Group of the Capital Red Guards Committee's Politics and Law Commune, "A Shocking Case of Counterrevolution: An Investigative Report into the Attempt by Peng Zhen, Lu Dingyi and their Sinister Lieutenants to Concoct a Counterrevolutionary Phony Medical Diagnosis Aimed at Shielding the Active Counterrevolutionary Element Yan Weibing," *Xingxingsese de Anjian: Liu Deng Peng Luo Shixing Zichanjieji Zhuanzheng de Yangban (All Types of Cases: Model Examples of the Bourgeois Dictatorship Exercised by Liu, Deng, Peng and Luo)*, June 1968, pp.18-33. A whole separate study could fruitfully be done on the topic of the close convergence of political and popular-psychological language during the Cultural Revolution, and on the wholesale semantic degradation that resulted. When the Red Guards accused Mrs. Yan of "insanely attacking" Lin Biao, for example, they meant it both as a serious political allegation and also, more randomly, as a form of sheer political abuse. On a deeper discursive level, however, they seem also to have been acknowledging that she probably was mentally ill, and the phrase "insanely attacking" may thus have been intended as a kind of pseudo-medical, politically reductionist explanation for her allegedly deviant mental behavior. On a much simpler level, of course, the question inevitably arises: who was the more "crazy," she or they?

In fact, Yan had been under psychiatric diagnosis and treatment, including frequent insulin coma therapy, for several years for a mental condition that senior Chinese psychiatrists had determined to be some form of paranoid behavioral disturbance.[102] She suffered frequent outbursts of uninhibited anger, much of which was apparently aimed at Lin Biao's wife, Ye Qun, and to whom she had been sending copious amounts of politically colored "hate mail" in recent years. In the months leading up to the full-scale outbreak of the Cultural Revolution in May 1966, her husband Lu had been considering having her compulsorily admitted to the Anding Hospital for treatment. In the event, all of the psychiatrists and senior government officials responsible for Yan's earlier care and treatment (including Shen Yucun, who survived to become the principal editor of the major PRC textbook on psychiatry after 1978 and head of the WHO's mental health liaison office in Beijing) were branded by Red Guards as having been centrally involved in a "counterrevolutionary conspiracy" to falsely diagnose Yan as mentally ill so that she could be spared punishment for her "insanely hostile" letters against Lin Biao and his wife; at least one of them committed suicide as a result.[103]

The real target of the Red Guards' displeasure, of course, was Lu Dingyi himself, and the evidence of his wife's letters formed a crucial plank in their efforts, soon thereafter successful, to have him dragged from power. Yan's persecutors thus had little time for diagnostic niceties and their final verdict on her mental state was as follows: "What was Yan Weibing's real mental illness? A counterrevolutionary disease of the heart![104] Her mind was extremely alert...and her state of anxiety [reflected only] her high degree of

---

[102] The precise diagnosis, made by psychiatrists two weeks after Yan was formally arrested, was: "Paranoid state on the basis of a sub-acute hysterical personality type" (Ibid., p.31).

[103] The psychiatrist was Shi Shuhan, an official at the Ministry of Health; he took an overdose of barbiturates on August 25, 1966. Among the numerous senior psychiatrists and health officials denounced and punished as "counterrevolutionary conspirators" as a result of the Yan Weibing "false diagnosis" case were: Qian Xinzhong, Minister of Public Health; Huang Shuze, deputy Minister of Public Health and head of the ministry's healthcare bureau; Xue Bangqi, director of the East China Hospital in Shanghai; Shen Yucun, a psychiatrist in the brain medicine department of Beijing Hospital (and wife of Qian Xinzhong); Su Zonghua, director of the Shanghai Hospital for the Prevention of Mental Diseases; Xu Yunbei, a former Party Secretary at the Ministry of Health; Zhang Ziyi, former deputy head of the Party's Propaganda Department; Zheng Xuewen, head of the medical treatment department of the Ministry of Health; and Geng Dezhang, the personal physician of Lu Dingyi.

[104] "Fan'geming de xin-bing."

counterrevolutionary vigilance." She had been under investigation by the Ministry of Public Security for many months on account of the letters to Lin Biao's family, and on April 28, 1966, the central authorities ordered her arrest on charges of counterrevolution. Yan and her husband were to spend the next twelve and a half years in solitary confinement at Qincheng Prison, during which time they were denied even a single meeting together.[105]

Accounts from senior-level cadre victims of the Cultural Revolution purges go only a small way toward explaining, however, the extremely widespread incidence of forensic-psychiatric "cases of a political nature" that was later reported to have occurred during those years. A perhaps more typical story was one related many years later to a Western human rights organization by a former political prisoner, identified only as "Mr. C," who spent a total of more than sixteen years in various labor camps, detention centers and prisons for the "mentally disordered" in China. His account conveys with great clarity the grotesque ironies and injustices that characterized legal psychiatry at that time:

> Summer 1969. After I was arrested as a counterrevolutionary, I was interrogated three times. I did not want to accept any charge for a crime that I had not committed, nor did I want to name any person as having committed any crime. Therefore I was sent to Jiangwan Number 5 [in Shanghai]. This place was known as the "Institute for Diagnosing Mental Disorder" — the setting of my most terrifying experiences during my entire 16 years of imprisonment.

> The whole "institute" was a large cage from within which one could not see the skies. Inside this large cage there were many small cages, which were only half as high as an average person. One could only squat or lie in them, and I had to crawl in and out of mine. They were no better than chicken houses. All those detained in the "institute" were suspected of mental disorder, but being there would truly drive a mentally normal person insane. There, one could constantly hear frightening screams. The wardens tried to stop people from screaming and, when failing to do so, would administer drugs to cause

---

[105] For a detailed account of Lu Dingyi's and Yan Weibing's persecution during the Cultural Revolution, see Chen Qingquan and Song Guangwei, *Lu Dingyi Zhuan* (*A Biography of Lu Dingyi*), (Zhonggong Dang Shi Chubanshe, Beijing, December 1999). Prior to the publication of this book, it was not known what became of Yan following her arrest in April 1996 (Ibid., p.541).

people to lose consciousness and thus become silenced. Once awakened from the drug, one felt very dull, depressed and uncomfortable.

People sent to this institute were mostly those who had committed serious counterrevolutionary crimes such as shouting anti-Mao slogans in public. In order to avoid sentencing of death, these people pretended to be mentally abnormal by screaming nonsense, only to be cruelly beaten and drugged. They were allowed to go out of their small cages to be "aired" once a day, and were given two meals of very thin porridge each day.

Whenever the wardens appeared, I would tell them that I was not mentally disordered and that I would like to talk to them about my problems if only they would let me out of the "institute." Usually, people insisted on their lunacy in order to receive a reduced sentence. Therefore, when I very soberly proclaimed that I was normal, they truly believed me to be a madman.

I did not know how long I would be treated like an animal in a place where fear alone could suffice to drive a person crazy. Many of the inmates I met had been there for more than ten years; some had been imprisoned there for over twenty years. Worse still, when an inmate was diagnosed to be a normal person, he or she would either be executed, given a more severe sentence, or shut up in the cage forever as a "politically insane" criminal.

I was there for only about 100 days. A good-hearted warden, knowing that I was a college student from reading my personal files, secretly released me. I hid for a while, then was arrested again soon after.[106]

---

[106] "Shanghai Detention Center for the Mentally Disordered: An Interview with Mr. C," *Human Rights Tribune* (journal of the New York-based monitoring group Human Rights in China), vol. 1, no. 5 (October 1990), p.16; HRIC's journal is now called *China Rights Forum*.

The place where Mr. C was held — "Jiangwan No. 5" — is believed to be the same institution that in 1987 was renamed as the Shanghai Public Security Bureau's Ankang Center for the Custody and Treatment of the Mentally Ill, located just south of the Fudan University campus on Guoquan North Road. Apart from the appalling conditions of detention that Mr. C describes, what is most striking about his story is the Orwellian complexity and intricacy of the classification of the inmates. Most were arrested "counterrevolutionaries" who had shouted banned political slogans and then been suspected of mental illness. Others, presumably "genuine" counterrevolutionaries, had adopted the survival stratagem, after their arrest, of feigning mental illness in order to avoid being executed for shouting such slogans. Meanwhile Mr. C himself, another political offender, was regarded as indisputably insane by the warders because he had actively chosen to reject this stratagem by declaring himself quite sane. The normal language and conceptual armory of forensic-psychiatric science would seem to be of little direct use as a means of understanding or construing a situation of such utter medico-legal absurdity as this one.

One further issue that should be briefly addressed here concerns the extent and quality of psychiatric care available to criminal offenders in general in China since 1949. The focus here is on the theme, as noted above, of medical neglect, rather than of either hypo-diagnosis or hyperdiagnosis; in practice, though, these various divergent themes were often complexly intermingled. The U.N.'s basic document in this area, the Standard Minimum Rules for the Treatment of Prisoners, stipulates that seriously mentally ill persons are not to be held in prisons and that less severely disturbed inmates are to be given appropriate medical care.[107]

Since prison systems in most countries are notoriously under-resourced in terms of their ability to provide psychiatric treatment for mentally ill offenders, in practice these provisions are often widely ignored. China's shortcomings in this respect should thus, in principle, occasion little surprise or blame. For decades after 1949, however, the PRC prison authorities applied a policy of actively withholding appropriate medical care in the case of major political

---

[107] See especially Article 82 of the Standard Minimum Rules and Procedures for the Effective Implementation of the Rules, (United Nations [New York: Department of Public Information, 1984]), adopted by the United Nations on August 30, 1955: "(1) Persons who are found to be insane shall not be detained in prisons and arrangements shall be made to remove them to mental institutions as soon as possible. (2) Prisoners who suffer from other mental diseases or abnormalities shall be observed and treated in specialized institutions under medical management. (3) During their stay in a prison, such prisoners shall be placed under the special supervision of a medical officer. (4) The medical or psychiatric service of the penal institutions shall provide for the psychiatric treatment of all other prisoners who are in need of such treatment."

prisoners suffering from mental illness. According to Article 37 of the 1954 PRC Regulations on Reform Through Labor, prison authorities were not permitted to take custody of offenders suffering from mental illness or other serious diseases, "except in the case of major counterrevolutionary criminals."[108] Since the great majority of all convicted prisoners in China during the 1950s and 1960s were "counterrevolutionaries," this discriminatory policy inevitably meant that large numbers of mentally-ill political prisoners were denied access to proper care throughout their imprisonment. Another abusive practice that seriously compounded this general problem was that, until fairly recently, both sentenced counterrevolutionaries, irrespective of their mental state, and common criminals suffering from mental illness were frequently held in solitary confinement cells throughout their term of imprisonment.[109] An extreme example of the conditions of squalor and misery that could result from this practice was related in a 1983 directive from the Ministry of Public Security:

> In December 1980, the authorities at Yingshan Prison, Guangxi Province, placed a mentally disturbed prisoner in solitary confinement and kept him there for more than two years. They afforded him neither medical treatment nor ideological education. No one cleared away the prisoner's excrement and urine, with the result that a mound of fecal matter thirty-five centimeters high accumulated inside the cell. During the winter of 1982, the prisoner was not supplied with any additional clothing or bed quilt, and as a result of the extreme cold and the noxious gases created by the fermentation of the decaying excrement, the prisoner died in

---

[108] See also Xu Shoubin, "The Legal Protection and Restriction of Rights of the Mentally Ill," *Fazhi Shijie (World of Legality)*, no.6 (1994), p.26. The prohibition on penal institutions taking in mentally ill prisoners was reiterated by the Ministry of Public Security (whose No.11 Bureau ran all such facilities until July 1983 when jurisdiction was transferred to the Ministry of Justice) in Article 9 of the Ministry's 1982 "Detailed Rules on the Disciplinary Administration of Prisons and Labor-Reform Detachments (Trial Draft)," in *A Compilation of Standard Interpretations of the Laws of the People's Republic of China: Supplementary Volume* (Jilin People's Publishing House, 1991), p.798. However, the provisions of Article 37 of the 1954 Regulations remained in force.

[109] Even common criminals with mental illnesses were rarely dealt with according to the provisions of the 1954 Regulations, since virtually no mental healthcare facilities were to be found anywhere in the country's prison system; as late as 1988, the penal network reportedly still contained only two specialized mental hospitals ("Penal-System Medical and Health Work Has Been Greatly Strengthened and Developed in Recent Years," *Fanzui Yu Gaizao Yanjiu [Research in Crime and Reform]*, no.4 [1994], pp.53-55).

January [1983] from the combined effects of cold exposure and gas poisoning.[110]

The same directive ordered that mentally ill prisoners were henceforth not to be placed in solitary confinement and must be given proper medical care and attention. In March 1998, however, a leading southern Chinese newspaper reported the case of a violent prisoner suffering from chronic schizophrenia who had been kept locked by police in an outdoor cage for at least the previous five years. As a result of the publicity, the man was subsequently freed from the cage and placed in a secure mental asylum. According to the newspaper account,

> Reporters found Deng Qilu, the "man in the cage," at Beitan Village, Nanxiang Township, Xuwen County last weekend. The cage had been made [by the police] by welding together reinforced steel pipes and had an area of approximately two square meters inside but had no exit. It was situated in an open yard at the side of the village. The caged man looked to be a little over 40 years old, had grown long whiskers, and was stark naked. When we strangers walked close to the cage, his eyes showed fear and panic.[111]

---

[110] "Notification of Bureau No. 11 of the Ministry of Public Security On Strengthening and Reorganizing the Management of Solitary Confinement Cells (July 12, 1983)," *Zhonghua Renmin Gongheguo Falü Guifanxing Jieshi Jicheng (A Compilation of Standard Interpretations of the Laws of the People's Republic of China)*, (Jilin People's Publishing House, October 1990), pp.1591-1593. (A heavily censored version of the same directive appears in: *Zhonghua Renmin Gongeheguo Jiancha Yewu Quanshu (A Compendium of PRC Procuratorial Work)*, (Jilin People's Publishing House, July 1991), pp.1496-1497.) The directive ordered an immediate tightening up of the administration of solitary confinement units throughout China. For a full translation of China's regulations at that time on the administration of solitary confinement cells (Articles 60–64 of the Ministry of Public Security's February 1982 "Detailed Rules for the Disciplinary Work of Prisons and Labor Reform Detachments"), see Asia Watch (now Human Rights Watch/Asia), "Democracy Wall Prisoners: Xu Wenli, Wei Jingsheng and Other Jailed Pioneers of the Chinese Pro-Democracy Movement," vol. 5, No. 6, March 1993, pp.21-23.

[111] "Man Detained in Iron Cage for Ten Years in Guangdong," *Yangcheng Wanbao*, March 28, 1998; translation from BBC Summary of World Broadcasts, April 13, 1998. (Chinese press reports on the case varied on whether the man had spent five or ten years in the cage.) The background to the case was described in another news report as follows:

> On 29th May, 1999, Deng was detained for investigation after he suddenly stabbed and inflicted serious injury upon a police officer with a sharp weapon measuring 80 cm in length. On 30th July of the same year, the Zhanjiang City Hospital for the Prevention and

A related issue concerns the question of prisoners who went insane or were driven mad during their time in prison. This type of phenomenon, known as "prison psychosis," is common to prison systems around the world, but it was especially frequent and severe in China during the Cultural Revolution.[112] In particular, the police pressure on those arrested for alleged political offenses was often so great that many people began to believe that they actually had committed "towering crimes against the people," notably conspiracy, espionage and political subversion, and in the course of their daily forced-confessional writing sessions in prison, they began to reinterpret large sections of their own pasts in lurid and entirely fabulatory terms. In some cases, this unusual and highly specific form of "politically induced" prison psychosis was driven, at some vestigial level of the person's sanity, by a realization that it was only by constantly amplifying the scale and seriousness of the imagined crimes that one might hope to prolong the police investigation and thereby postpone the day of eventual punishment, which not infrequently meant death.[113] Clinically speaking, the people concerned were already acutely mentally disturbed, but their flights of confessional fantasy, of whose veracity they themselves were quite convinced, would frequently be given blanket credence by the authorities and taken as grounds for criminal conviction.

Treatment of Mental Disease and a forensic psychiatry appraisal team of Zhanjiang City determined: "Deng Qilu has been suffering from dementia praecox for a period of 16 years... In this connection, it is suggested that he be placed under long-term, intensified custody to prevent him from committing violence and injuring others." ("'Caged Man' Set Free," *Yangcheng Wanbao*, March 29, 1998; also in BBC Summary of World Broadcasts, April 13, 1998.)

[112] Recent data, however, show that the condition was rarely if ever diagnosed in China until fairly recently. According to one local study published in 1998, no cases were recorded during the 1980s, but during the 1990s the condition was said to have accounted for 9.2 percent of all cases of forensic psychiatric examination (Zheng Chengshou et al., "*80 Niandai yu 90 Niandai Sifa Jingshenbingxue Jianding Anli de Duizhao Yanjiu* [A Comparative Study on the Case Expertise of Forensic Psychiatrics Between the 1980s and 1990s]," *Zhonghua Jingshenke Zazhi* [*Chinese Journal of Psychiatry*], no.4 [1998], pp.228-230).

[113] One such case from the Cultural Revolution is described at length in Shen Yucun, ed., *Jingshenbingxue*, pp.1106-1107. See also Jia Yicheng, *Shiyong Sifa Jingshenbingxue*, p.513. This particular condition is referred to in Chinese psychiatry as either "delusion-like fantasy syndrome" (*lei wangxiangxing huanxiang zheng*) or "reactive confabulatory syndrome" (*fanyingxing xugou zheng*); the latter diagnosis may be clinically related to a condition known elsewhere as "Korsakoff's syndrome."

In 1979, soon after Deng Xiaoping's return to power, the judicial authorities issued a directive instructing that — "in the interests of revolutionary humanism and so that these offenders do not die in prison" — a nationwide review be carried out of the cases of all "aged, weak, sick and disabled or mentally ill prisoners," and that the majority of such persons be set free.[114] As late as the 1990s, however, reports from the legal-medical literature indicated that many severely mentally ill prisoners in China continued to be held in solitary confinement cells in regular prisons, watched day and night by a roster of prison guards and assigned prisoner "trusties," due to the continued widespread lack of secure psychiatric treatment facilities.[115]

---

[114] "Joint Directive of the Supreme People's Court, Supreme People's Procuratorate and Ministry of Public Security Concerning the Clearing Out of Aged, Weak, Sick and Disabled or Mentally Ill Prisoners," April 16, 1979. All mentally ill (or otherwise infirm) prisoners serving sentences of death with a two-year suspension of execution (*si-huan*) were, however, specifically excluded from the scope of this official amnesty order. A sanitized version of the April 16, 1979, directive, omitting the statistical and other details cited above, appears in many PRC legal anthologies; the unexpurgated version referred to here can be found in *Jiancha Gongzuo Shouce* (*A Handbook of Procuratorial Work*), vol.1 (Kunming: Yunnan Sheng Renmin Jianchayuan, December 1980), pp.281-283. Grateful acknowledgement is due to Lalagy Pulvertaft for kindly providing the uncensored version of this document.

[115] See, e.g., Lin Huai, ed., *Jingshen Jibing Huanzhe Xingshi Zeren Nengli He Yiliao Jianhu Cuoshi* (Capacity of Mental Illness Sufferers for Criminal Responsibility and Measures for Their Medical Guardianship), (Renmin Fayuan Chubanshe, 1996), p.67.

In December 1994, a new Prisons Law of the PRC (passed on December 29, 1994, at the 11th Session of the Standing Committee of the 8th National People's Congress) finally superseded the 1954 PRC Regulations on Reform Through Labor (see *Laodong Gaizao Tiaoli*, in *Gong'an Fagui Huibian* (1950-1979) [Beijing: *Qunzhong chubanshe*, 1980], pp. 397-409). Surprisingly, the current law entirely omits the previous "strict" prohibition on prisons accepting mentally ill offenders into penal custody; this move may perhaps be attributable to the authorities' decision several years earlier to set up the Ankang network of facilities specifically for this purpose, but it still merits further examination. According to Article 17 of the new law, "Prisons shall perform physical examinations on all prisoners turned over to them for punishment. If through physical examination either of the following conditions is found in a prisoner sentenced to life imprisonment or to fixed-term imprisonment, they may temporarily not admit the prisoner into prison custody: 1) A serious illness that requires release on bail for medical treatment; 2) pregnancy, or nursing of an infant." Besides omitting any mention of the previous prohibition on prisons accepting mentally ill offenders, Article 17 uses a much less emphatic phrase than before to describe the action to be taken in respect of the types of offenders who are still mentioned. Whereas now, prison authorities "may temporarily not admit the prisoner into prison custody", previously they had "to refuse to take into custody" not only the two categories of offender cited above but also any prisoner suffering from mental illness.

The total number of mentally ill prisoners falling within the scope of the government's 1979 amnesty order was officially said to be 4,600, many of whom were over eighty years old and one third of whom had already been in prison for ten years or more. Among this large group of prisoners were no doubt many of those former mental patients from the early 1960s whose psychiatric symptoms had included "strange political utterances" and who had been harassed and beaten into "confessing their sanity" during the Cultural Revolution. The main lesson of experience drawn by the authorities in the late 1970s, however, was not that "political lunatics" of this sort should never have been criminally detained in the first place. Instead, the new and reform-minded viewpoint was simply that they should henceforth be relieved of their "criminal liability" and placed in police-run psychiatric custody, rather than in regular prisons as before.

Psychiatric Abuse in the Post-Mao Era

> *In some countries in the West, the relationship between law and human rights often ends up in a self-contradictory predicament. The so-called human rights of the mentally ill, such as the right to refuse treatment and the right to refuse hospitalization, are clear examples of the kind of phony human rights advocated by Western jurisprudence.*
> — Chinese textbook on forensic psychiatry, 1989[116]

If the political misuse of psychiatry had ended with the inauguration of the Deng Xiaoping era in 1978, the above account of the first thirty years of forensic psychiatry in China would be of primarily historical interest. The official repudiation of the Cultural Revolution in the late 1970s and the commencement of the policy of "opening and reform," however, did not bring an end to such practices. Over the next two decades, China's forensic psychiatrists continued to diagnose certain categories of dissident-type individuals as being "dangerously mentally ill" and to send them to long-term custody in special mental asylums. According to official accounts, there was a substantial decrease in the overall scale and incidence of these practices after the Cultural Revolution. For example, a retrospective study of forensic psychiatric assessments carried out at the Hangzhou No. 7 People's Hospital, published in June 1987, reported:

---

[116] Chen Shouyi, in preface to Shen Zheng, *Falü Jingshenbingxue*, p. 9.

> According to this hospital's statistics, cases of antisocial
> political speech and action accounted for 54 percent of all
> cases [examined] during the year 1977; currently, the
> proportion of such cases has fallen to a level of 6.7 percent.
> This shows that the present situation of stability and unity in
> China has resulted in a marked fall in the number of cases
> arising from such factors.[117]

While highly welcome, this reduction in the overall scale of political
psychiatric abuse in China needs to be viewed and evaluated in an appropriate
conceptual context. The statistics generally cited for the incidence of "cases of a
political nature" in Chinese forensic psychiatry during the Cultural Revolution
decade (in this case, 54 percent) are, by any objective standard of assessment,
quite staggeringly high. They point to a situation whereby miscarriages of legal
and medical justice were so widespread and pervasive as to be almost mind-
boggling in their ethical implications. By contrast, the 1987 figure of 6.7 percent
for such cases appears low. However, even the latter statistic would suggest a
rate of political psychiatric abuse in China during the past two decades that is at
least comparable to, and quite possibly higher than, that reported in the case of
the former Soviet Union.[118] Furthermore, official sources give alternative
statistics on this count for China during the period since 1978 that go
substantially beyond 6.7 percent. The problem thus appears to remain serious.

A brief outline of the research methodology adopted in the remainder of
this article may be useful. In a book published in 1989, Dr. Semyon Gluzman, a
Soviet psychiatrist who famously broke ranks with his colleagues in the early
1970s to speak out against the political abuses within his profession and then
spent several years in prison as a consequence, proposed three different ways to
approach the study of the political misuse of psychiatry.[119] Gluzman's "three

---

[117] Zhong Xingsheng and Shi Yaqin, "A Preliminary Analysis of 210 Cases of Forensic
Psychiatric Medical Assessment," *Chinese Journal of Nervous and Mental Diseases*, vol.
20, no.3 (1987), pp.139-141. As Veronica Pearson has commented, regarding this report
from 1987, "There is no discussion of whether this is an absolute drop in numbers due to
a decrease in that kind of crime, or whether the officials of the Public Security Bureau
now only take notice of such behavior if it is very extreme" (Pearson, "Law, Rights and
Psychiatry in the People's Republic of China," p.413).

[118] For a detailed discussion of the statistical size and extent of the political psychiatry
problem in China since 1980, see Section VII., "Official Statistics on Political
Psychiatry," below.

[119] See Semyon Gluzman, *On Soviet Totalitarian Psychiatry*, p.33-35.

methods of collecting evidence and analyzing the situation" have direct methodological relevance for our present topic:

> The first approach is to personally and objectively examine those who were found non-imputable by reason of insanity after being charged with political and religious crimes... During such an examination, at least the following should be established. 1) Was the victim in fact persecuted for political or religious crimes? 2) Did the victim show any signs or symptoms of psychiatric illness? ... 5) What is the internationally accepted standard of psychiatric practice in such cases (including the finding of "diminished capacity" in countries where it is in use? ...

In Gluzman's view, this approach to establishing and proving abuse of psychiatry was both procedurally very difficult and also "not in itself effective."[120] However, he argued, "This work must be done: real people, victims of abuse, need protection and help, not academic discussion about humanism and justice." He continued:

> The second approach should combine a systematic study of the precepts of Soviet psychiatric theory, consideration of the differences among different school[s] of thought, and serious discussions in which specific disagreements can be focused on, and expert statisticians can be consulted. In my view, this is a very effective approach. But I doubt that such a discussion is feasible because it would require commitment and patience on both sides."

Gluzman's other proposed methodology was as follows:

> The third approach is very complex and laborious. It is necessary to examine an enormous number of Soviet

---

[120] "First of all, every instance of unjustifiable exculpation indicates only professional incompetence and the responsibility of a particular psychiatrist does not reveal an institutional phenomenon. Secondly, it is difficult to collect such information and therefore the proof cannot be complete. The many difficulties in obtaining all legal psychiatric documentation for an objective study make this approach very difficult" (Ibid., p.34).

psychiatric publications that are available in open libraries, administrative norms, regulations, professional guidelines, monographs, collections of articles, scientific journals, dissertations, etc. As far as I know, nobody in the USSR or abroad has ever undertaken such a study. The advantages of such an approach are self-evident; no "discovery" can be disputed and such "content analysis" will inevitably show who abused their profession and when. It will also reveal their theoretical justifications.

In the case of the Soviet Union, in practice, it was largely by means of the first of these methods, the individual case-based approach, that the problem of political psychiatry first became known in the West,[121] and this remained largely true throughout the subsequent campaign to end psychiatric abuse in the Soviet Union.[122] In China, the practical difficulties associated with this approach are at least as great, and probably much greater, than was the case even in the former Soviet context. In particular, the task of carrying out objective and independent psychiatric assessments of Chinese individuals who have been placed in forensic psychiatric custody solely, apparently, on account of their political or religious views is something that may only become feasible at some point in the future, if and when the Chinese government begins to allow direct outside scrutiny of its practices in this field. At present, in most cases, we do not know even the names of the individuals discussed in the official documents excerpted below. The Falun Gong cases are important exceptions, though by no means the only ones.

Similarly, in the case of China, Gluzman's second approach, that of initiating a direct and sustained theoretical dialogue between Chinese psychiatrists and their Western counterparts over allegations of politically-directed psychiatric practice, represents a highly desirable aim but one that is unlikely to be practically attainable in the immediate to near future. While all appropriate efforts should certainly be made toward establishing this kind of intra-professional dialogue, the key determinant to the success of any such efforts, and more importantly, to ending the abusive psychiatric practices at

---

[121] That is to say, significant numbers of Soviet dissidents and others still managed, despite the politically repressive environment, to collect substantial numbers of individual case details on people placed in mental asylums on account of their political or religious views, and to transmit these to international human rights groups and the foreign news media. This has only recently begun to happen in China's case.

[122] Gluzman's misgivings about the effectiveness of the method seemingly relate more to the subsequent, "post-mortem" phase of investigations into the Soviet case.

issue, will undoubtedly remain the political will and attitude of the Chinese government.[123]

Since the relatively closed nature of official Chinese society renders, for the meantime, alternative avenues of investigation largely impracticable, the principal methodology used in compiling the evidence of psychiatric abuse in China presented below has conformed, in the main, to the third approach advocated by Gluzman. The principal source of information relied upon has been the wide range of professional legal and psychiatric publications issued officially by the Chinese government since the early 1980s. These include a series of major textbooks and manuals on forensic medicine and psychiatry, legal studies dealing with the psychological dimensions of crime, journals and periodicals dealing with all aspects of law and jurisprudence, various national, provincial and municipal-level laws and regulations on the handling of mentally ill offenders, including rules for the involuntary committal of those viewed as especially "dangerous" to society, and several specialized medical periodicals, notably the *Chinese Journal of Psychiatry* and the *Chinese Journal of Nervous and Mental Diseases*.[124] In addition, a number of first-hand accounts written by

---

[123] At present, the general signs in this area are far from being good: in recent years, despite the continuing economic reforms, the Chinese security authorities have redoubled their efforts to suppress all forms of perceived political or religious dissonance in society; and notwithstanding China's current participation in bilateral "human rights dialogue" sessions with Western countries and the European Union, Beijing continues to view human rights issues in general as representing a major "battle front" in its relations with the West.

[124] *Zhonghua Jingshenke Zazhi* and *Zhongguo Shenjing Jingshen Jibing Zazhi* (formerly known as *Zhongguo Shenjing Jingshenke Zazhi*; for purposes of consistency, the latter two titles are both referred to in the present article by the journal's current English name, the *Chinese Journal of Nervous and Mental Diseases*). Each journal appears four times a year.

former inmates of the Ankang system and other Chinese psychiatric detention facilities have been examined.

Although the officially published sources contain little in the way of detailed individual case material and offer scant insight into the prevailing conditions of treatment and incarceration in China's police-run secure psychiatric facilities, they manifest in full measure the advantages referred to by Gluzman above. First, unlike victim or refugee accounts for example, they are, by virtue of their provenance, not amenable to disputation or refutation by the authorities. Second, they provide a productive source of information for a content analysis-based examination of the issues. Finally, they afford major insight into the various theoretical justifications used by Chinese psychiatrists, in their collaborative endeavor with the security authorities to medically criminalize certain forms of dissent.

IV. A SHORT GUIDE TO POLITICAL PSYCHOSIS

As a preface to more detailed discussions of the Chinese medico-legal concept of political insanity since the Cultural Revolution, it may be helpful to have before us a capsule definition of what, more specifically, the Chinese judicial and psychiatric authorities have in mind when they speak of "political cases" involving the commission of crimes by the allegedly mentally ill. The following passage, taken from a textbook on forensic psychiatry produced in 1983 by the official publishing house of the Ministry of Public Security, fulfills this purpose well. Published less than five years after the official denunciation of the Cultural Revolution, it affirms and incorporates key elements of the still deeply-entrenched abusive concepts and practices of that era, while at the same time seeking — in accordance with the more modern and "scientist" official ethos of China in the 1980s — to cloak them in the terminology of modern medical science. Moreover, it provides a virtual roadmap of the political abuse aspects of the system of forensic-psychiatric evaluation and custody that, only four years later, was to be formally adopted and developed by the Chinese government as the Ankang regime.

Manifestations of Counterrevolutionary Behavior by the Mentally Ill [125]

As Article 90 of the [1979] Criminal Law points out: "All acts carried out with the aim of overthrowing the political power of the dictatorship of the proletariat and the socialist system, and which endanger the People's Republic of China, are crimes of counterrevolution." Under the dominant influence of pathological thinking and other symptoms of psychological disease, mentally ill people may engage in behavior that sabotages the proletarian dictatorship and the socialist state. In terms of form and consequence, these acts constitute crimes of counterrevolution. The most commonly encountered pathological states involving counterrevolutionary behavior by the mentally ill are delusions of grandeur and delusions of persecution.

---

[125] See Liu Anqiu, ed., *Sifa Jingshenbingxue Jichu Zhishi* (*Basic Knowledge in Forensic Psychiatry*), (Beijing: Qunzhong Chubanshe, 1983), pp.18-19.

A mentally ill person suffering from delusions of grandeur, for example, may think that he is the "head of the Central Committee" or a "leading political figure" [*lingxiu renwu*], and may formulate "guidelines" and "policies" as a replacement for existing policies, laws or decrees that he thinks are unreasonable. In one case, a mentally ill person proclaimed himself as a "peasant revolutionary leader" and called for a new political party to be set up in order to carry out a second revolution, and he openly drew up a manifesto and handed out leaflets.

People suffering from delusions of persecution with a certain specific content, for example those who deludedly [sic] harbor feelings of suspicion towards the Party organization, government departments and certain leading officials, may adopt all kinds of retaliatory measures against them, thereby occasioning counterrevolutionary behavior. Still other kinds of mentally ill people, those suffering from disorders of thought and logic, try to interpret and understand the present political situation [in China] from the standpoint of pure theory. A mentally ill person, for example, owing to his divorcement from reality, applied the former political orthodoxy to China's present-day context: the patient insisted that the Cultural Revolution had been entirely necessary and extremely timely, and he even went around publicly arguing his case with others. In addition, people with pathological personality disorders may also engage in various kinds of counterrevolutionary behavior.

Identifying Counterrevolutionary Behavior by the Mentally Ill

Counterrevolutionary behavior carried out by mentally ill people is to be distinguished from the commission of such behavior by genuine counterrevolutionary elements. The following basic hallmarks will assist us in ascertaining those in the former category:

In analyzing the personal history of an individual engaging in counterrevolutionary behavior, no historical origins or social background showing any logical relationship [with the behavior in question] can be identified. That is to say, no conformity can be found between the nature of the counterrevolutionary behavior and the person in question's previous political demeanor, ideological make-up and moral or ethical quality.

The content of the behavior displays a certain degree of absurdity and lack of commensurability with the actual status and capacity of the person concerned. For example, an ordinary student expressing the wish to become a major and important figure: most people would regard this as being something quite unimaginable. Or a person who groundlessly suspects the leadership of persecuting and harming him and then proceeds to focus his resentment upon the entire Party organization: this represents a marked deviation from normal logical reasoning and inference.

The person concerned carries out the counterrevolutionary behavior in a brazen and flagrant manner and with no sign of scruples or misgivings. In a publicly confrontational manner, he or she will hand out leaflets in broad daylight and deliver speeches on the main road or at street corners. Naturally, some mentally ill people may act in a more covert manner than this; yet as soon as they're caught, they admit to everything quite frankly and unreservedly. In addition, mentally ill people may write anonymous letters, but often these are not genuinely anonymous but rather a manifestation of some mental impairment. For example, a person suffering from mental illness wrote a letter to all Military Regions in the country and to the Central Committee, signing his name as "Chen Zhenli" ["Chen the Truth"]; this was not his real name, but he still wrote his actual address on the envelope. After the case was cracked and he had been caught, the person was asked why he had written this anonymous letter. He replied that it was actually an open letter: he'd used the name "Chen Zhenli" because he had the truth on his side and the viewpoints he expressed were all "true."

The various elements of the counterrevolutionary-behavior process are generally only loosely interconnected and may be logically self-contradictory. They can also show a lack of consistency over time — sometimes active and positive, but at other times passive and negative — and may even be self-repudiatory in nature.

The most important grounds for ascertaining the commission of counterrevolutionary behavior by the mentally ill is where, necessarily, a correspondence exists between the particular manifestation of mental abnormality and the mental illness in question. A detailed investigation of the person's background and medical history may reveal additional psychiatric symptoms, and the counterrevolutionary behavior will then be seen as simply one manifestation or symptom of the mental illness.

The official literature on forensic psychiatry in China in recent decades is replete with formulations expressing, more or less overtly, all of the theoretical themes and contours mentioned above. To show that the general theory is alive and well in contemporary China, it should suffice to cite at length one further authority, Long Qingchun, a leading forensic psychiatrist at the Beijing Ankang institute, who included the following comparative discussion in a textbook which he edited in 1994:

What Is the Difference Between a Paranoiac and a Political Dissident?[126]

There is a certain type of person with the mental illness of paranoid psychosis [*pianzhixing jingshenbing*]. The content of the fantasies and delusions of such persons does not come from their having been persecuted, but is mainly about state policies and principles. Such persons continually submit petitions, and are often taken by non-specialists to be political dissidents [*chi butong zhengjianzhe*]. But there is a difference in nature between the two.

---

[126] See Long Qingchun, ed., *Sifa Jingshen Yixue Jianding Zixun Jieda* (Consultative Questions and Answers for Forensic-Psychiatric Medical Evaluations), (Beijing: Chinese University of Politics and Law Publishing House, 1994), pp. 58-59.

Paranoiacs, commonly known as "document crazies" [*wen fengzi*], manifest [their illness] through their loss of reason in political theory. With respect to all sensitive [political] issues, they listen only to themselves and think, "Only I am right." Although they might focus on one or two specific issues, generally they have both historical problems and current problems.[127] Their political theory and their political stance are mutually contradictory; although they oppose the [government's] general line and policies, they also support Marxism-Leninism and materialism. Political dissidents are relatively specific. They have dissenting opinions about certain specific issues, and don't simply oppose everything.

Paranoia is a kind of morbidity; therefore, the delusions and fantasies are self-contradictory. They are not plausible and consistent, and have no capacity to spread to others. That which is expressed by political dissidents is logical and has a certain capacity to spread to [literally: "infect"] others.

A paranoiac will take any opportunity to peddle his views, without regard to time, place, or audience. A political dissident will choose the time, place, and audience for expressing his views; he will not start talking to just anyone he runs into.

The acts and views of paranoiacs do not match their education, reading, and status. There was, for example, an old retired worker with only three years of elementary school education who worked untiringly to write a "Manifesto of Scientific

---

[127] "...*wangwang shi ji you lishi wenti, you you xianshi wenti.*" In China, the phrase "having historical problems" generally indicates that the person in question was accused of (and usually punished for) "bourgeois" or "counterrevolutionary" views or activities in the past; similarly, the phrase "having current problems" often indicates that the person is a current target of such political suppression (c.f. the terms "*lishi fan'geming*" and "*xianxing fan'geming*," meaning "historical counterrevolutionary" and "active counterrevolutionary"). A better translation of "*wenti*" in this context might thus be "political record" or "political taint."

Communism."[128] He bought a typewriter and printer with his own money and sent his "work" out everywhere. Neither his wife nor his children could convince him to stop. The acts and views of political dissidents are consistent with their learning and their status; moreover they generally have better sense than to pursue something in complete disregard of the [legal] consequences.

Disarmingly enough, the basic distinction that Long appears to be drawing here between political lunatics and dissidents is that while the former engage in nonsensical rambling, what the latter say makes a lot of sense and is broadly convincing to others. Two more central points should be noted in this context however. First, the political dissidents in question, while escaping psychiatric incarceration for their oppositional viewpoints, would for the most part have been severely dealt with under criminal law provisions against "counterrevolution," since 1997 renamed as "crimes of endangering state security." Second, those diagnosed as being "paranoid psychotics" following their arrest on similar charges of political subversion will, in most cases, neither be freed from police custody nor given appropriate treatment, whether out-patient or in-patient, for their alleged politico-psychiatric disorders. Rather, they will be declared "not legally responsible" (i.e. non-imputable) and then placed indefinitely in Ankang custody or similar. A third vital issue also arises in all such cases: whether the person concerned was genuinely suffering, in fact, from any internationally recognized mental disorder. These various topics will be addressed at greater length and in different contexts below.

For now, it should suffice to note that in both of the above passages from 1983 and 1994, respectively, a basic distinction was drawn between "genuine" political offenders, counterrevolutionaries, on the one hand, and mentally disordered political offenders, or what the authorities colloquially call "political lunatics" and we may perhaps refer to as "pseudo-counterrevolutionaries," on the other. This was certainly progress as compared to the situation of forensic psychiatry during the Cultural Revolution, when the dividing line in this area became grotesquely blurred. But what did not change after 1978 was the authorities' firm insistence that, in both types of situation, a serious political crime had been committed.

---

[128] See Section VII. "An Illustrative Case," below, for a detailed account of this case.

V. THE LEGAL CONTEXT

Legal Norms and Judicial Process

In an article published in 1974 in the British Medical Journal summarizing his findings from a recent study visit to Soviet psychiatric hospitals, the British psychiatrist J.K. Wing expressed with neat precision the unusual ethical dilemma he encountered in evaluating his Soviet colleagues' handling of cases of political offenders alleged to be mentally ill. After discussing two other problematic issues that arose,[129] Wing wrote,

> The third conceptual problem concerns [legal] "responsibility." This is the most difficult one for the British psychiatrist to comment on since it means trying to answer a ludicrous non-question: should a person who is not severely mentally ill by our standards be regarded as responsible for an action which we would not regard as a crime?[130]

The same central issue hovers disquietingly over any discussion of the formal legislative and procedural aspects of the ways in which "political lunacy" cases are handled in the Chinese forensic psychiatric context. The range of cases falling within the system's scope and purview is much wider, of course, than this one specific category, and it seems reasonable to assume that the great majority of cases dealt with under the system involve the commission of genuine and serious offenses (such as murder, rape and arson) by mentally ill people. The following descriptive account thus has a general applicability, and critical observations are directed toward the significant minority of cases where the system claims and applies jurisdiction over people, such as peaceful dissidents, sane or otherwise, who have not committed any internationally recognized criminal offense.

Until 1979, the main judicial yardstick in this field was a brief directive issued by the Supreme People's Court in 1956, according to which persons found to have been mentally ill at the time of committing criminal offenses were not to be held legally responsible for their actions.[131] The mental state of the

---

[129] These were, the fact that "there is nothing in our criminal law equivalent to the Soviet category of crimes against the State," and secondly, that "the concept of mental illness, particularly of schizophrenia, is a good deal wider [in the USSR then, as in China today] than in the U.K."

[130] J.K. Wing, "Psychiatry in the Soviet Union," *British Medical Journal*, no.1 (March 9, 1974), pp.433-436.

[131] See "Reply of the Supreme People's Court on the Question of the Handling of Crimes Committed by Mentally Ill Persons," June 2, 1956. Soon after the Cultural Revolution,

defendant was to be ascertained by "the relevant medical departments" and through interviews with the person's neighbors.[132] In 1979, the first Criminal Law of the PRC codified this longstanding policy, although in somewhat simpler terms than before.[133] Then in March 1997, an extensively revised version of the Criminal Law was promulgated which significantly amended the previous provisions in this area:

> Article 18. If a mental patient causes harmful consequences at a time when he is unable to recognize or control his own conduct, upon verification and confirmation through legal procedure, he shall not bear criminal responsibility, but his family members or guardian shall be ordered to keep him under strict watch and control and arrange for his medical treatment. When necessary, the government may compel him to receive medical treatment.
>
> Any person whose mental illness is of an intermittent nature shall bear criminal responsibility if he commits a crime when he is in a normal mental state.
>
> If a mental patient who has not completely lost the ability of recognizing or controlling his own conduct commits a crime,

---

during which legal norms had collapsed almost entirely, the Supreme People's Court reiterated the validity of the June 1956 directive (Supreme People's Court, Document No. 17 [78], August 4, 1978).

[132] The directive also stipulated: "Counterrevolutionary elements and their families, or landlords and rich-peasant elements, should not be dealt with differently." This seems to run counter to Article 37 of the 1954 Regulations on Reform Through Labor, which excluded "major counterrevolutionary offenders" from the rule that prisons were not allowed to admit criminals suffering from mental illness. In practice, however, any contest at that time between the court system and the prison system (which was run by the all-powerful Ministry of Public Security) would generally have ended in the latter's favor.

[133] According to Article 15 of the 1979 Criminal Law (Adopted July 1, 1979 and effective as of January 1, 1980; available in *U.S. Journal of Criminal Law and Criminology*, Spring 1982): "A mentally ill person who causes dangerous consequences at a time when he is unable to recognize or unable to control his own conduct is not to bear criminal responsibility; but his family or guardian shall be ordered to subject him to strict surveillance and arrange for his medical treatment. A person whose mental illness is of an intermittent nature shall bear criminal responsibility if he commits a crime during a period of mental normality. An intoxicated person who commits a crime shall bear criminal responsibility."

he shall bear criminal responsibility; however, he may be given a lighter or mitigated punishment.

Any intoxicated person who commits a crime shall bear criminal responsibility.[134]

The main changes were as follows. First, "expert forensic evaluation" must now be performed in order to ascertain whether or not a defendant was mentally ill at the time of committing an offense. Except during the Cultural Revolution, in practice this was hitherto also generally the case, but the statutory inclusion of a forensic-psychiatric appraisal procedure is still important. Second, the new law stipulated for the first time that mentally ill defendants may be ordered by the government to undergo "compulsory medical treatment." While not specifically mentioned, involuntary committal is certainly among the intended range of available legal options. Again, this merely codifies a longstanding police prerogative, but the new law's mention of compulsory medical treatment has particular significance in light of the Chinese government's post-1987 program for creating a nationwide network of Ankang institutions. Finally, whereas previously a judgment of either full legal responsibility or total absence of such responsibility had to be officially rendered when evaluating a defendant's mental state, the intermediate option of "limited legal responsibility" (*xianding zeren nengli*) can now be adopted; while this too was frequently done in the past, it is now fully lawful. Significantly, the lack of such an intermediate option in the legal code of the former Soviet Union was a frequent target of criticism from the dissident community there.

---

[134] Similar provisions appear in the 1996 PRC Law on Administrative Punishments (passed by the National People's Congress on March 17, 1996 and effective as of October 1, 1996, see BBC Summary of World Broadcasts, FE/2585, April 13, 1996), which governs all of the wide-ranging forms of non- or extra-judicial punishment currently available to law enforcement agencies in China. According to Article 26 of this law, "If a mental patient commits an illegal act at a time when he is unable to recognize or cannot control his own conduct, no administrative penalty shall be imposed on him, but his guardian shall be ordered to keep him under close surveillance and arrange for his medical treatment. Administrative penalty shall be imposed on a person whose mental illness is of an intermittent nature and who commits an illegal act when he is in a normal mental state." The same general provisions appear also in Article 10 of the 1994 revised version of the PRC Regulations for the Punishment of Public Order Offenses (see *Guowuyuan Gongbao* [Bulletin of the PRC State Council], 1994, pp.440-448), which allow police to impose (without trial) custodial sentences of up to fifteen days for minor offenses.

The legislative basis for conducting "expert evaluations" had been formally laid down in March 1996 in a revised version of the Criminal Procedure Law of the PRC. According to Article 119 of that law, "When certain special problems relating to a case need to be solved in order to clarify the circumstances of the case, experts shall be assigned or invited to give their evaluations." Article 120 of the same law added, "If an expert intentionally makes a false verification, he shall assume legal responsibility." And Article 121 continued: "The investigation organ shall notify the criminal suspect and the victim of the conclusion of the expert verification which will be used as evidence in his case. A supplementary expert verification or another expert verification may be conducted upon application submitted by the criminal suspect or the victim." An especially problematic area where criminal defendants suspected of mental illness are concerned relates to the lawful time limits on pretrial detention. According to Article 9 of the government's 1984 "Supplementary Provisions" on this question, all time limits on detention specified in the 1979 Criminal Law could be dispensed with during the period that a criminal defendant was being held in custody for forensic-psychiatric appraisal,[135] and Article 122 of the revised Criminal Procedure Law proceeded to formalize this dubious legal practice: "The period during which a criminal suspect is undergoing appraisal for mental disorder shall not be included in the calculation of time limits for handling the case."[136]

Separately, the police are accorded wide legal powers to detain and hospitalize alleged offenders who are suspected of being mentally ill. According to Article 14 of the 1995 Law of the People's Police of the PRC,

> The people's policemen of public security organs may take protective measures to restrain a mentally ill person who seriously endangers public security or other people's personal safety. If it is necessary to send the patient to a designated

---

[135] See Supplementary Provisions of the Standing Committee of the National People's Congress Regarding the Time Limits for Handling Criminal Cases (*Guanyu Xingshi Anjian Ban'an Qixian de Buchong Guiding*, passed by the NPC Standing Committee on July 7, 1984; in Wang Huai'an et al, eds., Zhonghua Renmin Gongheguo Falü Quanshu [Changchun: Jilin Renmin Chubanshe, 1989], p.223).

[136] Another relevant provision of the new Criminal Procedure Law (adopted on March 17, 1996 and effective as of January 1, 1997, see "PRC: Amended PRC Criminal Procedure Law," FBIS, April 10, 1996), Article 48, reads as follows: "All those who have information about a case shall have the duty to testify. Physically or mentally handicapped persons or minors who cannot distinguish right from wrong or cannot properly express themselves shall not be qualified as witnesses."

institution or place for guardianship, the matter shall be
reported for approval to the public security organ of a people's
government at or above the county level, and his or her
guardian shall be notified without delay.

This law does not require the police to arrange either prior or subsequent
forensic psychiatric assessment of persons whom they decide to send to a
"designated institution," which in practice may be either an Ankang custodial
facility or, in the case of lesser offenses, the secure ward of a regular mental
hospital; they merely have to report the matter to a superior police authority.[137]
The police may choose, at their discretion, to send the detainee for forensic
psychiatric examination; and in cases where the alleged offense was a serious
one, the procuracy, the prosecuting authority, would no doubt require that such
an examination be carried out and a subsequent finding made of non-
imputability by reason of mental illness as a precondition for agreeing to
suspend criminal proceedings against the person. However, Chinese law remains
highly vague in this general area, and in practice offenders suspected of being
mentally ill may end up being first committed by the police, and then left in
prolonged custodial limbo while other authorities decide if and when an expert
evaluation of their mental state is needed. In most criminal cases, the authority
of the courts is circumvented at an early stage, since either the police or the
procuracy normally suspend criminal justice proceedings once a forensic finding
of non-imputability has been made. The latter authorities then decide, on the
basis of their assessment of the "degree of dangerousness" of the offense in
question, whether or not custodial care is required.

Moreover, since China broadly follows the "commensurability principle"
of forensic psychiatric practice, whereby an offender deemed to be legally non-
imputable by reason of insanity for a given crime is generally held in secure
psychiatric custody for at least as long as the period of penal incarceration to
which they would have been sentenced if ascertained to have been sane at the
time of committing the offense, the authorities' inclusion of certain types of
peaceful political prisoners (alongside psychotic murderers and the like) among
the "most serious and dangerous" category of alleged mentally ill offenders

---

[137] The police in many countries are empowered, in emergency situations, to take
suspected mentally ill people into custody and to transfer them to psychiatric hospitals if
they fear that dangerous consequences might otherwise ensue. In the case of China,
however, it is the lack of any clear legal requirement for prompt forensic psychiatric
evaluation then to be conducted that renders this police power liable to misuse and
therefore problematic from a human rights point of view.

means that such people can end up being psychiatrically detained on an indefinite or even permanent basis.

The question of the civil rights entitlements and "capacity for civil action" of mentally ill people in China is dealt with in various provisions of the 1987 General Principles of the Civil Law of the PRC. For example, Article 13 states: "A mentally ill person who is unable to recognize his own conduct shall be a person having no capacity for civil conduct and shall be represented in civil activities by his agent ad litem." It continues by saying that those "unable to fully recognize" their own conduct shall be regarded as having "limited capacity" for civil conduct and may engage in "civil activities appropriate" to their state of mental health. In other articles, issues relating to the guardianship of mentally ill people are addressed. The General Principles do not, however, contain any provisions on such important matters as the legal procedures and criteria for the compulsory hospitalization and treatment of the mentally ill. In particular, there appears to be little, if any, in the way of legislative interconnect or cross-over between, on the one hand, the handling of mentally ill offenders under the Criminal Law and, on the other, the broader issue of their civil rights entitlement as laid down in the General Principles.[138] Whatever may be the situation of those subjected to civil psychiatric committal in China,[139] it is clear from the relevant official literature that criminal detainees found not legally responsible by reason of insanity may also, by virtue of this finding, lose most if not all of their civil rights.[140]

---

[138] Indeed, simply by virtue of being ill, even mentally ill people who do not commit offenses may suffer significant reduction of their civil rights; confidential regulations state, for example, that the police "should delay issuing [citizens'] identity cards to...persons who are mentally ill" — so placing them in a broadly similar category of official treatment as that applied to persons placed under formal arrest or serving terms of imprisonment, who are to be denied identity cards altogether (see Liu Guangren, ed., *Hukou Guanlixue* (*The Administration of Household Residence*), (Beijing: Zhongguo Jiancha Chubanshe [volume marked "for distribution within the public security organs only"], 1992), p.324.

[139] A more detailed discussion of the civil law aspects of the treatment of mentally ill people in China can be found in Pearson, "Law, Rights and Psychiatry in the People's Republic of China," pp.417-420.

[140] Specific procedures for the courts to make findings of civil competence and incompetence are set forth in Articles 170-173 of the Civil Procedure Law of the PRC (adopted by the 4th session of the 7th National People's Congress on April 9, 1991 and effective as of same date). Courts may declare a mentally ill person to have "lost the capacity for civil action" and they may also reverse such rulings (Article 19 of the General Principles of Civil Law, adopted at the 4th Session of the 6th National People's Congress on April 12, 1986 and effective as of January 1, 1987), although the former (as in other countries) is not an essential prerequisite for compulsory civil psychiatric

In 1985, a prominent authority in the field of legal psychiatry, Wu Jiasheng, acknowledged the urgent need for China to take legislative action in this area:

> Legislation to protect and safeguard society in the area of mental illness should be promptly formulated. The most pressing problems are those concerning compulsory custodial treatment; at present, there are no clear guidelines on the applicable scope of such treatment, on the means by which it should be carried out, the types and methods of treatment, the time limits on detention, or the rights of the mental patient. From the viewpoint of building a healthy and complete socialist legal system, it is essential that we formulate relevant laws and regulations soon.[141]

The same year, the Chinese government began preparing to enact comprehensive national legislation on the treatment of the mentally ill, and since then, ten different draft versions of a "Mental Health Law of the PRC" have been produced and widely circulated among psychiatric professionals around the country; the World Health Organization has also provided input on the draft law.[142] The question of involuntary psychiatric committal and treatment has been addressed in considerable detail by the law's drafters, with provisions on such matters as the criteria for compulsory admission, the civil legal capacity of those committed, and the permissible use of restraints on inmates. In addition, the draft law contains several stipulations on the basic rights and interests of the mentally ill (for example, that "inhumane treatment of patients is not allowed"

---

committal. In the case of criminal psychiatric committal, however, the courts in China appear to have an almost negligible role to play, either in terms of authorizing and approving such treatment, or as regards providing those psychiatrically detained with legal channels for appeal and possible redress.

[141] Wu Jiasheng, "*Qiantan Jingshenbingren Weifa Zhaohuo Xingwei de Zeren Nengli* (A Brief Discussion of the Legal Capacity of Mentally Ill Persons Who Behave Unlawfully and Create Disastrous Incidents)," *Faxue* (*Jurisprudence*), no. 40 (1985), pp.43-45.

[142] The law-drafting group is headed by Professor Liu Xiehe of the Institute of Forensic Medicine at the West China Medical University in Chengdu. The most recent joint initiative between China and the WHO on drafting a mental health law was a high-level symposium held in Beijing on November 11, 1999, attended by Dr Gro. Harlem Brundtland, the WHO's Director-General, and thirteen vice-ministerial-level Chinese officials. The full text of Brundtland's speech at the conference can be found at http://www.who.int/director-general/speeches/1999/english/19991111_beijing.html.

and that those compulsorily hospitalized should have their mental state "systematically assessed at least once every half year"); and it even briefly addresses the rights of mentally-disordered criminal defendants and provides a basic legal framework for the operation of forensic psychiatric custodial centers.[143] The passage of a well-crafted mental health law is clearly vital to any attempt to reform the system and safeguard the rights of those psychiatrically detained.[144] However, there is no indication that the government intends to enact formal legislation regulating official behavior in this sensitive area anytime soon.

In August 1989, the Chinese government issued a long-awaited set of formal rules — the Temporary Regulations for Judicial Appraisal of the Mentally Ill — specifying legal procedures for the conduct of expert psychiatric

---

[143] In the 1988 draft, these were referred to as "Guardianship Hospitals for the Mentally Ill" (*Jingshenbingren Jianhu Yiyuan*), which were to be organized and led by the Public Security departments; such hospitals were therefore clearly the same as the ones now more commonly referred to as "Ankang."

[144] For useful and authoritative practical guidelines on this field of legislation, see World Health Organization, *Mental Health Care Law: Ten Basic Principles*, 1996 (WHO/MNH/MND/96.9). The legislative experience of the former Soviet states in this area also provides an important comparative frame of reference. According to two well-qualified observers,

> Establishing a proper legal foundation for mental health care has been the top priority for reformers in transforming psychiatry in practically all post-Soviet and post-socialist countries... The [July 1992] Russian law merits particular attention because it has provided a sound model for the other countries of the former Soviet Union. The law has many positive features that will help to facilitate the transformation of Russian psychiatry. (1) It codifies the fundamental norms and principles that should guide psychiatric care, including confidentiality, informed consent, and medical necessity. (2) It declares and reinforces the fundamental idea that psychiatrists are expected to be independent in making their decisions, which — as the law states — should be based only on "medical indications, medical duty and the law." (3) It establishes formal procedures for judicial review of involuntary hospitalizations, and of alleged violations of the rights of hospitalized patients. (4) Finally, the law opens psychiatric institutions to outside scrutiny and thereby promotes accountability to patients' families and to the society at large. The State is directed to "set up a service independent of health agencies for the protection of rights of psychiatric patients," and the law also specifically authorizes associations of psychiatrists, families or other citizens to monitor the observance of patients' rights and to file complaints on behalf of aggrieved patients. Enactment of this law was itself a remarkable achievement... (Bonnie and Polubinskaya, "Unraveling Soviet Psychiatry," pp.292-294.)

appraisals in criminal, civil, administrative and other types of cases.[145] According to Article 1 of the Temporary Regulations, they were intended, among other things, "to safeguard the lawful rights of mental illness sufferers," but in fact they contained almost no specific provisions on this topic. On more institutional matters, the Temporary Regulations instructed that Psychiatric Judicial Appraisal Committees were to be established at all provincial, regional and major municipal levels of government, and that these should comprise "responsible officials and experts" from the courts, procuracy, and public security, judicial administration and health departments. These committees were also to appoint, for specific cases that arose, Technical Appraisal Groups consisting of not less than two expert assessors, and the latter's expertise was to be sought in all cases where questions of mental competence had arisen in respect of criminal defendants, parties to civil or administrative litigation, persons undergoing administrative punishment (primarily, those sentenced without trial to up to three years in "re-education through labor" camps), criminal offenders serving custodial sentences, and also "other persons involved in the case who require [such] appraisal." The only "right" specifically accorded to the subject of the appraisal appears in Article 8: "The Appraisal Committee may, depending upon the circumstances, accept a request from the person being examined for a supplementary appraisal, a fresh appraisal or a review of the [original] appraisal to be performed."

The principal task of the appraisers was to ascertain whether or not, at the time of "carrying out dangerous behavior," the person concerned was mentally ill, and, if so, to identify the specific nature and severity of the illness. Depending on the type of case involved, the appraisers would also be charged with ascertaining the level of mental capacity and responsibility of those being examined in one or more of the following areas: overall legal responsibility for criminal acts committed; capacity to distinguish between right and wrong actions; ability to control one's behavior and actions; capacity to stand trial (capacity for litigation); to serve a sentence or undergo other punishment; to testify or provide evidence; and (in the case of mentally ill victims of alleged

---

[145] See *Guanyu Jingshen Jibing Sifa Jianding Zanxing Guiding* (Temporary Regulations for Judicial Appraisal of the Mentally Ill), issued jointly by the Supreme People's Court, Supreme People's Procuracy, Ministry of Public Security, Ministry of Justice and Ministry of Civil Affairs, July 11, 1989. The regulations came into force on August 1, 1989. This followed an earlier set of rules on the same topic issued in October 1985 by the Anding psychiatric hospital in Beijing, which were "to be adopted by all provinces" in China (see Pearson, "Law, Rights and Psychiatry in the People's Republic of China," p.411).

sexual assault) to exercise either self-defense or sexual consent.[146] Two other important points should be made. First, only the "judicial organs" (i.e., courts, procuracy, police) were accorded the right to present a person for forensic psychiatric appraisal. Second, although the Temporary Regulations do not state as much, it was clearly understood that the findings of the expert appraisers were not binding on the judicial organs and that any final decision on whether to institute charges or to proceed to trial would be made solely by the latter.

The 1989 Temporary Regulations are still China's authoritative governing document in this area. In early 2000, however, the Ministry of Health issued a "recommendatory draft" version of a new document entitled "Administration Methods for Psychiatric Judicial Appraisal,"[147] the final clause of which states that the 1989 Temporary Regulations are to be superseded by the new document once it comes into force. The Administration Methods themselves were based to a very large extent on a similar document issued by the Beijing municipal government in January 1998,[148] and it is likely that they are already being implemented on a trial basis in several parts of China. It should be noted at the outset that none of these regulations list or refer to the enjoyment of any statutory rights or protections by the person being evaluated, and no provision is made for the lodging of appeals against eventual committal on grounds of criminal insanity.

The main additional measures and stipulations found in the new draft regulations are as follows. First, a new national-level governing body is to be instituted. According to Article 5, "The Supreme People's Court, Supreme People's Procuracy, Ministry of Health, Ministry of Justice and Ministry of Public Security shall jointly form a State Committee for the Coordination of Psychiatric Judicial Assessments, which shall be responsible for coordinating all such work throughout the country." This State Committee will stand at the apex of the system of provincial-level Psychiatric Judicial Appraisal Committees

---

[146] The Chinese terms for these various criteria are (in order of listing above): "*xingshi zeren nengli,*" "*bianren nengli,*" "*kongzhi nengli,*" "*susong nengli,*" "*fuxing (shou chufa) nengli,*" "*zuozheng nengli,*" and "*ziwo fangwei nengli.*"

[147] See Ministry of Health, *Jingshen Jibing Sifa Jianding Guanli Banfa* (Administration Methods for Psychiatric Judicial Appraisal), issued informally sometime in early 2000. The full Chinese text of this document can be found on the Internet at http://www.fmedsci.com/sfjs/sfjs11.htm.

[148] See Beijing Municipal Bureau of Health, *Beijing Shi Jingshenbing Sifa Jianding Guanli Banfa* (Beijing Municipal Psychiatric Judicial Appraisal Management Rules [1998]). The full Chinese text is available on the Internet at http://www.fmedsci.com/sjfs/sfjs3.htm. The document came into force on January 1, 1998.

created in virtue of the 1989 Temporary Regulations, and will establish offices in the various health departments under the jurisdiction of the State Council, China's highest administrative body. Second, the new draft regulations stipulate a wide range of new measures aimed at imposing tighter regulation over the existing forensic-psychiatric appraisals system, especially in respect of the legal and academic accreditation of Technical Appraisal Groups and of individual expert assessors, the various time limits within which appraisals must be applied for, organized and completed (for example, assessors are to complete their appraisal within 30 days of first examining the person), and the requirement that complete case documentation, including all relevant police files, must be provided to the assessors before they can proceed. And third, the draft regulations introduced a number of significant legal-procedural safeguards. For example, officials or assessors having a close family connection with the examinee or any other personal interest in a case must withdraw themselves (the rule of recusal), and the examinee or other concerned persons have the right to request this. Technical Appraisal Groups must comprise no fewer than three assessors, and any expert opinions dissenting from the group's final recommendations should be separately noted on the official record. Also, private individuals and bodies may now also apply for expert appraisal to be carried out.

All these pending reforms are no doubt highly worthwhile, and they may well have an important impact on ensuring the overall accuracy, quality and consistency of forensic psychiatric appraisals in China. The bottom line, however, as far as our main topic, the treatment of alleged mentally ill political offenders, is concerned, is that none of those experts or officials working in the various committees and groups listed above have any say or discretion in the selection of the people whom they are required to examine. The identity of those individuals is determined solely by the nature of the country's criminal justice system; if the law says that a certain action is a crime, and if the offender is then arrested and brought for forensic psychiatric assessment, the expert assessors are required, unless they are ill or have some other acceptable reason for declining the job, to carry out an appraisal of the person's mental condition. It is not their task to determine whether or not a crime was actually committed, but rather to evaluate the detainee's sanity and then reach a conclusion as to whether or not he or she should bear "legal responsibility" for whatever offense the police claim was committed.

When the charge in question is a political one, however, this task immediately becomes, for the expert assessor, not only highly politicized in the general sense, but also, given China's overall history and track record in this particular area, potentially fraught with considerable personal risk. The safest course of action in such cases, undoubtedly, is for psychiatric assessors to "go by the book" — and as we have seen, Chinese forensic psychiatric textbooks still, even today, define certain types and instances of the uninhibited public expression of officially banned views and ideas as being clearly indicative of mental pathology. We do not have any first-hand accounts from Chinese forensic psychiatrists as to how they feel in such situations, but the following account of the situation of their former Soviet counterparts may provide some useful comparative insights into the matter:

> When the psychiatrist is finally confronted with the dissident, he knows he is dealing with someone who stands accused of committing what is considered by the authorities to be a serious crime. He is on his toes. He probably does not know, in most cases, whether a high-level decision has been made by the KGB to hospitalize the dissident, or whether the KGB investigator had genuine doubts about the dissident's mental health. The safer course is to assume that the KGB would like the dissident to be hospitalized. The psychiatrist himself is often in a special group to begin with: he is a forensic psychiatrist, usually a consultant to the KGB, and is particularly sensitive to the expectations of authorities. If he is sure that the expectation of hospitalization exists, then much less evidence of illness is needed to establish a diagnosis. If he does not know, then his need to play it safe may influence him to see more symptoms than he ordinarily would — sufficiently more to justify a diagnosis of illness.[149]

At another level, moreover, ethically conscientious assessors face the following invidious choice: to find the defendant to be sane and hence "legally responsible" for the alleged political offense, in which case he or she will almost certainly be found guilty and sentenced to a long term of imprisonment; or to make a finding of insanity and legal non-imputability, in which case the person

---

[149] Walter Reich M.D., "Diagnosing Soviet Dissidents," *Harper's*, August 1978, pp.31-37. At the time of writing this article, Dr. Reich was Lecturer in Psychiatry at Yale University and chairman of the program in the medical and biological sciences at the Washington School of Psychiatry. Over the previous six years he had interviewed a number of Soviet dissidents and psychiatrists.

will most likely be committed for an indeterminate period to an Ankang or similar-style center for psychiatric custody and treatment?[150]

Counterrevolutionary Crimes in China

Since the police allegations in most cases involving the use of politically directed psychiatry in China have concerned the charge of "counterrevolution," we should examine this category of crime in greater detail. The world of criminal jurisprudence was first introduced to the concept of counterrevolution during the French Revolution, in a decree issued by the Jacobins on March 10, 1793 establishing the system of "revolutionary tribunals." The works of Marx and Engels are replete with references to "counterrevolution," and Lenin eventually enshrined the concept in the Soviet criminal code after describing it as being not merely a useful legal device but also an "instrument of terror" that would awe the opponents of the Bolshevik Party into submission. The term was subsequently incorporated into the criminal codes of several Soviet satellite states, although the USSR itself later dropped the term in favor of the less political-sounding "crimes of state."[151] In China, somewhat ironically, the concept was first enshrined in law by Chiang Kai-shek, the leader of the KMT, whose government on March 9, 1928, promulgated a Temporary Law on the Punishment of Crimes of Counterrevolution, aimed primarily at the Communist Party of China.[152] Soon after establishing its first territorial base in Jiangxi Province, the Communist Party took steps to establish a similar legal regime, but aimed at suppressing the "KMT bandits" and their supporters among the local rural elite. On April 8, 1934, the Communist Party enacted its first formal law in

---

[150] In his report to the *British Medical Journal*, J.K. Wing posed a tantalizing ethical question that might also be asked of Chinese legal psychiatry: "Assuming for the moment that the Soviet psychiatrists have made their diagnosis in good faith, the question looks quite different to them: is a person who is suffering from a slowly developing form of schizophrenia responsible for an action that is likely to land him, at the very least, in a labor camp for three years? The Soviet doctor claims that he is acting humanely and that, in essence, the part he plays is no different from that of the American psychiatrists who saved Ezra Pound from execution" (J.K. Wing, "Psychiatry in the Soviet Union").

[151] The Chinese term for "crimes of state" is "*guoshi zui.*"

[152] See *Zanxing Fan'geming Zhizui Fa* (Temporary Law on the Punishment of Crimes of Counterrevolution). According to the latter law, "All attempts to subvert the Chinese Nationalist Party and the National Government...are defined as crimes of counterrevolution." As the KMT's Judicial Yuan expressly proclaimed, moreover: "Cases involving the Communist Party are to be dealt with as counterrevolutionary offenses."

this area: the Regulations of the Chinese Soviet Republic on the Punishment of Counterrevolution.[153]

Upon the Communist Party's assumption of power in October 1949, the clear evidence of widespread wrongful executions and imprisonments perpetrated by the Party's secret police since the 1930s proved to pose no obstacle to the systematic expansion of the same kind of legal regime that had produced these earlier injustices.[154] In February 1951, the Central People's Government passed a law, titled "Regulations of the PRC on the Punishment of Counterrevolution,"[155] which would serve as the main legal basis and justification for the systematic persecution of political dissidents and all other opponents of the Party for most of the next three decades. With Deng Xiaoping's return to power in late 1978, the growing trend towards an official condemnation and repudiation of both the 1957 Anti-Rightist Movement and the Cultural Revolution, together with rising public demands for the rehabilitation of the legions of counterrevolutionary political victims created during those two periods, acquired major new impetus. Over the next five years or so, virtually all of the hundreds of thousands of people who had been condemned, imprisoned, or executed for alleged counterrevolutionary offenses during the Cultural Revolution decade were exonerated by the new regime and declared to have been victims of the myriad "trumped-up cases and miscarriages of justice" perpetrated by the former radical Maoist leadership, the "Gang of Four," and its

---

[153] See Han Yanlong & Chang Zhaoru, eds., *Zhonghua Suweiai Gongheguo Chengzhi Fan'geming Tiaoli*, (Regulations of the Chinese Soviet Republic on the Punishment of Counterrevolution), in *"Zhongguo Xin Minzhuzhuyi Geming Shiqi Genjudi Fazhi"* (Legal System of the Base Areas During the Revolutionary Period of New Democracy)," in *Wenxian Xuanbian* (Selected Documents), vol. 3 (Zhongguo Shehui Kexue Chubanshe, Beijing, 1981), pp. 5-11.

[154] For example, as the State Council noted in 1983: "Some work-units and individuals have recently submitted petitions on behalf of comrades who were unjustly killed during the period of the Second Revolutionary Civil War [1927-37]...requesting that these wrongly executed comrades be commemorated as martyrs" (PRC State Council, State Council Document No. 91, 1983, *Guowuyuan Pizhuan Minzhengbu Guanyu Dui Di'erci Guonei Geming Zhanzheng Shiqi Sufanzhong Bei Cuosha Renyuan de Chuli Yijian de Tongzhi* [Notification of the Ministry of Civil Affairs, As Approved and Circulated by the State Council, Concerning the (Ministry's) Opinion on How to Handle the Cases of Persons Wrongly Killed in the Course of Campaigns to Suppress Counterrevolution During the Period of the Second Revolutionary Civil War], in *Xinfang Gongzuo Shiyong Zhengce Fagui Shouce, Zhonggong Zhongyang Bangongting* [A Handbook of Policies, Laws and Regulations for Use in Petitions and Visits Work], issued by the Office of the CPC Central Committee [document marked "for internal distribution only"], [Falü Chubanshe, July 1992]).

[155] *Zhonghua Renmin Gongheguo Chengzhi Fan'geming Tiaoli.*

followers. Similarly, the great majority of those branded as "rightists" in 1957 were finally rehabilitated, although Deng's role as Party General Secretary in overseeing the purges of that time meant that many simply had their political "hats" removed, rather than being officially pronounced innocent.

Overall, the Party's use of charges of counterrevolution against its political enemies and opponents — real or imagined — during the second half of the twentieth century undoubtedly generated more miscarriages of justice and devastated the lives of greater numbers of innocent people than any other single factor on China's judicial landscape. The only just and appropriate governmental response to such an appalling judicial track record would have been for Deng and his colleagues, in the late 1970s, to have set about dismantling the entire legal category of "crimes of counterrevolution," thereby repudiating the manifest judicial failings of the past and holding out the promise of a more politically neutral criminal justice system. But instead, in July 1979, the new leadership chose to give pride of place in the country's inaugural criminal code to an entire chapter on counterrevolutionary crime, laying down penalties ranging from several years in jail to life imprisonment or even death. Since then, at least ten thousand people or more have been consigned to long terms in prison on charges of counterrevolution that were no less politically determined and legally unsound than in the past.

By the mid-1980s, however, the incidence of counterrevolutionary crime as a proportion of the total number of criminal offenses recorded each year in China had dropped, according to official figures, to a very low level as compared with the situation during the first two decades or so of the People's Republic.[156] Until quite recently, the total number of imprisoned counter-revolutionaries was classified by the government as top secret, but the example of one province may serve to illustrate the general trend. In October 1959, Heilongjiang Province recorded a total prison inmate population of some 97,332 persons, of whom no fewer than 57,933, or just under 60 percent of the total,

---

[156] This reduction in the number of counterrevolutionary cases in China does not mean that the authorities have become substantially more tolerant of political criticism than before. Rather, a clear trend has been evident since 1980 towards sentencing political dissidents and other "enemies of national stability" on alternative and less obviously political legal grounds: for example, on common criminal charges such as alleged economic malfeasance, soliciting prostitutes, and even for violating restrictive regulations on the ownership of fax machines. In many cases, these charges have clearly been trumped-up and devoid of factual basis. Another recent trend has been towards imposing "administrative sentences" on dissidents and others in the form of up to three-year terms of "re-education through labor" (*laodong jiaoyang*) — an extremely widespread form of detention without trial that is applied solely at the discretion of the police authorities.

were counterrevolutionaries. By 1981, out of a total prisoner population of 23,685, the number of counterrevolutionaries had fallen to only 577, or 2.5 percent of the total.[157]

This reduction did not occur in a gradual or phased manner, but rather took the form of a sudden drop over a brief several-year period from December 1978 onwards. By 1982, for example, the government had officially exonerated the victims of more than 27,800 counterrevolutionary cases (involving a much greater number of actual defendants)[158] that had been falsely adjudicated in courts across the country during the two-year period from September 1976, when Mao died, until late 1978, when Deng returned to power. Similarly, in Fujian province alone during 1977-78, altogether 750 counterrevolutionaries were sentenced by the courts, of whom ninety-three received the death penalty and were executed. Again, the great majority of those sentenced were eventually rehabilitated.[159] These various figures show the extensive use that was still being made of such charges even after the conclusion of the Cultural Revolution.

Thereafter, according to official statistics, the numbers declined sharply. From 1980 to 1984, Chinese courts tried a total of 7,123 cases of counterrevolution (again accounting for many more defendants, only a tiny handful of whom would have been acquitted).[160] The question of possible

---

[157] Heilongjiang Provincial People's Procuracy, *Heilongjiang Jiancha Zhi* (Annals of the Heilongjiang Procuracy), (Harbin: Heilongjiang Renmin Chubanshe, 1988). Of the 577 persons imprisoned in 1981, just under half were said to be "historic counterrevolutionaries," that is, political prisoners who had probably already been held in jail for several decades.

[158] Many criminal "cases" (*anjian*) in China involve multiple defendants, and this was especially true in the case of counterrevolutionary offenses carried out during the early 1980s, when numerous "reactionary organizations" dedicated either to the restoration of Cultural Revolution-era policies or (at the other end of the political spectrum) to the promotion of Western-style democracy appeared in many parts of the country.

[159] For documentary sources on the above statistics, see *Sichuan Shengqing* (A General Account of Sichuan Province), published "for internal use only" by Sichuan People's Press, December 1987, p.548; and "Many 'Unjust, False and Erroneous' Verdicts Also Found Among Cases Tried Between 1977 and 1978," *Renmin Sifa Xuanbian* (A Compilation of Articles from "People's Justice" Magazine), (Law Publishing House, February 1983), pp.116-8 (volume also marked "for internal use only"). Among twenty-one of the counterrevolutionaries sentenced by the Fuzhou Intermediate Court, the latter report added, "Seventeen, or 77 percent of the total, were found to have been completely innocent... The original verdict was upheld in only one case." And of nine such verdicts rendered by the Xiamen Intermediate Court, "All were found to have problems."

[160] *Dangdai Zhongguo de Shenpan Gongzuo* (Judicial Work in Contemporary China), vol.1, (Contemporary China Publishing House, 1993). According to this book, the figure

rehabilitation and release did not arise in these cases, however, since by that time the government had completed its post-Cultural Revolution "rectification of the political line," and therefore those sentenced in the 1980s and later were all considered to be "genuine" political enemies of the State. By the mid-1980s, the annual numbers of sentenced counterrevolutionaries were down to single digits in many Chinese cities. Foshan Municipality in Guangdong Province, for example, had tried and sentenced 1,861 such cases in 1951; 2,165 in 1955; 3,298 in 1959; 178 in 1972; and 275 in 1976. During the entire nine-year period from 1979 until 1987, moreover, a total of only forty-seven cases of counterrevolution were tried by the Foshan court system, representing an average of 0.5 percent of all the criminal cases tried by local municipal courts during those years.[161] As of the late 1990s, the government's official accounting for the total number of sentenced counterrevolutionaries still held in prisons throughout China stood at around 2,000.

However, an analysis of the changing composition of cases of counterrevolution since the early 1980s, that is, the relative proportions of those convicted of the various types of counterrevolutionary offenses during different periods, reveals a striking trend. The 1979 Criminal Law specified more than ten varieties of counterrevolutionary crime, ranging from carrying out "subversion" and "espionage" to organizing "reactionary sects" and "counterrevolutionary groups." The main judicial weapon used by the government in the punishment of non-violent acts of speech and expression, however, was the Article 102 charge of "counterrevolutionary propaganda and incitement." The specific meaning and content of this offense was explained in detail by the Supreme People's Procuracy in 1992 as follows:

> There are four main forms of expression [of Article 102 crimes]: 1) shouting counterrevolutionary slogans in public and making counterrevolutionary speeches; 2) writing, posting up or distributing in public places counterrevolutionary leaflets, banners, and big-or small-character posters; 3) extensively mailing out counterrevolutionary-propagandist letters or sending threatening and alarmist letters to [government] organs, [social] bodies, and universities or

---

of 7,123 counterrevolutionary cases accounted for 0.43 percent of all criminals sentenced during the period in question.

[161] *Foshan Shi Fayuan Zhi* (Annals of the Foshan Municipal Courts), compiled and published by the Foshan Municipal Intermediate Court (year of publication not known, but probably 1988 or 1989).

colleges; and 4) editing and issuing reactionary publications and publishing counterrevolutionary articles. The first two of these four categories...account for two-thirds of all cases of counterrevolutionary incitement.[162]

Between 1980 and 1991, the proportion of sentenced counterrevolutionaries convicted under Article 102 rose steeply. According to one authoritative account, the average incidence of Article 102 offenses as a proportion of all counterrevolutionary offenses during the 1980s was "approximately 20 percent."[163] By 1990, however, an official law journal noted: "During the most recent period, counterrevolutionary propaganda and incitement cases have accounted for around 80 percent of all the counterrevolutionary cases accepted and dealt with by the people's courts."[164] Far from declining after the Cultural Revolution, therefore, both the government's sensitivity to dissident-style criticism and the extent to which it was determined to punish such acts of free political expression had, by the early 1990s, significantly increased as compared to the frequency with which it prosecuted and punished other alleged forms of counterrevolution. It should be emphasized that dissident-style individuals brought for forensic psychiatric examination in China in recent decades have also, for the most part, been initially charged with the same offenses as those singled out for attention by the Procuracy in the passage quoted above: namely, political speech making, sloganeering, leafleting and poster sticking.

---

[162] Supreme People's Procuratorate, *Xingshi Fanzui Anli Congshu — Fan'geming Zui*, (Criminal Case-Studies Series: Vol.1: Crimes of Counterrevolution), (Beijing: Zhongguo Jiancha Chubanshe, November 1992), p.238.

[163] Ibid., p.238. According to the same source, the incidence of counterrevolutionary crimes as a percentage of all criminal offenses committed during the period 1980-89 varied from between 0.08 percent and 0.8 percent; and "even in the highest year, it did not reach 1 percent of the total."

[164] Li Li and Li Shaoping, "*Lun Fan'geming Xuanchuan Shandong Zui de Rending* (On the Determination of Crimes of Counterrevolutionary Propaganda and Incitement)," *Xiandai Faxue* (*Contemporary Jurisprudence*), no. 1 (1990). One factor behind this relative surge in Article 102 offenses was no doubt the government's June 1989 nationwide crackdown on the Tiananmen Square pro-democracy movement, which had been officially condemned as a "counterrevolutionary rebellion." However, the incidence of all categories of counterrevolutionary offense (notably "leading and organizing a counterrevolutionary group" [Article 97] and "counterrevolutionary sabotage" [Article 100]) rose dramatically after the June 1989 crackdown, so the high predominance of Article 102 offenses at this time was still of considerable statistical significance.

In March 1997, the Chinese government finally responded to years of intense international criticism over its cavalier use of the statutes on counterrevolution as a means of suppressing peaceful political and religious dissent by ostensibly removing them from the Criminal Law. In their place, however, came a whole range of new but very similar offenses known as "crimes of endangering state security."[165] In essence, the concept of peaceful and non-violent political crime in China was not abolished as a result of this move, but merely remodeled in a form ostensibly more acceptable to international legal opinion. Far from attempting to hide the fact that this was in large part a mere change of name with little change in substance, the Chinese leadership went out of its way to stress this point, in what was probably an attempt to mollify domestic conservatives who feared it was another step down the road toward liberalization. The first indication that it would be "business as usual" after the legislative changes in question came from Wang Hanbin, Vice-Chairman of the National People's Congress Standing Committee, in a speech to the national parliament introducing the revised criminal code: "The punishment meted out for crimes of counterrevolution in the past will remain valid and cannot be altered."[166] This ruled out any question of amnesty or early release for those already sentenced on such charges. The protracted legal debate that preceded the new legislation's introduction made the matter even clearer. According to one commentator, "By altering the name of this legal weapon [the statutes on counterrevolution], we will be changing neither its basic nature, its tasks nor its combat effectiveness; still less will we be discarding it. All that will be involved is the adoption, in line with today's changed circumstances, of a new and more appropriate designation for the weapon."[167] And as another pointed out, "The proposal to redesignate counterrevolutionary offenses as crimes of endangering

---

[165] A detailed analysis of the significance of these legislative changes can be found in Human Rights Watch/Asia and Human Rights in China, "Whose Security? An Analysis of "State Security" in China's New Criminal Code," *A Human Rights Watch Report*, vol. 9, no. 4 (c), April 1997. Another very detailed and informative account of the topic can be found in Donald C. Clarke, *Wrongs and Rights: A Human Rights Analysis of China's Revised Criminal Code*, (New York: Lawyers Committee for Human Rights, 1999).

[166] Speech by Wang Hanbin to the Fifth Session of the Eighth National People's Congress, March 6, 1997.

[167] Guo Qun, "*Guanyu Fan'geming Zuizhang de Tiaozheng* (On Readjusting the Chapter on Crimes of Counterrevolution)," in Cui Qingsen, ed., *Zhongguo Dangdai Xingfa Gaige (Reform in China's Contemporary Criminal Code)*, (Shehui Kexue Wenxian Press, November 1991).

state security means nothing more than a change of name; in no way does it imply the 'deletion' or 'abolition' of those offenses."[168]

Since March 1997, the Chinese security authorities have proceeded to apply the new charges to precisely the same types of people — political dissidents, ethnic rights activists, independent trades unionists, unofficial religious believers and so forth — who previously were judicially dealt with on charges of counterrevolution; if anything, the sentences passed on such people for "endangering state security" in recent years have been even harsher than those previously imposed for counterrevolutionary offenses.[169] Legal reform in China since 1978 has brought many new and valuable benefits to the country as a whole. There has been no sign, however, that the authorities are prepared to slacken off or display greater tolerance in their longstanding judicial war against dissident freedom of expression and association in the key realms of politics, ideology and religion. Essentially, insofar as the country's criminal justice system is concerned, all that has changed in the post-Mao era is the specific content of what is officially regarded to be "counterrevolutionary" or "threatening to state security."

For this same reason, "cases of a political nature" will no doubt continue, much as before, to account for a significant proportion of offenses committed by the "dangerously mentally ill" in China. For much of the past two decades, certainly, the officially reported incidence of "pseudo-counterrevolutionary" cases as a proportion of all cases of forensic psychiatric appraisal (somewhere

---

[168] Li Wenyan, *"Fan'geming Zui Gaiwei Weihai Guojia Anquan Zui Qianyi* (My Humble Views on the Changeover from Counterrevolutionary Crimes to Crimes of Endangering State Security)," *Fazhi Ribao (Legal Daily)*, March 14, 1991.

[169] The following examples illustrate the draconian manner in which the new state security laws have been applied. On December 21, 1998, the veteran dissident Xu Wenli, 55, was sentenced to 13 years' imprisonment for "conspiring to subvert state power" after he attempted to legally register a peaceful opposition group, the China Democracy Party (CDP); the following day, his colleague Qin Yongmin, 49, was sentenced to 12 years' imprisonment on the same criminal charge. On December 27 the same year, Zhang Shanguang, a Hunan labor activist, was sentenced to 10 years' imprisonment after a two-hour trial held behind closed doors which found him guilty of "providing intelligence to institutions outside the borders," a charge relating to his attempts to establish an "Association to Protect the Rights and Interests of Laid-off Workers" in Xupu County. In July 1999, Yue Tianxiang, a labor rights activist, was sentenced to 10 years' imprisonment for "subversion"; Yue, who was detained on January 11 and formally charged on January 26, 1999, formed the China Labor Rights Observer in Gansu Province to protect the rights of laid-off workers. And on August 6, 1999, Liu Xianbin, a leading CDP member in Sichuan, was sentenced to 13 years' imprisonment for alleged conspiracy to subvert state power; Liu was unable to find defense counsel as a series of lawyers withdrew from the case following pressure from the authorities.

between five and fifteen percent) has been markedly higher than the reported incidence of cases of "genuine" counterrevolution as a proportion of the total number of criminal offenses committed (much less than one percent). The precise significance of these puzzling statistics is unclear, but they evidently do not point in the direction of any major systemic reforms in the medico-legal handling of the former variety of cases. In summary, so long as the notion of "political crime" continues to hold sway in police stations and courtrooms around the country, forensic psychiatry in China seems set to remain mired, to a greater or lesser extent, in the unethical practices of the past, tainting the ability of Chinese psychiatrists to perform their proper and legitimate role within the criminal justice system.

VI. THE ANKANG: CHINA'S SPECIAL PSYCHIATRIC HOSPITALS

In the mid-1980s, China's leaders, perceiving the emergence of an "ideological vacuum" among the populace, caused mainly by the official downplaying of politics in national life since the Cultural Revolution, launched a campaign to build "socialist spiritual civilization"[170] across the country. The purpose was to create a spiritual counterpart to China's already fairly well developed "material civilization," the national infrastructure and the economy. Since in Chinese the words for "spiritual" and "mental" are the same, the new movement was also an attempt to expand "mental civilization," and thus had important implications for the field of mental health work. In October 1986 in Shanghai, the ministries of health, civil affairs and public security convened the country's Second National Conference on Mental Hygiene Work, the first national-level meeting of this kind in almost thirty years.[171] The main item on the agenda was the sharp increase in the rate of mental illness among China's population in recent years: since the 1970s, the rate was said to have risen from seven per thousand members of the population to as many as 10.54 per thousand.[172] The level of violent crime in society was also rising rapidly, and China's severe lack of healthcare facilities for the mentally ill was identified as a major causal factor.

In April 1987, the three concerned ministries drew up a list of proposals designed to address these problems. According to the resulting policy document, "An especially urgent need is for the public security organs immediately to set up institutions for the custody and treatment of mentally ill people who break the law and create disastrous incidents... Owing to the lack of management over the mentally ill, many of them are spread over society at large and they create endless disastrous incidents that pose a very serious threat."[173] The ministries'

---

[170] *Shehuizhuyi jingshen wenming.*

[171] The first one had been held in 1958.

[172] According to a website run by the Beijing Institute of Forensic Medicine and Science (*Beijing Shi Fating Kexue Jishu Jianding Yanjiusuo*), the rate of mental illness among China's population currently stands at 13.47 per thousand. See http://fmedsci.com/sfjs/sfjs09.htm.

[173] "*Weisheng Bu, Minzheng Bu, Gong'an Bu Guanyu Jiaqiang Jingshen Weisheng Gongzuo de Yijian* (Opinion of the Ministries of Health, Civil Affairs and Public Security on the Strengthening of Mental Health Work)," April 20, 1987, in *Zhonghua Renmin Gongheguo Weisheng Fagui Huibian 1986-1988* (*PRC Compilation of Laws and Regulations on Health, 1986-1988*), (Law Publishing House, June 1990), pp.366-369.

main policy recommendations were threefold: first, to speed up the passage of a national mental health law; second, to further develop forensic appraisals work; and third, to establish a national network of police-run centers for the custody and treatment of severely mentally ill offenders. Further important meetings swiftly followed. In June the same year, the First National Academic Symposium on Forensic Psychiatry was held in the southern city of Hangzhou, and in December, the First National Public Security Conference on Custody and Treatment of the Mentally Ill took place in Tianjin.[174]

At some point in the course of these meetings, it was officially decided that the name "Ankang," meaning "Peace and Health," would be used as a uniform designation for the proposed new network of custodial facilities for mentally ill offenders. In December 1987, the Ministry of Public Security formed a National Ankang Work Coordinating Group, one of whose deputy chairmen was Wang Guiyue, director of the Tianjin Ankang facility and recent founder of a "stereotactic brain surgery" unit there.[175] A small number of institutions for the criminally insane had already been in existence in China for many years; known locations include Beijing, Shanghai, Tianjin, Dalian and Jilin Province. After the April 1987 conference decision, however, moves to establish institutions of this type elsewhere proceeded apace, and by May of the following year, a total of sixteen Ankang centers had been established and brought into service. A series of guiding documents were then drawn up by local public security authorities, including the "Administration Methods for Ankang Hospitals," "Detailed Implementation Rules for Nursing Work in Ankang Hospitals" and "Rules for the Admission and Treatment of Mentally Ill People Who Seriously Endanger

---

[174] This latter meeting was held at the Tianjin Public Security Bureau's Custody and Treatment Center for the Mentally Ill, which was shortly thereafter renamed as the Tianjin Ankang institute. Since that time, "national academic conferences on the custody and treatment of the mentally ill," attended mainly by practicing forensic psychiatrists, have been convened in various Chinese cities approximately every two years; the first, for example, was in Wuhan in May 1988 (see *Renmin Gong'an Bao* [People's Public Security News], May 20, 1988), and the third was in Hangzhou in October 1990 (see *Hangzhou Ribao* [Hangzhou Daily], October 24, 1990.)

[175] *Renmin Gong'an Bao*, May 24, 1988, p.1. A report two years later in the same newspaper confirmed the independent observer's account, cited above, of the establishment of a high-technology lobotomy unit at the Tianjin Ankang facility ("*Gong'an Xitong Jingshenbing Guan-Zhi Gongzuo Chengxiao Xianzhu* [Public Security System's Work of Custody and Treatment of the Mentally Ill Achieves Conspicuous Results]," *Renmin Gong'an Bao*, May 18, 1990, p.1).

Public Security."[176] By 1992, the total number of such institutions had risen to twenty, with several others under construction.[177] According to one source, large Ankang centers can accommodate around 1,000 inmates;[178] the Tianjin facility, however, is now believed to have around twice that capacity. According to another official source, the average length of stay for mentally ill offenders in the Ankang system is five and a half years, with some inmates being held for as long as twenty years.[179] The government's eventual goal is to establish one Ankang center for every city in China with a population of one million or above.[180]

The institutional model for the new Ankang forensic-psychiatric regime set up in China after 1987 was the Shanghai Municipal Hospital for Custody and Treatment of the Mentally Ill, which had been first established in May 1985.[181] This institute, now known as the Shanghai Ankang, is located in the same part of the city that previously housed "Jiangwan No. 5," the scene of Mr. C's ordeal during the Cultural Revolution; indeed, it is highly probable that they are one and the same place. In April 1986, the Shanghai government took the national

---

[176] These regulations are mentioned in *Renmin Gong'an Bao*, May 18, 1990; however, no actual copies of the documents have as yet come to light.

[177] Long Qingchun, ed., *Sifa Jingshen Yixue Jianding Zixun Jieda*, p.152. The twenty places having Ankang facilities as of 1992 were the cities of Tianjin, Beijing, Shanghai, Shenyang, Dalian, Tangshan, Wuhan, Xi'an, Suzhou, Chengdu, Hangzhou, Hefei, Fuzhou, Ningbo, Jinhua and Shaoxing; and also Heilongjiang Province, Jilin Province, Ningxia Autonomous Region, and Inner Mongolia Autonomous Region (city locations for the latter four are unknown). As of late 1999, the total number of Ankang facilities was reportedly still twenty (Zheng Zhanpei et al., *"Woguo Sifa Jingshenbingxue Jianding Gongzuo de Xianzhuang ji Zhanwang* [Present Situation and Future Prospects of China's Judicial Psychiatric Appraisals Work]," *Chinese Journal of Psychiatry*, vol.32, no.4 [1999], p.201).

[178] Lin Huai, *Jingshen Jibing Huanzhe Xingshi Zeren Nengli He Yiliao Jianhu Cuoshi*, pp. 54-55.

[179] Gu Xiangdong et al., *"Shehui Jineng Xunlian Dui 32 Li Zhuyuan Manxing Jingshenfenliezheng Huanzhe de Liaoxiao Guancha* (An Examination of the Efficacy of Social Skills Training for 32 Chronic Schizophrenic Patients)," *Chinese Journal of Nervous and Mental Diseases*, vol. 20, no. 2, pp.85-87.

[180] *Renmin Gong'an Bao*, May 24, 1988, p.1.

[181] The Chinese name for this institute was *"Shanghai Shi Jingshenbing Guan-Zhi Yiyuan."* In 1987, it was renamed *"Shanghai Shi Gong'an Ju Ankang Jingshenbing Guan-Zhi Yuan"* (Shanghai Municipal Public Security Bureau Ankang Institute for the Custody and Treatment of the Mentally Ill). The same wording is now used (after substitution of the specific city or province name in question) as a uniform designation for all the various Ankang centers in China.

lead by promulgating a detailed set of regulations for the compulsory hospitalization of mentally ill people who "create incidents or disasters" (*zhaoshi zhaohuo*).[182] These regulations are still the most specific thus far issued in China on the crucial procedural matter of how mentally ill offenders actually get admitted to Ankang care: expert forensic psychiatric appraisal of the detainee was to be performed, but once a finding of legal non-imputability had been made, the public security authorities were then accorded complete authority to issue the necessary paperwork for compulsory psychiatric admission; the courts had no visible role in the process.[183] Shortly thereafter, municipal and provincial governments elsewhere in China, including Tianjin and Guangdong, issued similar sets of regulations.[184]

Specific criteria outlining the various types and categories of mentally ill offenders who are to be compulsorily admitted to Ankang can be found in several published sources in China. These criteria vary slightly from source to source, but the most complete and exhaustive version appears in an official encyclopedia of police work published in 1990. The encyclopedia begins by explaining the three main types of people who are to be taken into police psychiatric custody: .

---

[182] "*Shanghai Shi Jianhu Zhiliao Guanli Zhaoshi Zhaohuo Jingshenbingren Tiaoli* (Shanghai Municipal Regulations on the Guardianship, Treatment and Management of Mentally Ill People Who Create Incidents or Disasters)," promulgated on August 29, 1986, in *Shanghai Gong'an Nianjian, 1988* (*Shanghai Public Security Yearbook, 1988*), (Shanghai Social Sciences Publishing House [volume marked: "for internal distribution only"], December 1988), pp.343-346. The regulations came into force on October 1 the same year.

[183] An argument that the courts should be given a leading role in this process is made in Lin Huai, *Jingshen Jibing Huanzhe Xingshi Zeren Nengli He Yiliao Jianhu Cuoshi*, pp.53-54.

[184] See "*Tianjin Shi Shouzhi Guanli Weihai Shehui Zhi'an Jingshenbingren Banfa* (Tianjin Municipal Methods for the Shelter and Management of Mentally Ill People Who Endanger Public Order)," undated and unpublished document on file with the author; and "*Guangdong Sheng Shourong Anzhi Zhaohuo Zhaoshi Jingshenbingren Zanxing Banfa* (Guangdong Provincial Temporary Methods for the Shelter and Settlement of Mentally Ill People Who Create Disasters or Incidents)," issued by the Guangdong Provincial People's Government on January 17, 1990, in *Guangdong Sheng Fagui Guizhang Huibian* (*A Compilation of Guangdong Provincial Laws, Regulations and Rules [January 1989-December 1990]*), edited and published by the Office of the Guangdong Provincial People's Government, pp.275-276.

The first are those commonly known as "romantic maniacs" [*hua fengzi*],[185] who roam around the streets, grab food and drink from others, expose themselves naked, or look unkempt and disheveled, and so have an adverse effect on social decorum.

The second are those commonly known as "political maniacs" [*zhengzhi fengzi*], who shout reactionary slogans, write reactionary banners and reactionary letters, make anti-government speeches in public, and express opinions on important domestic and international affairs.

The third are those commonly known as "aggressive maniacs" [*wu fengzi*], who beat and curse people, pursue women, elderly people and children, smash up public property, commit murder or arson, or who otherwise endanger people's lives and the safety of property.

The encyclopedia then lists the following more specific and operational criteria for dealing with mentally ill people falling within the three categories:[186]

The public security organs have primary responsibility for the management and treatment of the following five kinds of severely mentally ill persons, all of whom pose a relatively grave threat to social order:

---

[185] The term "*hua fengzi*" (literally: "flower crazies") is a euphemistic one whose broad meaning encompasses aspects of the English terms "hippy," "nutcase," and "sex maniac"; however, it does not have the often violent or non-consensual overtones of the latter term.

[186] Another important category of persons liable to be sent to Ankang facilities is those who develop "prison psychoses" of various kinds (as discussed above) during their confinement in regular prisons. The incidence of this type of mental illness has apparently risen sharply in China in recent years. One significant subgroup of such sufferers is reportedly those sentenced to death and awaiting execution; if the stress and anxiety of impending execution leads them to become mentally ill, they are regarded as "incompetent to undergo punishment" and are then placed in Ankang custody for treatment until they become sane enough to be executed. Moreover, prisoners who stage hunger strikes in jail are often regarded as suffering from a subtype of this particular illness and are therefore also sent to Ankang centers for secure psychiatric treatment.

- Persons carrying knives who commit violent or injurious acts; those who are suicidal; and those who commit arson or other acts that seriously disturb social order, with definite consequences.

- Persons who disrupt the normal work of Party and government offices or who disrupt normal work and production in enterprises, scientific and educational institutions, thereby posing a danger.

- Persons who frequently expose themselves naked, or otherwise harm social morals, in busy crowded areas or in public places.

- Persons who shout reactionary slogans, or who stick up or distribute reactionary banners and leaflets, thereby exerting an undesirable political influence.[187]

- Mentally ill people who drift in from other areas and disrupt the public order of society.

- Upon encountering any of these five types of people, the public security organs are to take them into custody for treatment.[188]

Finally, the police encyclopedia adds, "The taking of mentally ill people into custody is especially important during major public festivals and when foreign guests arrive for visits, and it should be appropriately reinforced at such

---

[187] "Huhan fandong kouhao, zhangtie sanfa fandong biaoyu, chuandan, zaocheng buliang zhengzhi yingxiangde."

[188] Zhongguo Gong'an Baike Quanshu (China Encyclopedia of Public Security), (Jilin People's Publishing House, February 1990), p.1964. A similar set of criteria for enforcing police custody of the mentally ill is listed in Zeng Wenyou et al., ed., Jing Guan Bi Du (Essential Reading for Police Officials), (Police Officials Publishing House, Beijing, October 1992), (volume marked "for internal circulation only"), p.163. A more readily accessible source, giving roughly the same kinds of guidelines and discussing the role and purposes of the Ankang system more generally, is Liu Dechao, "Dui Weihai Shehui Zhi'an de Jingshenbingren de Chuli (On the Handling of Mentally Ill People Who Endanger the Public Order of Society)," Xiandai Faxue (Modern Jurisprudence), no. 2 (1990), pp.69-71. Finally, a 1996 book states that the various criteria for compulsory Ankang admissions were first formulated at the First National Public Security Conference on Custody and Treatment of the Mentally Ill, held in Tianjin in December 1987. See Lin Huai, Jingshen Jibing Huanzhe Xingshi Zeren Nengli He Yiliao Jianhu Cuoshi, p.111.

times."[189] For our present purposes, the most important categories of alleged mentally ill people listed above as being targets for Ankang-style custody and treatment are, first, "political maniacs," namely those displaying "dangerously" political dissident-like behavior, including "expressing opinions on important domestic and international affairs"; and second, those accused of disrupting "the normal work of Party and government offices," since in practice this category is often taken to include the kinds of persistent petitioners and complainants whom the police regard as suffering from "litigious mania." As mentioned earlier, most countries need to maintain institutions for the criminally insane in order to protect the public from genuinely dangerous psychotic offenders. At least in the modern era, however, few countries have ever regarded the above-mentioned types of mentally ill people as being legitimate targets for forced psychiatric custody. The former Soviet Union was the most prominent such country, and to the extent that it now follows a similar set of practices, China's recently established Ankang system appears to be performing a role much the same as that of the Soviet Interior Ministry-run "Special Psychiatric Hospitals," which were used to incarcerate, in a medically unjustifiable way, hundreds and possibly thousands of peaceful Soviet dissidents.

Owing to the highly secretive nature of these institutions, little is known about the conditions of detention and treatment currently found within them. One first-hand account of conditions at the Shanghai facility on the eve of its transformation into an Ankang center, however, painted a disturbing picture of widespread fear among the inmates arising from the frequent resort by warders and nursing staff to various abusive methods of punishment. The account, which was written by a female dissident and former political prisoner who had been placed in the Shanghai facility in early 1987 and which contained case details of several other "political maniacs" held there at the time, reads in part as follows:

> The only difference between [prison and this hospital] was that the two used different methods of punishment. The instruments of punishment in prison were common handcuffs, whereas the hospital used medical appliances...

> If patients were disobedient in the hospital, the doctors would increase their medication. Besides eating, they only felt like sleeping, and often suffered from cramps. This is not a civilian

---

[189] The rounding-up by police of mentally ill citizens in advance of important public events and visits by foreign dignitaries was also a highly characteristic feature of political psychiatry in the former Soviet Union.

hospital that you can leave in three or five months. There, three or five years was considered to be a short time. Moreover, you had to work for seven hours a day. Those who were on more medication dribbled saliva constantly. Their eyes often rolled upwards helplessly in their sockets. They walked slowly and stumbled frequently.

If such and such a person was to be punished, her bed would be taken to the area between the dining hall and the workshop, and she would be tied by her four limbs to the bed by straps looped through the metal bed frame. In this way the nurses could supervise her from morning till night. In the daytime during working hours the dormitory was locked. Sometimes two people could be punished at once. During the daytime when everyone was working, we looked at the women's hands and feet tied to the bed. We all kept silent, lowered our heads and carried on working. In the evening when we returned to the dormitory, we would watch the bed carried away, and see the empty space where it had stood. A cold shiver would go through your heart. You didn't know when it would be your turn. Maybe you would be punished because the doctors discovered you had smuggled a letter out to some visitors, or maybe because you had had an argument with the doctors or nurses. When they wanted to punish someone, the alarm outside the dormitory (in the dining room) would sound and several police would arrive at once, and tie you to the bed.

Another kind [of punishment] was injections. One kind was muscular injection and the other intravenous, which was much more painful. I saw some patients after intravenous injections, whose tongues were so swollen they bulged out of their mouths. After a few days of injections, their facial muscles were all stiff, their eyes fixed and staring. Their faces were like waxwork masks -- they couldn't turn their heads and would have to slowly turn their whole body if they wanted to look at something.

Yet another kind of punishment was acupuncture with an electric current. The patients called it the "electric ant."[190] It uses electrically controlled acupuncture needles. There are three levels of current. The higher the current, the more painful, and the degree of pain also depends on the particular acupuncture points used. There is the *taiyang* point (on the temple), *hegu* (also known as "hukou," on the palm of the hand between the thumb and the index finger) and the heart point on the sole of the foot. The people who have suffered this say the heart point on the sole of the foot is the most painful. In civilian hospitals, when a patient is subjected to electric shock treatment it is forbidden to let the other patients watch, but in this [kind of] place, treatment was no longer about curing illness and saving peoples' lives. It had become the penal code the doctors used to maintain control. When they wanted to punish someone, they would make all the patients stand around her bed, while the patient twitched in agony and pitifully cried, " I won't do it next time... I won't do it again, please let me go..." After it was over, the nurses admonished all the other patients that whoever violated the rules next would suffer the same treatment as her. Everyone would lower their heads, fearing that their faces had turned pale.[191]

---

[190] The treatment method of electric acupuncture, which is in widespread use in China (and is found also as an "alternative" therapy in many other countries nowadays) is to be differentiated from the use of ECT. When properly administered, electric acupuncture has no ethically abusive connotations. Like many other legitimate medical treatments, however, electric acupuncture can, as the above account indicates, be misused for purposes of inflicting pain and punishment.

[191] Handwritten account circulated to various human rights groups in 1995; the writer cannot presently be identified for reasons of personal safety. According to the account, the ward in which she was placed held twenty women, three of whom were political dissidents of various kinds. Moreover, "[inmates] convicted of murder were allowed to talk freely together, but political prisoners were not permitted to do the same." The reason why one of the three dissidents had been admitted was, according to the same account, as follows: "She had gone onto the streets to make a speech protesting about the high increase in the cost of living. She said that skyrocketing prices had made people's lives worse, and that political corruption nowadays meant officials made a fortune through their official posts, something that could not have happened in Mao Zedong's day."

The most recent confirmed case of a political dissident being sent to the Shanghai Ankang facility is that of Li Da, a young worker at an electrical appliances firm in the city who had apparently been involved in the May 1989 pro-democracy movement. On three separate occasions, prior to his arrest in July 1998, he stood outside the Shanghai No. 1 Department Store handing out leaflets calling for the rehabilitation of victims of the June 4, 1989 government crackdown, for greater political democracy in China, and for the right to commemorate Taiwan National Day. Li's case was briefly reported on by Voice of America in February of the following year, on the basis of a letter he had smuggled out of the Shanghai Ankang facility. There has been no further news about him since.

Another account, this time involving a fatality at the Ankang facility in Beijing, suggests that staff violence against inmates was still commonplace in institutions of this type at least as late as 1993. In March that year, as part of China's bid to host the 2000 Olympic Games, a delegation from the International Olympic Committee arrived in Beijing to inspect the city' sporting and other facilities. Over the preceding few weeks, among other preparations designed to enhance China's chances of winning its bid for the games, the Beijing authorities had removed large numbers of homeless, indigent or mentally ill people from the streets of the city and shipped them out of town either to their original place of residence or to temporary holding centers, and in the case of mentally ill targets of this "cleanup" operation, the Beijing Ankang center was apparently also used for this purpose. One such person was a 41-year old mentally retarded man named Wang Chaoru, who lived with his parents in the southern part of the city. According to a detailed account of Wang's case that was subsequently written by Nicholas Kristof and Sheryl WuDunn, the Beijing correspondents of the New York Times during that period, a policeman arrived at the family's door, accompanied by a woman named Zhang from the local Street Committee, two days before the IOC delegation's arrival in Beijing:

> The policeman wanted to take Wang away, but the retarded man began shrieking his protests. So the policeman and Zhang left. The next morning, Zhang returned, this time with two policemen. They had no arrest warrant, no detention warrant, and they didn't suggest that Wang had broken any law or endangered anybody. They didn't give any reason for wanting to take him away, but they insisted that he had to leave with them. "I don't want to go," Wang cried out in fear. "Mama, Papa!" He raced to the corner of the big bed, shielding his

head with his arms. His parents knew that it would be futile to resist, so they watched helplessly as the two policemen dragged away their terrified son. Wang had reason to be frightened. A year earlier, as part of their efforts to beautify Beijing in preparation for the annual session of the National People's Congress, the police had taken him to a sanatorium on the outskirts of Beijing and beaten him to a pulp. A few days later, they drove him to the Temple of Heaven, where they deposited him in a wounded clump at the front gate. It took Wang two hours of walking to find his way home.

As the Olympic delegation toured Beijing's sports facilities on March 7, Wang's parents waited anxiously for news about their son. Two days later, shortly after dawn,

A police car came to pick them up, but the police officer said that only one of the parents could go. The parents, now desperate with worry, imagining their son beaten bloody, perhaps even in a coma, insisted that they both go. The police backed down and drove them out to Fangshan, a hospital closely associated with the Public Security Bureau... When they arrived, the police took the parents into an office that was bare except for several chairs and a table. "The person has died," an officer informed them matter-of-factly. "We have inspected the body." Wang Shanqin and An Yulian were devastated. They felt responsible for their son, who had depended on them. He had pleaded with them to let him stay, yet they had allowed the police to take him away.

Wang's father demanded to see the body, and he and his wife were then led down a long corridor to the hospital's morgue. Later, the couple described to the foreign journalists what they found on arrival:

"There was blood all over his face," the father recalled slowly and hesitantly, like a man fighting with himself, negotiating between his desire to tell the world and the pain of remembering. "His hair was all red with blood. His lips were cut up, and his eyes — they were pierced, as if they had burst open and then swollen shut." ... In his back, there was a big hole. Someone must have stuck a police baton into his back,

boring it into the flesh. And his behind was all bruised" ...
"The back of my son's legs," he continued, as he rubbed his
hands under his kneecaps, "had these huge bumps, these
swellings. I told them I wanted to sue, and you know what
they said? 'You'll never win.' On the day we cremated him,
they gave me a bag with 5,000 *yuan* in it. They didn't say
what the money was for."[192]

The Beijing Public Security Bureau has a close organizational affiliation
with only two hospitals in the capital: one is the Binhe Penal Hospital, located
until recently within the grounds of the Beijing No. 1 Municipal Prison (this
facility was torn down and relocated about five years ago); the other is the
Beijing PSB Ankang Institute for the Custody and Treatment of the Mentally Ill,
which is located in Fangshan District, a suburban area to the southwest of the
city.[193] Even today, very few foreigners living in China have ever heard of the
name "Ankang," so it is unsurprising that the authors of the above account did
not specifically identify the place of Wang Chaoru's death as being the Beijing
Ankang facility. But that is undoubtedly where he died.

---

[192] Nicholas D. Kristof and Sheryl WuDunn, *China Wakes: The Struggle for the Soul of a
Rising Power* (Random House, 1994), p.98. The authorities' version of Wang's death was
as follows: "'The police said that my son had died on the night of the sixth,' [said the
father.] That was just hours before the Olympic delegation arrived. 'They said he went
mad and died on the streets. That's impossible! When they said that, I yelled at the
policemen. They were just too inhumane. How could they hate my son so much?'"

[193] A detailed official description of the organization and functions of the Beijing Ankang
facility can be found in Lin Huai, *Jingshen Jibing Huanzhe Xingshi Zeren Nengli He
Yiliao Jianhu Cuoshi*, pp.111-116; the account was written by Zhang Hu, a leading
forensic psychiatrist who formerly worked at the Harbin No. 1 Special Hospital
(*Ha'erbin Shi Diyi Zhuanke Yiyuan*) and for the past ten years or so has been based at the
Beijing Ankang institute. In his article, Zhang said that the Beijing Ankang is divided
into three parts: a closed and highly secure zone (*fengbi qu*), where all new admissions
are placed; a semi-open zone, holding around half of the inmates; and an open zone,
mainly devoted to work-therapy activities, where inmates scheduled for release are held.
According to Zhang, the facility is run "fully in accordance with humanitarian
principles," although he also acknowledges that "many problems remain to be solved." In
his view, Ankang centers should primarily be places of treatment, rather than detention or
punishment: "If the reverse were true, so that the medical objectives became secondary,
and the principal purpose was simply to lock up the patients and keep them in custody,
then it would be wrong, and the nature and aims of Ankang hospitals would no longer be
the same" (Ibid., p.113). Another description of the Ankang regime can be found in Li
Congpei, *Sifa Jingshenbingxue*, pp.385-386.

VII. THE MATRIX OF THEORY AND PRACTICE: READINGS FROM THE LEGAL-MEDICAL LITERATURE

The Dangerousness Criterion

Under international legal and medical standards, a number of key principles are held to be paramount in the field of psychiatry. First, compulsory hospitalization is, in most cases, only justified where the patient's mental state poses a direct danger, usually physical, either to his or her own health and safety, or to that of others; alternative considerations, such as concern by the authorities that a person's mental state or behavior may prove injurious to "social stability," do not meet the requirements of this key "dangerousness" criterion.[194] As a U.N. Special Rapporteur noted in 1983, "It is not satisfactory to generalize about 'dangerousness' in the abstract. One must distinguish between 'danger to self', danger to others', and 'danger to the public'... The argument of 'overprediction of dangerousness' poses a grave threat to the human rights and fundamental freedoms of the patient."[195] Second, it is a commonplace of international law, starting with the Universal Declaration of Human Rights, that

---

[194] The U.N. Principles for the Protection of Persons with Mental Illness and for the Improvement of Mental Health Care (discussed above: see Section II) contain broader criteria for involuntary hospitalization than just that of dangerousness; for example, they also permit involuntary commitment in the case of a person suffering from mental illness whose judgment is impaired and who is likely to suffer further psychiatric deterioration if not hospitalized. This aspect of the Principles clearly goes well beyond the question of dangerousness to self or others, and as such is viewed as controversial by many experts in the field. For a detailed critique of this and other aspects of the December 1991, U.N. document, see Eric Rosenthal and Leonard S. Rubenstein, "International Human Rights Advocacy under the 'Principles for the Protection of Persons with Mental Illness,'" *International Journal of Law and Psychiatry*, vol.16 (1993), p. 257. However, while the Principles may create a certain potential for abusive practices by allowing involuntary commitment on the grounds of possible further deterioration in the patient's subjective mental condition, they nonetheless still define the objective "dangerousness" criterion quite narrowly. Since the Chinese authorities invariably cite this particular criterion (and in the much wider form, moreover, of a putatively "social" or "political" type of dangerousness) when explaining why certain types of political nonconformists require to be psychiatrically detained, it is important to emphasize that China is in violation of international standards in this specific and key respect. Certainly, official concern that the mental state of those involved might "further deteriorate" unless they are forcibly committed never appears, in the Chinese legal-medical literature, as being either the whole or partial grounds for such action having been taken by the authorities. Finally, it is again vital to stress here that one is talking, in the Chinese case, about people being *criminally* detained and then subjected to *forensic* psychiatric appraisal — a very different matter from the kinds of involuntary civil commitment cases to which the psychiatric "deterioration" provisions in the U.N. Principles might well give rise.

[195] Erica-Irene A. Daes, *Principles, Guidelines and Guarantees*, p.20.

no person may be subjected to detention, arrest, trial or any other form of persecution on account of their peacefully held political or religious views and activities.[196] And third, as a logical extension of these two principles, it is flatly impermissible for government authorities to subject any person, whether mentally ill or otherwise, to involuntary psychiatric treatment or hospitalization on criminal charges relating to the person's political or religious views and beliefs — or indeed, to do so for any other reasons of governmental convenience.

The following questions should be borne in mind, therefore, in seeking to evaluate the cases of those described as "mentally ill political offenders" in China. Were the individuals concerned in fact mentally ill? If so, did they pose a genuine and direct danger to themselves or to others? And did their activities, as officially described, in any way justify their being placed under arrest and subjected to the authority of the State's criminal-psychiatric assessors? The first question is, in most cases, difficult if not impossible to answer on the basis of the fragmentary case material available, although certain useful insights can often be gleaned. The remaining two issues boil down, in essence, to the dangerousness criterion and how it is defined and interpreted by the authorities. The understanding of dangerousness as a medico-legal category varies considerably in legal systems around the world,[197] but the question of a mentally ill person's potential for doing physical harm to himself or others is of central and primary concern in most jurisdictions; secondary considerations may include psychological harm, danger to property, or damage to the environment.[198] China, however, is today the only country known specifically to

---

[196] See for example, Articles 9, 18 and 19 of the Universal Declaration of Human Rights.

[197] For an informative account of this topic, see Timothy Harding and Cleopatre Montandon, "Does Dangerousness Travel Well? A Cross-National Perspective on Medico-Legal Applications," in John R. Hamilton and Hugh Freeman, eds., *Dangerousness: Psychiatric Assessment and Management* (Gaskell, 1982), pp.46-52. A fuller and more in-depth discussion of the various issues involved can be found in John Gunn, "Dangerousness," in John Gunn and Pamela J. Taylor, eds., *Forensic Psychiatry: Clinical, Legal and Ethical Issues* (Butterworth & Heinemann, 1993), pp.624-645.

[198] The dangerousness criterion is a contentious issue among psychiatrists at the best of times, even when it is narrowly restricted to the potential for committing physical violence. According to one writer,

> Furthermore, the evidence is pretty overwhelming that psychiatrists are not very good at predicting dangerousness; their success rate in correctly identifying future violence varies from a high of 40 percent...to a low of something like 0.3 percent... The role of psychiatrists in sentencing and detaining procedures is also

include "political harm to society" within the scope of what the medico-legal authorities officially regard as being dangerous mentally ill behavior.[199]

How high or prominently, then, do so-called political cases figure in the Chinese psychiatric establishment's general hierarchy or ranking of "serious crimes committed by the mentally ill"? This important issue has a close bearing upon the further question of whether the offenders concerned, once evaluated as being "not legally responsible" for their actions, will end up, variously: a) being set free and placed under a "family surveillance and control" order, or instructed to undergo either outpatient or inpatient psychiatric treatment at a normal hospital; b) being placed under involuntary committal in the secure ward of a regular mental hospital or, for those with no means of financial support, in a similar closed section of one of the numerous Ministry of Civil Affairs-run "social welfare institutes"[200] found throughout the country; or c), being forcibly confined without limitation of time in an Ankang institute for the criminally insane. As the following passage from 1988 makes clear, "cases of a political nature" are deemed by the Chinese medico-legal establishment to rank among the most serious and dangerous of all possible forensic-psychiatric offenses:

> challenged, on the grounds that they cannot even agree amongst themselves on a definition of dangerousness. I myself like the simple one of it being the potential to cause serious physical harm to others, although there is a case for psychological harm to be included also. (Hamilton and Freeman, *Dangerousness*, pp.1-3.)

[199] This is not to say that no other countries still practice political psychiatry; a handful do, notably Cuba. For the background history, see Charles J. Brown and Armando M. Lago, *The Politics of Psychiatry in Revolutionary Cuba* (Freedom House, 1992). For a more recent case report, see "Dissidents Stage Fast to Protest Reincarceration," Agence France Presse, February 27, 1998; in FBIS same day. But so far as is known in these other cases, the notion of political harm is not actually written into the formal definition of psychiatric dangerousness. It is also worth noting that even where the dangerousness criterion is validly and legitimately applied, "The level of security applied to a patient should always be the minimum level which is compatible with safety and good management" (John Gunn and Pamela J. Taylor, *Forensic Psychiatry*, p.635). In practice this means that unless a crime has already been committed, a violent mentally ill person may be detained in, for example, the secure ward of a normal mental hospital; those who commit serious crimes of violence may, by contrast, end up in a secure prison mental hospital. In China, as the Ankang admissions criteria listed earlier clearly indicate, non-violent and alleged mentally ill "political offenders" are among those most likely to receive the latter kind of treatment.

[200] These institutes serve, simultaneously, as warehouses or dumping grounds for indigent elderly people, abandoned or orphaned infants and small children and also the destitute mentally ill. For further information, see Human Rights Watch/Asia, *Death By Default: A Policy of Fatal Neglect in China's State Orphanages* (New York: Human Rights Watch, 1996), Chapter 2 and *passim*.

Of the 222 cases in the present group where diagnoses of schizophrenia were made, sixty-six cases (or 29.7 percent) involved murder or serious injury (a figure closely approximating the findings of Li Congpei *et al* in their study); there were fifty-five cases of a political nature; and forty-eight cases involved disturbances of social order. The combined total for these three categories came to 169 cases, accounting for 76.1 percent of all cases committed by schizophrenics. From this, we can ascertain the major gravity of the threat posed to social order and personal safety by schizophrenia sufferers who commit crimes, and also the severity of the consequences thereof.[201]

Thus, so-called political cases and also those involving disturbance of public order[202] are evidently seen by China's legal-medical authorities as representing no less serious and dangerous a threat to society than cases of murder and injury committed by genuinely psychotic criminal offenders. In other words, psychiatric detainees of both these political categories are prime candidates for long-term admission into Ankang. But the official view goes still further than this, for it sometimes seeks actually to equate violence and dissidence, by depicting the latter as being a form of "violence" in itself. A

---

[201] Shen Muci, Jin Wei, Cai Jianhua, and Han Baojin, "*Sifa Jingshen Yixue Jianding 654 Li Fenxi* (An Analysis of 654 Cases of Forensic-Psychiatric Medical Evaluation)," *Chinese Journal of Nervous and Mental Diseases*, vol. 21, no.3 (1988), p.166-168. As can be seen, "cases of a political nature" accounted for as much as 25 percent of all the schizophrenia cases forensically examined in this study.

[202] Many cases of "disturbing public order" in China also merit inclusion under the general heading of "cases of a political nature," since state-appointed forensic examiners frequently diagnose such persons as suffering from "litigious mania" (*susong kuang*) also known as "processomania." The latter diagnostic category was reportedly first posited by a French psychiatrist in the 19th century, and was widely applied by Soviet forensic psychiatrists (who generally regarded it — as do their Chinese counterparts today — as being a subspecies of "paranoid psychosis") in the cases of politically dissident detainees up until the late 1980s. Western systems of law acknowledge a category of persons known as "vexatious litigators"; but this term is applied only in civil cases (most commonly, in judicial denial of the right to bring suit on the grounds that the plaintiff's allegations are frivolous or unwarranted), and certainly not as a psychiatric label leading to incarceration on the grounds of criminal insanity. The various different types of "disturbing social order" in China that also properly qualify as "political cases" are further discussed below.

prime example of this mode of thinking can be seen in the following passage written by Li Congpei, probably the most eminent forensic psychiatrist working in China today, and several others, on the question of crimes committed by schizophrenics:

> Among the cases under discussion, outbursts of violent behavior[203] were characterized by several unusual features: for example, the person's "criminal" motive would frequently be vague and unclear or the reverse of what it originally seemed to be, and was thus difficult to fathom; or the person would often display absolutely no sense or instinct of self-preservation, for example by openly mailing out reactionary letters or pasting up reactionary slogan-banners in public places — and even, in some cases, signing his or her real name to the documents; and in cases where the "criminal" behavior had been relatively savage,[204] the person would later maintain an air of cool indifference.[205]

At the outset of this analysis of 386 cases of criminal behavior by schizophrenics, Li and his colleagues stated that the diagnostic criteria applied in the study were based, among other things, upon the psychiatric classification models laid down in the World Health Organization's International Classification of Diseases (ICD-9) and the American medical profession's Diagnostic and Statistical Manual of Mental Disorders (DSM-III). The authors' explicit characterization, however, of the relatively mild acts of public political protest referred to above as representing typical examples of violent psychotic behavior will no doubt dismay psychiatric professionals around the world who actually do base their work on these standard reference texts.

---

[203] "*shixing baoli xingwei*"

[204] "*jiaowei xiongcan*"

[205] Li Congpei, Li Yongzhi, Liu Jinsheng and Fang Mingzhao, "*Jingshen Fenliezheng Sifa Jingshenbing Jianding An Li Fenxi* (An Analysis of Cases Involving the Forensic-Psychiatric Evaluation of Schizophrenia)," *Chinese Journal of Nervous and Mental Diseases*, vol. 20, no.3 (1987), pp.135-138. It is worth noting also that the works of Georgi Morozov were cited as an authority in the footnotes to this article.

Official Statistics on Political Psychiatry

The frequency with which "cases of a political nature" are referred to in the official forensic psychiatric literature has been noted several times in this article, and we shall now examine these statistics in greater detail. According to these sources, the incidence of forensic psychiatric "political cases" has declined steadily over the past two decades, falling from a level of around fifteen percent in the 1980s to as low as one or a few percent in the late 1990s; the general trend thus appears to parallel the sharp decline seen in the numbers of "genuine" counterrevolutionary cases dealt with by the authorities over the same period.

At the outset, it should be noted that not all of the "political cases" cited in these official publications necessarily involved persons who were of entirely sound mind when detained by the security authorities for exercising their right to free expression. Many of them may indeed have been suffering from various mental quirks, disorders or abnormalities at the time in question, and a certain proportion may even have been in urgent need of psychiatric attention. Two key questions arise in all such cases, however. First, why were the numerous individuals who actually make up these statistics arrested by the police in the first place, since their only real offense seems to have been voicing opinions and viewpoints which, for a wide range of questionable reasons, the Chinese authorities viewed as politically unacceptable? The fact that these dissident, or pseudo-dissident, viewpoints were apparently directed, in a high number of reported cases, against the Communist Party of China neither represents a legally acceptable grounds for arrest, nor — still less — can it be regarded as a medically sound or valid reason for questioning the basic sanity of those involved. And second, why were so many of these individuals, sane or otherwise, seen by the authorities as posing such a serious "danger" or "threat" to society that, upon being arrested, they had to be labeled by forensic psychiatrists as "not legally responsible" for their dissident or pseudo-dissident activities, and then promptly divested, as a result, of most of their civil and litigious rights — notably the right to be tried in court — and finally, sent for indeterminate periods of time to police-run institutes for the criminally insane?

The following passages provide a typical cross-section of the numerous statistical references to such cases that have appeared in China's professional literature during the post-Mao era. During the 1980s, the overall statistical profile for political-style forensic psychiatric appraisals was broadly as follows. According to Shen Zheng, a leading authority in the field,

> In a research study of 1986 on eighty-three criminal cases where diagnoses of schizophrenia were made, Zhang Junxian

and others found that cases of murder and injury accounted for 55.4 percent, political cases accounted for 13.3 percent, and hooliganism and sexual crime accounted for 10.8 percent.[206]

More specifically,

> Of the eleven cases of antisocial acts or statements carried out by schizophrenics, six involved the writing of slogan-banners in public places, three involved the shouting of slogans amidst crowds of people, and two involved the sending of openly-signed letters by post.[207]

According to Zhang Xinzhi, an elderly forensic medical expert who had worked in the Chinese police force since 1954 (most recently as deputy-head of the Wuhan Municipal Public Security Bureau's department of forensic medicine),

> In criminal cases, mentally ill people, as a result of their pathological thoughts and hallucinatory delusions, may exhibit abnormal behavior in the form of anti-social acts and statements; for example: murder, arson, rape, theft, injury, disrupting traffic, and writing reactionary letters and posters or shouting reactionary slogans.

Out of a sample group of fifty criminal cases studied by Zhang in which the defendants were examined by police-appointed psychiatrists,

> Altogether six cases, or twelve percent of the total, involved the writing of reactionary letters; and another two cases, or four percent of the total, involved the shouting of reactionary slogans."[208]

---

[206] Shen Zheng, *Falü Jingshenbingxue*, p.302. For the study referred to by Shen, see Zhang Junxian, "An Analysis of the Forensic Evaluation of 83 Cases of Schizophrenia," *Fayixue Zazhi* (*Journal of Forensic Medicine*), vol. 1, no. 2 (1986), pp.33-36.

[207] Ibid., p. 305. (NB: In the *Columbia Journal of Asian Law* version of this article, the passage in question was wrongly attributed to Zhou Yingde, another Chinese forensic medical expert; see next Note.)

[208] Zhang Xinzhi, "A Preliminary Analysis of 50 Cases of Crime by the Mentally Ill," in Zhou Yingde, ed., *Fanzui Zhenchaxue Gailun: Cankao Ziliao* (*General Theory of*

The combined incidence of sixteen percent in this sample is broadly consistent with the 13.3 percent figure given for "political cases" by Shen Zheng. Moreover, out of an expanded group of 111 cases examined by Zhang from the period 1982-89 in which criminal defendants underwent forensic psychiatric evaluation,

> There were forty cases of murder, accounting for thirty-nine percent of the total; fifteen cases of rape, or thirteen percent of the total; fourteen cases of theft, also thirteen percent; six arson cases, or six percent; sixteen cases of injury, or fourteen percent; twelve cases of writing reactionary letters, or eight percent; four cases involving the shouting of reactionary slogans, or four percent; and four suicide cases, another four percent.[209]

The combined incidence for the two types of "political case" noted by Zhang in his expanded study was thus twelve percent, again broadly consistent with the figure of 13.3 percent officially recorded elsewhere in China during the mid- to late-1980s.

Similarly, a study by Shen Muci, Jin Wei and other psychiatrists from the Hangzhou No.7 People's Hospital published in the *Chinese Journal of Nervous and Mental Diseases* in 1988, found that out of 654 people subjected to forensic-psychiatric evaluation at the hospital between 1973 and 1986 in connection with alleged criminal acts,

> Altogether 103 cases were of a political nature; of these, forty cases involved the making of political statements, twenty-five involved [the display or distribution of] political slogan-banners or leaflets, twenty-one cases involved acts of

---

Criminal Investigation: Reference Materials), (Beijing 1987), pp.417-422 (volume marked: "Internal teaching materials: keep confidential").

[209] Zhang Xinzhi, "A Preliminary Analysis of 111 Cases of Crimes by the Mentally Ill," in Zhai Jian'an, ed., *Zhongguo Fayi Shijian (Forensic Medical Practice in China)*, (Beijing: Police Officers' Educational Publishing House, August 1993), pp.556–561. No fewer than 85 percent of the 111 criminal cases reportedly involved schizophrenics. (NB: This sample group of 111 cases appears to have included the fifty cases cited in the 1987 study by Zhang – see preceding Note.)

political propaganda; and seventeen cases involved [the writing and sending of] letters.[210]

Once again, the aggregate figure for "political-style" criminal-psychiatric cases in this particular sample group comes, coincidentally or otherwise, to almost sixteen percent — a figure surpassed only, moreover, by the 21.9 percent of those in the same forensic sample group who had allegedly committed murder or serious injury.[211]

In addition, the same study noted that a further one hundred of the 654 cases concerned acts that allegedly "disturbed social order," including twenty-nine cases of "unreasonably making trouble" (*wuli qunao*) — a code-phrase generally reserved by the authorities to denote the legions of "petitioners" (*shangfangzhe*) who regularly besiege the government offices around the country responsible for dealing with citizens' complaints about official malfeasance or corruption, and which are also supposed to handle citizens' applications for official redress of the countless past acts of political persecution and injustice committed by Chinese government agencies.[212] As mentioned above, many of those falling in this general category should also

---

[210] Shen Muci et al., "*Sifa Jingshen Yixue Jianding 654 Li Fenxi*," pp.166-168.

[211] According to the article, 80 percent of the political cases in this particular study were ones dating back from before 1980, a situation about which the authors comment: "This shows that [the incidence of forensic-psychiatric] cases of a political nature is closely related to [the question of] political movements and social stability" (Ibid., p. 168).

[212] Usefully, Shen and his colleagues also provide a break-down of the specific medical diagnoses made by state forensic psychiatrists in respect of the various criminal categories included within this large sample group. Notably, of the 103 "political cases," fifty-five (or more than half) were attributed to schizophrenia; mental retardation was said to account for five of the cases; eight were attributed to mania; seven were described as being due to anti-social or sociopathic personality disorders; nine were said to be due to reactive psychosis; three more were attributed, respectively, to prison psychosis, "other mental illness" and organic brain disease sequella; and in only sixteen (or 15 percent) of the numerous "political cases" were the defendants found to be "not mentally ill" — and therefore liable to criminal prosecution for their "anti-social" or "counterrevolutionary" acts. (It should be stressed, of course, that the majority of those in the "political" subcategory were not set free by the authorities after being found "not legally responsible" by reason of mental illness; rather, the legal issue then became: in what particular form of "non-penal" state custody would it be most appropriate to place such people in order that society could be afforded maximum protection from their "pathologically dangerous" political behavior.)

properly be seen as "political cases."[213] Out of the one hundred persons accused of "disturbing social order," forty-eight were diagnosed as suffering from schizophrenia, eight were said to have various personality disorders, thirteen were found to be not mentally ill (and so were "legally responsible" for their actions), while an additional five were diagnosed as being "paranoid psychotics." If cases of this secondary category are added into the various statistics for those primarily defined by the authorities as being "political" in nature, then the overall incidence rates for political psychiatry in China in the 1980s rises to somewhere in the region of 20 percent of the criminal psychiatric caseload.

Finally, it should be noted that of the 103 "political cases" in the group, only sixteen, or approximately 15 percent, were determined to be "not suffering from mental illness" and so were liable to criminal prosecution; the majority of the group was found to be mentally ill and thus liable for psychiatric custody. Similarly, of the 100 cases of "disturbing social order," only thirteen were determined to be not mentally ill, while all the rest were found to be not legally responsible and were also therefore candidates for involuntary psychiatric committal.[214]

---

[213] For further information on the authorities' application of abusive detention policies to mentally ill persons alleged to have "disturbed social order," see Human Rights in China, *Not Welcome at the Party: Behind the "Clean-Up" of China's Cities — A Report on Administrative Detention under "Custody and Repatriation"* (New York: Human Rights in China [HRIC], September 1999). In the late 1980s, even orphans and abandoned children, residents of the Shanghai Children's Welfare Institute, were sometimes forcibly sent to psychiatric institutions by the orphanage authorities; this was done to them as a punishment for daring to cooperate with an independent investigation then being carried out by the Shanghai municipal legislature into phenomenally high death rates among infants and young children at the orphanage. For details of two of these cases, see Human Rights Watch/Asia, *Death By Default*, pp.272-275.

[214] The authors of the study also offered a statistical break-down of the subjective "motives" (*zuo'an dongji*) underlying the "criminal acts" carried out by the individuals in question. Of the 103 "political cases," thirty-one were attributed (oddly enough, given the ostensible topic of discussion) to "pathological behavior" on the defendant's part, thirteen were attributed to "delusions of persecution," fifteen were attributed to "impairments of mental logic," nine were attributed to "auditory delusions," eight to "personality disorders," while a total of twenty were attributed to "non-pathological" motives (note that this figure exceeds by four, for some reason, the overall number who were determined to be "not suffering from mental illness"); the remaining seven cases were attributed, variously, to "delusions of jealousy" (one case), "relational delusions" (five cases), and "impairment of consciousness" (one case). Of the one hundred cases of "disturbing social order," altogether twenty-eight were attributed to "pathological behavior" on the defendant's part, sixteen to "delusions of persecution," and twelve to

Turning now to the present era, two recently published studies from China have provided a detailed statistical breakdown of the relative incidence of "political cases" in forensic psychiatric appraisals work during successive decades from 1960 to as recently as the late 1990s. The first of these, published in January 2000, examines the situation in one particular institution in the southwestern city of Kunming, the Yunnan Provincial Mental Hospital.[215] The authors of the study offer few specific observations on their various findings, but they provide a very useful set of data, contained in Table 1.

Table 1: Forensic Psychiatric Appraisals at the Yunnan Provincial Mental Hospital, 1960-97

Period		1960-1979	1980-1989	1990-1997
Total cases		575	1274	936
Violent cases	#	236	734	437
	%	41.04	57.61	46.69
Economic cases	#	13	92	131
	%	2.26	7.22	14.00
Sexual assault cases	#	23	79	60
	%	4.00	6.20	6.41
Political cases	#	288	54	9
	%	50.09	4.24	0.96
Divorce cases	#	0	40	52
	%	0	3.14	5.56
Sexual victim cases	#	1	87	98
	%	0.17	6.83	10.47
Mental injury cases	#	1	28	61
	%	0.17	2.20	6.52
Appraisals of sentenced prisoners	#	13	160	88
	%	2.26	12.56	9.40

"personality disorders"; eighteen cases were deemed to be "non-pathological" in motive; and the remaining twenty-six to various other motivating factors.

[215] See Yao Zuhua et al., "*Jin 40 Nian Sifa Jingshenbingxue Jianding Anli de Bijiao* (A Comparative Study on the Case Expertise of Forensic Psychiatrics Over the Past 40 Years)," *Chinese Journal of Psychiatry*, vol. 33, no. 1 (2000), pp.47-49.

According to the data, the reported incidence of political cases at this one hospital fell from a high point of around 50 percent in the 1960s and 1970s,[216] to just over four percent during the 1980s, and ended at an average level of just under one percent in the 1990s. It should be noted, however, that this hospital appears to have dealt with a comparatively low number of political cases during the 1980s; as we have seen, the reported level for that period elsewhere in China was around fifteen percent. Moreover, while the actual number of cases reported for the 1990s was only nine, this was merely the figure for one hospital. If typical for the rest of the country, this low figure would translate into a total for the country as a whole during the 1990s of several hundred "political cases," and possibly thousands.

The second recent study, published in January 1999, surveyed a total of 9,925 cases of forensic psychiatric appraisal that had been reported in 231 separate articles published in ten psychiatric legal-medical journals in China between 1976 and 1995. During the period in question, the authors found a total of 375 "political cases," representing an average incidence rate of 3.78 percent. The overall data from this considerably more representative survey was tabulated in the article as shown in Table 2.[217]

---

[216] Interestingly, regarding the figure of 50.09 percent for the 1960s and 1970s, the authors comment: "At that time, when applying for appraisals to be carried out, the judicial organs almost never requested that an appropriate determination of legal responsibility be rendered in respect of the person being examined; in the overwhelming majority of cases, therefore, only a medical diagnosis was made in the appraisal conclusion." This was probably because the police and procuratorial system was in tatters for much of this period: especially during the Cultural Revolution, all such work was subsumed under the activities of ad hoc "security committees" (*baowei weiyuanhui*) set up in all the localities of China.

[217] See Zhao Jiancong et al., "*Woguo Sifa Jingshenbingxue Xianzhuang de Yanjiu* (A Study on the Current Data of Judicial Psychiatry in China)," *Chinese Journal of Psychiatry*, no. 1 (1999), pp.53-54.

Table 2: Forensic Psychiatric Appraisals Listed in Ten Chinese Journals, 1976-95

Period	1976-1990		1991-1995		Total (1976-95)	
Cases	#	%	#	%	#	%
Murder and injury	2,016	40.90	1,841	36.85	3,857	38.86
Theft	617	12.52	605	12.11	1,222	12.31
Arson	129	2.62	172	3.44	301	3.03
Sexual crime	465	9.43	612	12.25	1,077	10.85
Sexual victims	373	7.57	1,178	23.58	1,551	15.63
Obstructing social order	591	11.99	331	6.63	922	9.29
Politics (*zhengzhi*)	272	5.52	103	2.06	375	3.78
Hooliganism	81	1.64	88	1.76	169	1.70
Other	385	7.81	66	1.32	451	4.54
Total	4,929	100.00	4,996	100.00	9,925	100.00

Although the time periods used in this survey are not strictly comparable with those in Table 1, what is clear is that among the sample data used, the total number of "political cases" for the five-year period 1991-95 was more than one third of that reported for the entire 15-year preceding period. In other words, viewed chronologically, rather than as a percentage of the total cases for each individual period, the absolute per-year numbers of political cases had hardly changed at all between 1976 and 1995. Moreover, even when viewed as a percentage of the total cases for each period, the incidence rate for "political cases" was still, apparently, proceeding along at the quite considerable level of 2.06 percent during the first half of the 1990s, or more than half the average rate for the entire period since 1976. Also important to note is the fact that the figure of 103 such cases for this period was by no means the total number that actually arose around the country. Rather, it was simply the number that happened to emerge in a rather large group of separately published local studies. The true figure for China as a whole at that time was undoubtedly far higher than this.[218]

---

[218] Another study published in April 2000, for example, noted that at a single psychiatric hospital, the Zigong Mental Health Center, altogether 956 cases of forensic psychiatric evaluation were performed over the period 1981-88. If this was roughly typical for the rest of the country, the total number of such evaluations conducted across China as a

Finally, many of those included under the heading of "obstructing social order" in the above table were probably also "political cases" in the wider Chinese forensic-psychiatric sense of the term, since this is often the police's criminal charge of choice in cases of "litigation mania," whistleblowing, persistent complaint against authority, and "false accusation" (*wugao*.)[219]

Armed with the above statistical data, we can now attempt to make a rough "ballpark" estimation of altogether how many political dissidents and people in other similar categories may have been branded as criminally insane and confined to forensic custodial facilities in China over the past two decades. It should be stressed that, given the fragmentary nature of the currently available statistical evidence, this is an inherently hazardous undertaking and one that can yield, at best, only a very approximate indication of the actual extent of the problem. As we have seen, "political cases" accounted, according to the official statistics, for around 15 percent of all forensic psychiatric appraisals carried out during the 1980s, and, during the 1990s, for somewhere in the region of several percent. The largest statistical indicator on this general topic thus far found in China's legal-medical literature appeared in a volume published in 1988 and was as follows:

> According to statistical materials presented at the First National Conference on Forensic Psychiatry, held at Hangzhou in June 1987, the total number of forensic psychiatric appraisals cases (most of which dated from 1980 and later) handled by a certain number of mental hospitals in China had already reached more than 10,000.[220]

---

whole during the same period would certainly have run into the tens of thousands, and possibly even the hundreds of thousands (Wei Qingping et al., "An Analysis of Expert Psychiatric Testimony on Epileptic Patients' Illegal Actions").

[219] For a detailed account of the forensic-psychiatric handling of cases of "false accusation" in China, see *Zhongguo Gong'an Baike Quanshu* (*China Encyclopedia of Public Security*), p.1965. As the article explains, those found guilty of false accusation are subject to the disturbing judicial principle of "reverse criminal culpability" (*shixing fan zuo zui*), whereby the offender is sentenced to whatever term of imprisonment would have been applied to the person accused in the event that the accusation had proved to be well founded. Whilst mentally ill offenders of this type are supposed be exempted from criminal judgment, they may nonetheless still be subject to the "commensurability principle" (see above, "Judicial Psychiatry in China and its Political Abuses," Section V.A) and so have to spend similarly long periods in psychiatric custody.

[220] *Jia Yicheng, Shiyong Sifa Jingshenbingxue*, pp.1-2.

According to the same source (at p.28), altogether twelve mental hospitals accounted for no fewer than 7,862 of the above-mentioned cases; findings of mental illness were made in 87.51 percent of these cases. In addition, the same source notes (at p.31) that three mental hospitals in Shanghai conducted a total of almost 1,000 cases of forensic psychiatric appraisal over the five-year period between August 1982 and August 1987; again, findings of mental illness were made in approximately 80 percent of these cases. However, another source states that between 1982 and 1989, a single hospital in the Shanghai area — the Shanghai Municipal Center for Mental Health — carried out as many as 1,034 forensic psychiatric appraisals.[221] Similarly, between 1983 and 1987, as noted earlier, a total of 931 cases of forensic psychiatric appraisal were conducted at the Beijing Anding Hospital alone. While figures for the total numbers of such appraisals carried out during the 1990s in China are as yet relatively scarce, it is clear from numerous officially published sources that the recent general trend here has been rapidly upwards.

To summarize briefly the above data, during the period 1980-97, twelve hospitals in China performed almost 8,000 forensic psychiatric appraisals, or an average number of 670 per hospital. Applying the average "political case" rate of 15 percent for this general period to the latter figure, one obtains a total figure of 1,200 "political cases," of whom approximately 90 percent (or 1,080) would have been found legally non-imputable by reason of insanity for their alleged crimes and hence (in most or all cases) sent to forensic custody (the remainder would almost certainly have been sent to prison as "counterrevolutionaries"). In addition, we see that the total numbers of forensic psychiatric appraisals that were conducted by individual mental hospitals in China reached, during the same general period, high triple figures. And finally, we know that the total number of such evaluations being conducted across China nowadays is rapidly rising each year.

In order to estimate, on the basis of these partial figures, the approximate sum total of forensic psychiatric "cases of a political nature" in China, we also need to know how many mental hospitals there are throughout the country and how many of those are engaged in forensic appraisals work. The former figure, at least, is known; according to a recently published article in the Chinese press, "575 hospitals and 77,000 doctors and nurses are dealing with mental diseases in

---

[221] See Lin Huai, *Jingshen Jibing Huanzhe Xingshi Zeren Nengli He Yiliao Jianhu Cuoshi*, p.133. (No rate for findings of mental illness in this group was given.)

China."[222] It is not known how many of these hospitals are qualified or officially authorized to perform forensic psychiatric evaluations.

Let us assume, however, that only one in twenty of the hospitals (that is, around thirty institutions) is so authorized; this is likely to be a considerable underestimate of the actual situation. If so, one could reasonably estimate, on the basis of the average number of cases examined by each of the twelve hospitals referred to above, that these institutions performed somewhere in the region of 20,000 forensic psychiatric appraisals during the first seven years of the 1980s alone, and that approximately 3,000 of these were probably "political cases." (It should also be remembered that many other cases — notably those involving "crimes of disturbing public order" — were appraised during the same period that did not fall within the scope of the authorities' own definition of "political cases," but which would nonetheless qualify as such from the international standards point of view.)

Even allowing for the officially reported decrease in cases of this general nature from the early 1990s onwards, therefore, it is reasonable to estimate that somewhere in excess of 3,000 "political cases" (broadly defined) have been dealt with by Chinese forensic psychiatric examiners countrywide over the past two decades, and moreover that the great majority of these were subjected, as a result, to some form and duration of forced psychiatric custody and treatment. This conjectural "ballpark" figure is almost certainly inaccurate, but it probably errs on the conservative side; and it provides, at least, a reasonable indication of the general order of magnitude involved. By comparison, in the case of the Soviet Union, existing studies indicate that the total confirmed number of political dissidents and others in similar categories who were wrongfully branded as mentally ill and sent to forensic custodial facilities during the 1970s and 1980s was somewhere (depending upon the study in question) in the region of two to three hundred, with unconfirmed estimates also extending into the several thousands.[223]

Diagnostic Concerns

A useful and pithy working definition of the abnormal mental condition allegedly responsible for the various civic-minded activities mentioned above

---

[222] See "Nation's Mentally Ill Need More Care," *China Daily*, November 27, 2000.

[223] See, e.g., the various estimates on this topic presented in Bloch and Reddaway, *Russia's Political Hospitals*, and Smith and Olesczuk, *No Asylum: State Psychiatric Repression*.

was provided as recently as 1994 in a textbook on forensic psychiatry written by
a leading official at the Beijing Ankang institute:

> Paranoid psychosis manifests itself, in clinical practice, in two
> different ways: one form is "litigious mania," in which
> delusions of persecution tend to predominate; the other form is
> "political mania," where the dominant role is played by
> "political delusions." The content of the delusions in "political
> mania" concern the line and policies of the State; those
> afflicted do avid research into politics and put forward a whole
> set of original theories of their own, which they then try to
> peddle by every means possible, thereby leading to court
> action.[224] For this reason, such people are sometimes viewed
> as being political dissidents.

> For example, one middle-aged person who was suffering from
> "political mania" wanted to do research into "modern
> humanism" and spontaneously resigned from his job. He spent
> all his time shut up at home, writing manuscripts tens of
> thousands of characters in length, which he then sent to the
> Academy of Social Sciences and the editorial departments of
> various newspapers and journals, hoping they would accept
> them. When all his efforts failed, he got in touch with some
> foreigners and asked them to publish his articles abroad,
> thereby causing a great deal of trouble.[225]

---

[224] "...*cong'er yinqi susong*" literally means "thereby leading to litigation." The text is
ambiguous as to whether it is the dissident or the government who initiates the
"litigation" in question. Since there is no known case of any Chinese political dissident
having ever launched court action against the government for pursuing "erroneous
politics" (i.e., an "incorrect" form of Marxist socialism), the above reference to
"litigation" or "court action" can only be understood as a somewhat euphemistic
indication by the author that the dissident in question was criminally prosecuted for his
contrarian political views and writings. This would also explain why he was being
subjected to forensic psychiatric examination: he had already been detained or arrested
for alleged political crimes.

[225] Long Qingchun, ed., *Sifa Jingshen Yixue Jianding Zixun Jieda*, pp.83-84.
Interestingly, the author adds: "The incidence of unlawful and calamitous behavior,
however, is markedly less common in the case of paranoid psychotics than in the case of
schizophrenics. The vast majority of such behavior is caused by the sufferers' paranoid
delusions... And in cases where, under the dominant influence of delusions of grandeur
or persecution, 'reactionary speech or action' ensues, then it will usually do so in public

With this definition in mind, we shall now consider a number of important medical diagnosis-related issues that commonly arise in the context of the forensic-psychiatric evaluation of "political cases" in China. The first concerns the high rate at which findings of legal non-imputability on grounds of mental illness are made. In reviewing a total of 931 cases of forensic-psychiatric evaluation performed at Beijing's Anding hospital during the period 1983-87, Tian Zu'en and other senior physicians at the hospital established, among other things, that altogether 301, or 32.3 percent, of the criminal defendants concerned were found to have "impaired ability to recognize" their actions; another 307, or 33 percent, had "impaired ability to control" their actions; and 323 others, or 34.7 percent, had "no impairment of legal capacity."[226] This finding is significant because, like numerous other officially published statistics on the same point, it indicates that a far higher proportion of criminal defendants brought before psychiatric evaluation panels in China, altogether 65.3 percent in Tian's case study, are found to be legally incapable by reason of insanity than is the case in most other countries.[227] An even more striking finding of the same

---

places, for example with the person concerned handing out leaflets or sticking up big-character posters, signed with his or her real name, in crowded public places."

[226] The Chinese terms for these categories, in order of above listing, are: "*bianren zhang'ai,*" "*kongzhi zhang'ai*" and "*falü nengli wu zhang'ai.*" See Tian Zu'en, Yu Qingbo, Qi Wei, Wang Ping, Chen Lifeng and Yu Tian, "*Jingshenbingren de Xingshi Falü Nengli* (Criminal Legal Capacity of the Mentally Ill)," *Chinese Journal of Nervous and Mental Diseases,* vol. 21, no.3 (1988) pp.169-171. Under Chinese law the presence of either "impaired recognition" or "impaired control" constitutes, by itself, sufficient grounds for a finding of "lack of legal responsibility."

[227] According to Richard J. Bonnie, Professor of Law at the University of Virginia School of Law and Director of the University's Institute of Law, Psychiatry and Public Policy:

In the United States, where most psychiatric evaluations of criminal responsibility are initiated by defense attorneys, forensic examiners find a clinical basis for an insanity defense in approximately 10-20 percent of cases, depending on the state. See, e.g., Warren, J.W., Rosenfeld, B., Fitch, W.L., and Hawk, G., "Forensic Mental Health Clinical Evaluation: An Analysis of Interstate and Intersystemic Differences," *Law and Human Behavior,* Vol. 21, 1997, pp.377-390. (In 1987-88, opinions favoring insanity were rendered by forensic examiners in 7 percent of evaluations in Michigan, 9 percent of evaluations in Virginia, and 13 percent of evaluations in Ohio.) Interestingly, forensic examiners in the former USSR tended to render opinions of non-imputability in a substantial majority of cases in which the defendant was found to have a mental disorder. (See Bonnie, R.J., "Coercive Psychiatry and Human Rights: An Assessment of Recent Changes in the Soviet Union," *Criminal Law Forum,* 1990, No.1, pp.319-346, at page 334:

study was that out of the nineteen political psychiatric cases specifically defined as being "counterrevolutionary" in nature, fourteen defendants, or 73.7 percent, were determined to have "impaired recognition" of their allegedly criminal acts, while the remaining five, or 26.3 percent, were found to have "impaired control" over their actions.[228] None of these nineteen pseudo-counterrevolutionaries was determined to be mentally normal.[229]

"[N]onimputability determinations...occur in a much larger proportion of criminal cases than appears to be the norm in the united States and other Western countries.") That practice appears to have continued in Russia. (Richard J. Bonnie, personal communication to author, December 7, 2000.)

See also "Statistics of Mentally Disordered Offenders 1999 — England and Wales," U.K Government, available at http://www.homeoffice.gov.uk/rds/pdfs/hosb2100.pdf; see in particular Table 6, p.12.

[228] Curiously enough, however, where the question of "criminal motive" (*fanzui dongji*) was concerned, Tian and his coauthors found that while the illegal political behavior of eleven of the nineteen "counterrevolutionary" forensic examinees had been inspired by "pathological motives" (*bingli dongji*), and that of three others by "unclear motives" (*buming dongji*), the remaining five examinees were said to have been prompted by "real" or "authentic" motives (*xianshi dongji*) — meaning (in the authors' own words): "motives arising from the conflicts and requirements of reality and having no direct or evident relationship to the mental illness from which the person is suffering." In other words, the five "mentally ill" individuals in question appear, by the authorities' own admission, to have been entirely sane and rational at the time of staging their banned political manifestations (Tian Zu'en et al., "Criminal Legal Capacity of the Mentally Ill," pp.175-177). The same article also discussed the correlation between motive and legal responsibility: out of the total group of 931 forensic-psychiatric examinees, all the 323 persons who were determined to bear "full legal responsibility" for their criminal acts were also said to have been inspired by "authentic" motivating factors, suggesting an officially perceived one-to-one correlation between these elements under normal circumstances; a roughly similar number of persons (352) were found to bear "limited responsibility" for their actions despite also having been prompted by real or authentic motives; and only twenty-three persons found to be similarly motivated were determined to bear "no legal responsibility" for their acts. Of 163 persons whose crimes were officially attributed to "pathological motives," all were declared to be not legally responsible, as were eighteen others who were said to have acted from "mixed motives." The remaining 52 persons from the group were said to have had "unclear" motives, and all were similarly held not legally responsible (Ibid., p.176).

[229] But again, they were caught on the horns of what might be called "psychiatric justice with Chinese characteristics." For had they been found to be sane, they would have proceeded to trial and almost certain conviction on charges of counterrevolution, the most serious offence in the Criminal Law. Since, however, the ostensibly political activities that brought them into the orbit of the criminal justice system in the first place are viewed by the government as being so "socially dangerous" that such persons must on no account be allowed to continue manifesting their "pathological symptoms" within society at large, the fact that they were determined to be mentally ill meant that they would instead, in all

These various figures suggest either that the standard of proof and evidence for determining criminal insanity is considerably less rigorous in China than elsewhere, or that far fewer cases of a frivolous, implausible or opportunist nature are presented for expert medical evaluation. The latter possibility can effectively be ruled out since virtually all such cases in China are put forward by the police or the state prosecutor, rather than, as generally occurs in the West, the counsel for the defense. Either way, it is clear that criminal defendants' chances of being "acquitted" of the suspicion of mental illness is in practice extremely low — a situation broadly similar to that found in the criminal trials system, where less than one percent of defendants are eventually found to be innocent. A volume published in 1999 by three experts from the Institute of Forensic Medicine at the West China Medical University in Chengdu, including Liu Xiehe, one of China's top forensic psychiatrists, sheds important light on this issue. Liu and his colleagues began by calling for his Chinese colleagues to adopt, along the lines of certain stipulations found in the Criminal Code of Canada, a "presumption of sanity" when conducting forensic psychiatric appraisals. As they explained,

> At present in China there are two main modes of thought. First, the "clinical mode of thought," which is mainly found among appraisals experts who have worked for many years as clinical psychiatrists and also, part time, as judicial psychiatric appraisers. When psychiatric experts of this kind have to perform judicial appraisals, they make a presumption that the person being examined is either mentally abnormal or afflicted by some form of mental illness. The reason for this is that they assume that the examinee would not have been sent for appraisal in the first place unless he or she was in fact mentally abnormal or suffering from mental illness; or else, they feel that the person must indeed have been behaving in some unusual kind of way, otherwise the judicial officers, lawyer or family members concerned would not have raised the request for an appraisal to be carried out. As a result of this general presumption, or feeling of probability, the appraiser will then go to great pains to avoid "being negligent," either by searching through the case files for any possible evidence

---

probability, be placed in closed psychiatric prison wards where they would be forced to undergo indefinite medical treatment for their exotic psycho-political disorders. For China's hapless "political lunatics," in short, freedom is seldom a viable outcome.

of mental abnormality or mental disease, or by urging the judicial officers, lawyer or family members to provide as much evidence of this nature as they can.[230]

The second main mindset, which the three writers call "the judicial appraisal mode of thought," was one generally found among full-time police forensic psychiatrists, who tended to take the opposite approach and presume that all criminal suspects sent for psychiatric appraisal were mentally normal. The reason they did so was in order to ensure that as many offenders as possible would receive due punishment for their actions. In the view of the book's authors, both of these tendencies were biased and unscientific, and they concluded by calling for China to adopt a similar "presumption of sanity" rule as that found in the Canadian legislation.

The situation described here clearly gives much cause for general concern. Where "cases of a political nature" are involved, however, the implications become more complex and troubling still. Basically, these have to do with the same general problem identified elsewhere in this discussion, namely the essentially specious nature of the Chinese judicial authorities' distinction between "genuine" and "mentally ill" counterrevolutionary offenders. At least where internationally recognized criminal offenses are concerned, the two "modes of thought" identified above might result, at worst, in either a mentally ill offender being sent to a regular prison and not receiving any medical treatment, or in a sane offender being wrongly diagnosed as mentally ill and sent to a forensic psychiatric asylum.[231] In China's "political cases," however, no internationally recognized offense has been committed, but simply an act of free expression protected by international law, so the general picture assumes a significantly different quality and character than this. Presumably, the former type of Chinese psychiatrist will tend to rush to assume that a person detained for political offenses is indeed mentally ill and needs to be forcibly committed, whereas those of the second mindset will insist that "due punishment" be meted out and that the person be sent immediately to jail. In short, political detainees

---

[230] Zhang Wei, Huo Kediao and Liu Xiehe, "*Fayi Jingshenbingxue Jianding de Siwei Fangshi* (Modes of Thought in Forensic Psychiatric Appraisals)," in *Fayixue Jinzhan yu Shijian* (*Advances and Practices in Forensic Medicine*) (Chengdu Science and Technology University Press, 1999). The passage quoted above can be found at http://www.legalmed.org/ref/99z1.html.

[231] There is, of course, a third possibility, namely that the person sent either to prison or a mental asylum will eventually turn out to have been innocent; such miscarriages of justice occur, from time to time, in all legal systems around the world.

are presumed to be either guilty, or insane. Given this essentially punitive medico-legal climate, whichever variety of expert appraiser the hapless Chinese dissident, or "pseudo-dissident," happens to encounter, it is evident that his or her chances of being allowed to walk free at the end of the day are effectively nil.

As if this were not unjust enough, there is sometimes a further subtle twist to the situation. One of the tasks of forensic psychiatrists everywhere is to ascertain whether or not the examinee is feigning symptoms of mental illness as a way of avoiding trial or punishment. This phenomenon, generally referred to as "malingering," was discussed in the context of the psychiatric examination of political offenders by one Chinese source as follows:

> *Counterrevolutionary behavior by the mentally ill*: In most cases, the mental illness takes the form of either delusions of grandeur or delusions of persecution. When the mentally ill person exhibits behavior that endangers the People's Republic of China, it is usually in the form of speech or writing, such as writing reactionary posters or banners, shouting reactionary slogans, or drafting reactionary manifestos. The hallmark of such counterrevolutionary behavior by the mentally ill is that one can generally find no immediate or proximate cause for it. The thoughts and actions appear illogical. The counterrevolutionary behavior is carried out in public, with no apparent fear of the consequences, in broad daylight and in a brazen and flagrant manner. However, one must be on the alert in such situations: the person concerned may simply be feigning mental illness as a cover for their actions, while all the time engaging in genuinely counterrevolutionary plots.[232]

The above passage also raises another diagnostic emphasis, or clinical predisposition, that appears to be central to the official forensic psychiatric mindset in cases of this type. In essence, this can be colloquially summed up as

---

[232] "...*jiu keneng shi yi weizhuang jingshenbing shouduan wei yanhu, jinxing zhenzhengde fan'geming goudang.*" See China Encyclopedia of Public Security, p.1967. The implied scenario — of a dissident being caught in the street red-handed by the police while pasting up banned political material, and then being forensically examined to see if he or she was only "pretending to be mad" — surely takes some beating, even by official Chinese standards of political diligence and correctness. The most suitable diagnostic label for such crafty and devious political offenders would perhaps be "pseudo-pseudo-counterrevolutionaries."

the belief: "You'd have to be crazy to do things like that in China." Underlying
this assumption, which itself is a reflection or facet of the "presumption of
insanity" issue, is the common understanding that any Chinese citizen in his or
her right mind would surely be aware that to publicly challenge the government
on questions of political ideology is an extremely high risk activity that most
likely will lead to one's arrest by the police. One writer succinctly conveyed the
official psychiatric viewpoint on this question in a book published in 1989:

> Political offenses of this kind are usually perpetrated in public
> places. The person concerned will write out reactionary
> documents, sign them in full, and then sometimes — as if afraid
> that people won't know his or her real identity — even add
> their full addresses and give details of their work unit. In other
> cases, the person involved will write out slogan-banners and
> then go walking down the street, in broad daylight and into
> crowded areas, with a whole pile of the things draped over his
> or her arm and begin pasting them up all over the place. When
> other people start noticing this performance and come over to
> see what's happening, the person often tries to "act casual" and
> pretend that he or she is some kind of a "big hero."[233]

With unintended irony, other Chinese forensic psychiatrists frequently note
that the mental instability of people of this type is further apparent because, in
"openly signing their real names" to such documents and then "failing to run
away" afterwards, they have clearly demonstrated a "lack of any instinct for
self-preservation."[234] The above passage, however, could easily have been
referring to the kinds of peaceful protest actions that took place on a daily and
hourly basis in Tiananmen Square, and most other parts of China, during the
May 1989 pro-democracy movement. While such activities are understandably
irksome to authoritarian governments who insist upon a high degree of public
conformity to official standards of thought and behavior, and while it is possible
that some, or perhaps even many, of the "political offenders" concerned may

---

[233] See Shen Zheng, ed., *Falü Jingshenbingxue*, p.305; the quoted passage was written by
Zheng Zhanpei.

[234] See, for example: Mao Shulin et al., "Chapter Seven: Psychopathology and Crime,"
Fanzui Xinlixue (*Psychology of Crime*), (Beijing: Qunzhong Chubanshe, 1985), p.222;
see also Jia Yicheng, *Shiyong Sifa Jingshenbingxue*, p.38. Similar references to the "lack
of instinct for self-preservation" shown in cases of this type can be found throughout the
Chinese legal-medical literature.

have been mentally or emotionally disturbed in some way, the fact remains that none of these people, according to the official account, committed murders, raped or molested anyone, set fire to public buildings, attacked important government leaders, or even exposed themselves naked in the street. Those who were indeed mentally ill should have been provided with prompt and appropriate medical care, while the rest should have been allowed, in conformity with internationally recognized standards, to go about their public business in an unrestricted fashion.

An Illustrative Case

The following case study appeared in a 1994 textbook on criminal psychiatric work edited by a leading official at the Beijing Ankang facility:

> *A retired worker threw himself wholeheartedly into the study of political economy, tirelessly and laboriously writing "A Manifesto of a Scientific Communist." Why was this mental illness?*[235]

> Subject of [forensic-psychiatric] evaluation: Zhu, male, 57 years old, married. Ethnically Han, lower middle school educational level, worker in a coalmine. No unusual aspects in his development since childhood. Upper-primary school [sic] educational level, entered the army in 1956, joined the Party in 1961, and enthusiastically studied the works of Chairman Mao. Was demobilized in 1963 and began work at the coalmine. During the "Cultural Revolution," served as vice-chairman of the mine's Revolutionary Committee and was quite an activist. His achievements in "grasping revolution and promoting production" were, moreover, publicized in the People's Daily, and because of this Zhu regarded the Cultural Revolution as the sole path to the realization of Communism.

> In 1979 he began to get ideas about writing books on political theory, and after he retired in 1986 he often used to seek out members of the leadership and expound his thoughts and ideas to them. In his view, [the policy of] taking economic

---

[235] See Long Qingchun, *Sifa Jingshen Yixue Jianding Zixun Jieda*, pp.174-175 (italics indicate subtitle of passage, in original).

construction as the focus [of national work] was entirely
mistaken, and he completely negated the principles and
policies laid down [by Deng Xiaoping in December 1978] at
the Third Plenum of the Party's 11th Central Committee. He
maintained that the international communist movement had
already entered a third high tide, that China had produced its
leader, and that this leader was none other than himself.[236]
Furthermore, he wrote a 100,000-character-long document
entitled "A Manifesto of a Scientific Communist" and mailed
it out to all the leading organs at central, provincial and
municipal levels. Zhu had discussed all these views with the
leadership of his work unit. He was normally a fairly quiet
man, and he never used to discuss politics with ordinary
members of the masses.

Most leaders of Zhu's work unit felt that while his political
viewpoints were wrong, they were not reactionary in content;
moreover, he had relayed them all to the leadership and the
organization, he had not disseminated them among the masses,
and when mailing them out he had signed his real name to
them. Also, Zhu had spent several thousand yuan of his own

---

[236] Many Western-trained psychiatrists might also identify this particular aspect of Zhu's
behavior as a possible sign of mental instability — as being, say, indicative of "delusions
of grandeur" or other forms of "overvalued ideation." Both these diagnostic concepts
appear with particular frequency, however, in Chinese forensic psychiatric discussions of
"political cases" (the Chinese terms used are, respectively, "*kuada wangxiang*" and
"*chaojia guannian*"), where those being psychiatrically assessed at the same time face
serious criminal charges for activities that a Western-trained examiner would be viewing,
at worst, as a potential medical problem. Moreover, it should be noted that much of
China's political culture during the first three decades after 1949, especially the
"individual heroic" mode of leadership embodied in the exemplary person and history of
Chairman Mao, served to instill in many Chinese people a strong and no doubt
exaggerated sense of personal responsibility for the entire "fate of China." A good
example is that of Chen Erjin, a young dissident who in 1974 wrote a book entitled *Lun
Wuchanjieji Minzhu Geming* (On the Proletarian Democratic Revolution), in which he
called for national democratic change in the direction of a socialist two-party system. In
1982, he was arrested and sentenced to ten years of imprisonment as a
counterrevolutionary for attempting to set up a "second Communist Party" in China.
According to several reliable informants who knew Chen well, however, he was in no
way mentally impaired or unstable (Chen Erjin, *Crossroads Socialism: A Manifesto for
Proletarian Democracy*, trans. Robin Munro [London: NLB/Verso Editions, 1984];
Chen's book was first published in the June 1979 issue of the Beijing dissident journal *Si-
Wu Luntan [April Fifth Forum]*).

money to buy a printing machine, which his wife used to print out his various writings, and so his behavior had seemed orderly and logical and he didn't appear to be mentally ill.

According to the masses, Zhu's everyday speech was quite logical; he behaved in a respectable manner, was always polite in his dealings with people, and had an orderly and regular lifestyle. In their view he wasn't mentally ill, just highly eccentric, and so they regarded him as being a political dissident.

In March 1987, Zhu was expertly evaluated and found to be suffering from paranoid psychosis, on the following main grounds:

The content of Zhu's "theories" was conceptually chaotic: for example, he maintained that "during the period of scientific socialism, it is the State that engenders [social] classes, the superstructure that determines the economic base, and the mode of rule that determines the mode of production," etc. He maintained that all the principles and policies laid down since the Third Plenum of the 11th Central Committee were wrong. He was the leader who would guide the international communist movement during its third high tide. All this was a form of "political delusion," a pathological mental disorder, and Zhu's behavior was thus obstinate, impervious to reason, and insoluble through criticism or discussion.

Under the influence of his "political delusions," Zhu's pathological willpower grew ever stronger. Upon his retirement, he declared that he would "keep on writing until his very last breath." He saved more than 4,000 yuan to buy a printing machine. Even after these materials had been sent back,[237] he continued writing and mailing out his articles just as before, thereby manifesting utter political lunacy.[238]

---

[237] Presumably, after confiscation by the authorities.

[238] "*biaoxianchu zhengzhi-shang de fengkuangxing*"

> Zhu's views and utterances were incompatible with his status, position, qualifications and learning; the great disparities here clearly demonstrated his divorcement from reality.
>
> Paranoid psychosis differs from schizophrenia in that, in the former, mental activity remains well balanced, the delusions are relatively systematic and not entirely absurd in content, and the integrity of the personality remains relatively intact. Aside from his "political delusions," therefore, Zhu's overall mental activity remained normal, he was able to lead a quite normal life, and even his own family had difficulty believing that he was mentally ill.

Crucially, this account contains no indication that Zhu had engaged, by international standards, in anything of a remotely criminal nature. From the case details provided, it seems clear that he was simply a committed leftwing thinker, of the kind to be found everywhere in China during the Cultural Revolution decade, but one who — inexplicably and inexcusably from the government's point of view — had failed to perform the requisite ideological *volte face* after the 1978 return to power of Deng Xiaoping and the Party's repudiation of Cultural Revolution-era political theory. It should also be noted that over the several years following Mao's death and the ascendancy of the new political line, thousands of Zhu's fellow "die-hard ultra-leftists" across China were arrested and sentenced to long terms of imprisonment on various counts of counterrevolution.[239] So why was Zhu, presumably following his initial detention or arrest on such charges, not dealt with in similar fashion, but rather referred by the police for forensic-psychiatric assessment and then found to be mad? Zhu's case affords several vital clues that help elucidate the curious dividing line drawn by China's medico-legal authorities between "political crime" and "political insanity."

The first aspect of Zhu's case that seems to have raised forensic psychiatric eyebrows was the fact that Zhu had in no sense acted covertly or "conspiratorially" in the way he developed and publicized his contrarian political theories: as was noted earlier, this is widely taken in China to be a prima facie indication of mental instability, on the implicit assumption that "proper" political dissidents have "sufficient sense of self-preservation" to

---

[239] The official sobriquet generally applied to such people at the time was "residual poisonous dregs of the Gang of Four."

assiduously conceal their activities from the authorities, through fear of the stern judicial punishment they would otherwise encounter.

Second, the authorities evidently saw Zhu's endeavors in the realm of political theory as somehow "incompatible" with his status as a mere worker. This condescending attitude may seem surprising in view of the strong emphasis placed by Mao on the importance of China rearing a new generation of "worker intellectuals" after 1949. But Zhu was a longtime Party member who had at one time risen to the relatively important position of vice-chair of his local Revolutionary Committee, so he was surely entitled to have more than a passing interest in political theory. What the authorities appear to have taken primary exception to, however, is Zhu's original authorial efforts in this field, and in particular their detailed and extensive nature. In the official medico-legal view, only academic scholars or Party theorists are supposed to engage in this type of activity; for ordinary members of the public to do so is apparently seen as being not just eccentric, but also — and especially where dissident-type theories are being advanced — indicative of an underlying mental abnormality.

Third, there was the alleged "conceptual chaos" of Zhu's theoretical writings: this represents perhaps the most sinister aspect of the authorities' forensic psychiatric "case" against his sanity. What is significant, however, is that no substantive evidence was raised to suggest that Zhu was in any way cognitively impaired, or that his thoughts were indeed "chaotic" or disconnected. To the contrary, he was officially said to be "logical...respectable...polite" and to have "an orderly and regular lifestyle." The evidence that was officially given pertained solely to his ideas and theories themselves: these were "wrong," "obstinate" and "politically deluded," and the fact that Zhu persisted in holding them, even after receiving an official warning, was identified as a sign of "utter political lunacy."[240] The authorities' stated belief that Zhu's "overall mental activity remained normal" and their observation that even his own family viewed him as sane, was seen, not as undermining the final diagnosis of "paranoid psychosis," but rather as in effect confirming it. As noted earlier, this particular diagnostic contradiction was the very hallmark of the Soviet-era political diagnosis of "sluggish schizophrenia."

---

[240] In point of fact, all the various theoretical viewpoints attributed to Zhu by the authorities (for example, that "the superstructure determines the economic base") are typical of mainstream Maoist thought from the late 1950s until Mao's death in 1976, and moreover are held in common by numerous 20th century Western schools of Marxism, in a tradition extending from Trotsky through to the various "New Left" European schools of thought of the 1960s and 70s. Zhu may well have been slightly "megalomaniac" by disposition, but then so, by some accounts, were many European New Left theorists.

The above case is not one drawn from the obscure archives of China's revolutionary past. It was published in Beijing in 1994 in an official training manual for Chinese forensic psychiatrists. It was thus presumably seen as a typical illustrative case, the concluding diagnosis being one fully appropriate for study and emulation by others in the legal-psychiatric profession today.

VIII. THE FALUN GONG: NEW TARGETS
OF PSYCHIATRIC ABUSE

The authorities in the former Soviet Union employed political psychiatry against a wide range of different types of people: political dissidents, religious sectarians and spiritual nonconformists, ethnic nationalists, labor rights activists, and Jewish people seeking emigration to Israel, among others. In China, the principal known target of such treatment since 1949 has been political activists of various kinds, together with a variety of people accused of "disturbing public order," such as petitioners, complainants, "whistleblowers" and "litigious maniacs." Our current lack of detailed information on individual cases does not, however, necessarily mean that people of other types and categories, similar to those seen in the former Soviet case, have not also been subjected to compulsory psychiatric treatment and hospitalization in China. For example, several cases of Chinese labor activists being dealt with in this manner have just recently come to light. Since the latter part of 1999, however, it has become abundantly clear that religious sectarians now also form a major target of politically repressive psychiatry in China.[241]

In April 1999, a hitherto obscure though numerically large spiritual community in China calling itself the *Falun Dafa* (Great Wheel of Buddha's Law) or *Falun Gong* (Cultivation of the Wheel of the Law)[242] staged an unannounced peaceful protest demonstration outside Zhongnanhai, the main Communist Party leadership compound in central Beijing. According to reports, more than 10,000 practitioners from the group, whose devotional activities center on the practice of a traditional form of Chinese physical and mental exercises known as *qigong*, took part in the silent, day-long vigil.[243] The source of their dissatisfaction was an escalating campaign of official criticism of the

---

[241] In recent years, religious sectarian movements in Russia have once again come under direct legal and medical attack from government authorities. See, e.g., "Duma Appeal on Dangerous Religious Sects," *Moscow Rossiyskaya Gazeta*, December 28, 1996; translated in FBIS, same date; and Lev Levenson, "Psychiatrists and Officers in Defense of Traditional Values," *Ekspress Khronika*, January 31, 1997.

[242] "*Fa lun*" is the Chinese rendering of the Sanskrit word "*dharma*" (Buddhist law).

[243] The practice of qigong has undergone a massive popular revival in China since the early 1980s. A detailed account of this phenomenon can be found in Zhu Xiaoyang and Benjamin Penny, eds., "The Qigong Boom," *Chinese Sociology and Anthropology*, vol. 27, no.1 (Fall 1994). On September 15, 2000, as part of the government's continuing crackdown on Falun Gong practitioners, the State Sports General Bureau issued new rules tightening up controls over the practice of qigong throughout China. See *Jianshen Qigong Guanli Zanxing Banfa* (*Temporary Methods for Administering Bodybuilding and Qigong*), available at http://www.sport.gov.cn/qigong.htm.

Falun Gong movement, and of its leader, a middle-aged former government official named Li Hongzhi. The public demonstration was the largest held in China since the Tiananmen protests of May 1989, and it apparently caught the government's security services completely by surprise. A flurry of official condemnations quickly followed, but no overt action was taken against the Falun Gong until July 19-20, when dozens of the group's leading organizers and practitioners were suddenly arrested by police in the middle of the night. Two days later, and thus retroactively, as far as those already detained were concerned, the government announced that the Falun Gong was a proscribed organization and that it was to immediately cease all activities throughout the country.[244] Since then, tens of thousands of practitioners nationwide have been detained, arrested, sent to jail or labor camps for periods of several weeks or years, or formally charged and sentenced to terms of up to 18 years' imprisonment.[245] As of November 2000, reports indicate that more than seventy detained practitioners have died as a result of torture or severe ill treatment at

---

[244] Proclamation of the Ministry of Public Security of the People's Republic of China, July 22, 1999. Using unusually strong language, the Ministry called for the Falun Gong to be "outlawed and extirpated" (*yuyi qudi*) throughout China. In a comprehensive denial of the civil rights of all Falun Gong practitioners, moreover, the proclamation stated: "It is forbidden to undertake assemblies, marches or demonstrations in defense or propagation of the Falun Dafa (Falun Gong), whether by means of sit-ins, petitioning the authorities, or any other such activities."

[245] As the trials of Falun Gong leaders unfolded, the sect's main overseas support network issued the following translation of a directive that it claimed had recently been issued by the Beijing Bureau of Justice, imposing restrictions on detained sectarians' right of independent access to legal defense:

> To All Law Firms and District and County Judicial Departments: All consultations and retainers in respect of Falun Gong issues must be reported immediately. Particular requirements are: 1) In no circumstances may a lawyer accept a retainer involving any client involved in Falun Gong issues. Such cases should be reported to the Regulation Section (telephone: 6340-8078) and will be decided upon only after being reported. 2) In any event where consultations are requested by a client involved in Falun Gong issues, any advice or explanations proffered by attorneys offices must conform to the law and be strictly in conformity with the tone of the Central Government. 3) All recent consultations and retainers on Falun Gong issues must be documented and faxed immediately to the Regulation Section on or before August 2, 1999. (fax: 6340-8034) ("An Announcement in Regards to Falun Gong Issues from the Regulation Section, Judicial Bureau of Beijing City," available at http://www.clearwisdom.net/eng/china/judicial_announcement.html.)

the hands of the authorities.[246] Despite this harsh campaign of governmental repression, thousands of Falun Gong practitioners have continued, on an almost daily basis, to travel to Beijing and other major cities to stage peaceful protests against the continuing crackdown; they are invariably arrested within moments and carted off to police holding centers to await their punishment.[247]

The most distinctive aspect of the government's protracted campaign to crush the Falun Gong, aside from its sheer scope and brutality, has been the flood of reports that began emerging in the latter half of 1999 indicating that large numbers of the group's detained practitioners were being forcibly sent to mental hospitals by the security authorities.[248] By late 2000, overseas Falun Gong support groups had documented well over a hundred such cases where the names and other details of the victims were known, while overall estimates of the total number dealt with by the authorities in this way had risen to around six hundred. These various reports have not yet been independently confirmed by international human rights groups or similar organizations, and instances of factual error or misreporting may eventually come to light, however, there is presently no reason or evidence for doubting their overall veracity.[249] Certainly, numerous Western journalists who have witnessed police raids on Falun Gong demonstrators, in Beijing and elsewhere, have frequently reported seeing detainees being severely beaten up in front of their own eyes, so there is no grounds for believing that such people receive any more humane treatment after their removal from the public arena.

---

[246] "Two More Falun Gong Members Reported Dead in Chinese Police Detention," *Agence France Presse*, December 7, 2000. According to the article, the number of reported Falun Gong deaths in police custody stood at seventy-four. By May 2002, the death toll of Falun Gong detainees in China reportedly had risen to more than 400 ("Young Woman Beaten to Death in Beijing Jail for Refusing to Identify Herself," statement issued from the Falun Gong website, May 2, 2002, http://www.clearharmony.net).

[247] For a detailed account of the human rights violations involved in the government's anti-Falun Gong campaign, see Amnesty International, *People's Republic of China: The Crackdown on Falun Gong and Other So-called "Heretical Organizations,"* March 23, 2000 (ASA 17/011/2000).

[248] See, e.g., Elisabeth Rosenthal, "China is Said to Hold Devotees of Sect in a Psychiatric Hospital," *New York Times*, January 21, 2000.

[249] The ethical teachings of Falun Gong reportedly make its practitioners so frank and honest that, when stopped by police while traveling on trains in recent months and asked if they are going to Beijing to petition or demonstrate on behalf of the sect, they invariably feel obliged to give a truthful reply, thereby leading to their forcible eviction from the trains or worse.

The accounts of the treatment meted out to detained practitioners in mental asylums around the country make frequent and consistent reference to the following kinds of practices: people are drugged with various unknown kinds of medication, tied with ropes to hospital beds or put under other forms of physical restraint, kept in dark hospital rooms for long periods, subjected to electro-convulsive therapy or painful forms of electrical acupuncture treatment, denied adequate food and water and allowed only restricted access to toilet facilities, forced to write confessional statements renouncing their belief in Falun Gong as a precondition of their eventual release, and then required to pay fines or unreceipted charges of several thousand *yuan* for their board and treatment in the hospital. Many have been held in mental asylums since the late summer and fall of 1999, when the news of this form of repressive treatment was first reported. Among the currently known victims have been university professors, medical workers, government functionaries, members of the police and armed forces (including several senior officers), farmers, students, housewives, and a judge.[250] Three of those sent forcibly to mental asylums are reported to have died as a direct consequence of the ill treatment they received there.[251] Thus far, it

---

[250] According to an Associated Press report on February 11, 2000, "A judge in southern China has been put in a psychiatric hospital and forced to take narcotics for refusing to renounce his belief in the banned Falun Gong spiritual movement, a rights group said today. The case of Huang Jinchun is the latest troubling sign that the communist government is using mental institutions to punish political or religious dissenters. Huang displayed no symptoms of mental illness either at work or after being sent to the hospital nearly three months ago, the Hong Kong-based Information Center of Human Rights and Democratic Movement in China reported, citing former colleagues and nurses. But at the Longqianshan Psychiatric Hospital in the southern Guangxi region, medical personnel gave Huang daily injections of a narcotic that left him sleepy and muddled, after he refused to stop practicing Falun Gong, the nurses said. 'The doctors and nurses made fun of me: "Aren't you practicing Falun Gong? Let us see which is stronger, Falun Gong or our medicines?" Huang related in an appeal posted earlier this week on an overseas Falun Gong website.'"

[251] See Dr. Shiyu Zhou et al., eds., "Chapter 3: Detention and Abuse in Mental Hospitals," *A Report on Extensive and Severe Human Rights Violations in the Suppression of Falun Gong in the People's Republic of China — August 2000 Update* (Golden Lotus Press, August 2000), pp.65-82. (The information in the report was assembled by a group of activists and researchers associated with the Falun Gong overseas support network's principal website, http://www.minghui.org.) According to this source, the circumstances of the three Falun Gong practitioners' deaths were as follows:

1) In December 1999, Yang Weidong, 54, a medical inspector in Weifang city, Shandong, was forcibly committed to the city's Kangfu mental hospital. Already in poor health after several weeks spent in police custody as punishment for having gone to Beijing to petition against the anti-Falun Gong crackdown, Yang developed edema of the liver while at the mental hospital.

appears that Falun Gong practitioners subjected to this treatment have been sent to regular mental hospitals rather than to Ankang custodial facilities; the main reason for this is probably that most Chinese cities do not yet possess any such specialized psychiatric detention facilities. Many outside observers, however, have found the Chinese government's continuing campaign against the Falun Gong to be closely reminiscent of the kinds of extreme and unbridled political campaigns waged by the Party during the Cultural Revolution. In this connection, it should be noted that the security authorities' current practice of detaining Falun Gong practitioners in normal psychiatric institutions, rather than going through the due process normally required for forensic committals, certainly appears to be a worrying reversion to the widespread pattern of arbitrary political-psychiatric abuse that prevailed during the Cultural Revolution.

The following reports and victim statements afford a vivid insight into current conditions and practices within mental hospitals where Falun Gong practitioners have been detained.[252]

According to the account, "Even the doctor in Kangfu Hospital was frightened upon seeing his condition. He told the guard who watched Yang Weidong: 'He is in a state of physical collapse, how come you do not send him home? His illness is already incurable.'" Yang reportedly died on December 25, several days after being released from the hospital.

2) In May 2000, a woman named Shi Bei reportedly died after being forcibly held and given psychotropic medication at the Hangzhou No. 7 Hospital, Zhejiang (see Section VIII below for further details of Shi's case).

3) In June 2000, a 32-year-old man named Su Gang, a graduate in computer science and employee at a chemicals plant in Zibo city, Shandong, died after nine days of forcible hospitalization and medication at the Changle Mental Hospital. He had earlier been held in police detention for around 130 days for his Falun Gong activities. According to the account, "At 6 p.m. on May 31, the security staff of Su Gang's workplace sent him back to his father, Su De'an. After nine days of brutal 'treatment,' which included daily over-dose injections with damaging effects on the central nervous system, Su Gang looked miserable...he was very slow in reacting and his limbs appeared stiff...He was not able to recover from the severe mental and physical damage he had suffered in the mental hospital. After a period of painful struggle, he left this world on the morning of June 10, 2000." Su's death in psychiatric custody was also reported in "Bad Medicine in China" (editorial), *The Washington Post*, June 23, 2000.

---

[252] These four case descriptions appear in *A Report on Extensive and Severe Human Rights Violations in the Suppression of Falun Gong in the People's Republic of China — August 2000 Update*, op. cit. The case accounts have been slightly edited to correct faulty English, but otherwise are as they appear in the original document. The full text of the report can be found at http://hrreport.fldf.net.

Tan Guihua, female, 42 years old, an employee from the Third Leather Shoe Factory of Qingdao, Shandong Province, detained at the Jiaozhou Mental Hospital in Shandong Province[253]

On September 12, 1999, Tan went home after appealing in Beijing for the Falun Gong. Before she could sit down, some officers from her work unit and the Politics and Law Commission broke into her home and took her to the mental hospital.

The officers dragged her into the mental hospital by force. By then, they had already prepared a big dose of injection and planned to give her the shot as soon as she arrived. Tan refused to take the injection. A tall nurse then went out and brought back eight mental patients. They pressed her down and gave her the injection. In only a few seconds, she began to feel faint and sick. Her heart started to beat extremely fast. She had to press her head against the wall and hold the ground firmly with both hands. While in great pain, she bit down tightly on the comforter in her mouth and tried not to make any noise. Her mouth bled from the biting. She then lost consciousness. She did not feel better until the effects of the drug gradually abated.

Later, a female doctor asked Tan daily whether she would continue to practice Falun Gong. Tan said "yes," and the doctor then shocked her with electrical needles. She was shocked in this way altogether seven times. Meanwhile, she had been force-fed medicines and given injections three times a day. She spent two months in the hospital like this.

Later, the female doctor asked a nurse named Ma to give her another kind of injection. It was said to be some kind of imported medicine, and the drug effect would last for over one month. After that injection, Tan's period stopped coming. Her eyeballs couldn't move and she became slow in reacting to

---

[253] Ibid., p.72.

things. A few days later, they added another medicine to the
injection. After this shot, Tan shook all over violently and
couldn't even hold the bowl. She was tortured like this for 20
days. When her family members finally picked her up, she
was all muddleheaded and could not see things clearly. Her
mind was totally blank and could not recall things for a long
period. Her whole body was puffy. Her eyes looked dull. Her
reactions became slow, and it took a long time for her to say a
single word.

A 22-year-old Falun Gong practitioner, detained at Jining Mental Hospital, Shandong Province[254]

> On October 25, I went to Beijing to peacefully
> appeal to the government. However, I was arrested
> and escorted back to my hometown on my third
> day in Beijing. I was first given 15 days of
> detention. Then, on the seventh day of my
> detention, I was sent to a mental hospital in Jining,
> Shandong province. I do not have any mental
> problems. I was sent to the mental hospital because
> the authorities wanted to destroy me mentally in
> order to prevent me from practicing Falun Gong.
>
> In order to put me into the mental hospital, the
> police department forced my father and the
> officials of my workplace to sign a statement
> saying that I had mental problems. They then
> forced me into the mental hospital. Four male
> doctors carried a very thick rope and forced me to
> put on the uniform used by mental patients. When I
> was changing clothes, a female doctor gave me an
> injection. I struggled desperately, but the four male
> doctors tied me to a bed with ropes. They gave me
> a lot of injections. Soon the medicine started to
> take effect. I tried my best to control myself but I
> could not keep myself balanced. I felt extremely

---

[254] Ibid., p.76.

anxious, very uncomfortable and thirsty. I bumped
against the wall and fell to the ground anxiously.
Thoughts of death flashed through my mind. Later
the doctor gave me another injection. I fell asleep.
On the second day, my mind became a blank. I had
a headache and I fainted. I could not think of
anything. My legs and arms had no strength. My
tongue felt stiff and stretched out from my mouth
as if something was pulling it out and I couldn't
control it. I also felt stiff in my neck, which
stretched forward at an extreme angle. I was unable
to consciously control these movements. In this
condition, I could not eat at all. So they inserted a
tube through my nose into my stomach and fed me.
The nurse said this was how they persecuted the
members of "an evil religion." Later, my nose
started to bleed. By that time, they had given me
nine injections in total.

On my third day in the mental hospital, they forced
me to take perphenazine.[255] At the beginning, they
only fed me one pill. Later they fed me four to five
pills because I had continued to practice Falun
Gong. The symptoms of taking perphenazine were
the same as being injected. I endured inhumane
mental and physical tortures like this for thirty-six
days.

Now Jining Mental Hospital has become a place to
persecute Falun Gong practitioners. There are still
many practitioners being detained there. I hope the
international community and all kind-hearted
people around the world will pay attention to our
sufferings.

---

[255] Perphenazine is an antipsychotic medication that can be administered either orally or
by intramuscular injection. According to Medscape, an Internet "registered users only"
website of information on psychiatry, "Perphenazine is used for the symptomatic
management of psychotic disorders. Drug therapy is integral to the management of acute
psychotic episodes and accompanying violent behavior in patients with schizophrenia..."
(see http://www.medscape.com.)

Han Jizhen, female, detained at the Nanjing Mental Hospital, Jiangsu Province[256]

My mother, Han Jizhen, is a Falun Gong practitioner living in Nanjing, China. She is now being detained in a mental hospital although she is perfectly normal.

On December 23, my mother went to Beijing to appeal on behalf of the Falun Gong, and was arrested by a young police officer who slapped her face madly. Later, she was escorted back to Nanjing and thrown into the Nanjing mental hospital (now called the Nanjing Brain Hospital). In the beginning, the hospital refused to treat her. However, under pressure from the government authorities, they eventually took her in.

The doctor said she was sent to the mental hospital because she was a Falun Gong practitioner, even though she had no mental illness. In the hospital, she was forced to take injections and medicines, which made her lose her strength and feel terrible. My family went to the hospital to ask for her release, but the doctor said, "Since the police sent her here, we have to give her medicines. Otherwise, if she continues to go to Beijing to appeal for Falun Gong in the future, we will be in trouble."

In the name of saving people from illnesses, the hospital has been pressed into political service by the Chinese Communist Party as a means of persecuting mentally normal people. The hospital has betrayed its working ethics.

---

[256] Statement by Wang Yongsheng, a Ph.D. student at the physics department of Houston University. See *A Report on Extensive and Severe Human Rights Violations in the Suppression of Falun Gong*, p.77.

Before the Chinese New Year, after petitioning by
my family, my mother was allowed to return home
for two days. Then, the police sent her back to the
mental hospital again because she refused to give
up her practice of Falun Gong. She is now still
being "treated" in the mental hospital. I feel so sad
that innocent people are being treated like this. I
appeal to the world for help.

**Chen Zhong, male, 55 years old, detained at the Treatment
Center for Mental Diseases in No. 102 Hospital, Changzhou,
Jiangsu Province[257]**

On the afternoon of July 25, the local police and officers from
the Civil Affairs Bureau asked Chen Zhong to go for
interrogation. Without any due legal procedure, he was then
taken to the Treatment Center for Mental Diseases in No. 102
Hospital, Changzhou, for examination. Without any attempt at
disguise, they said, "If you continue to practice Falun Gong,
we can make you crazy even if you are not." But he did not
give in.

On the afternoon of September 28, again using interrogation
as an excuse, the police took Chen Zhong to the Mental
Hospital of the No. 3 People's Hospital in Wujin County. He
was forcibly hospitalized and made to take medicines
normally used for mental patients. Chen Zhong refused to take
the medicine, so they proceeded to electrocute him. They later
did so again (altogether five times) and then forced him to take
the medicines. This went on for more than ten days.

In an audiocassette tape, he said,

I am feeling very cold as I only have a T-shirt on
me. My family does not know my whereabouts. I
do not have a change of clothes, nor can I shave. In
fact, the hospital, which calls itself a "humanitarian

---

[257] Ibid., p.82.

hospital," is detaining many people who appealed
to the government for various injustices they had
received. This hospital is an even worse place than
the [police] detentions centers, with many more
cruel mental and physical tortures. I am a Falun
Dafa practitioner and also a law-abiding citizen. I
practice   "Truthfulness,   Compassion   and
Tolerance,"[258] which is beneficial to both the State
and society. Why am I being treated like this?

Among the three Falun Gong practitioners reported to have died as a result
of their ordeals in Chinese mental hospitals in recent months was a woman
named Shi Bei. Under pressure from the police, hospital staff reportedly gave
her forced injections of high dosage sedatives and denied her food for one week
in order to prevent her from propagating her spiritual beliefs inside the hospital;
her precise cause of death remains unknown.[259] The hospital in question was
said to be the Hangzhou No. 7 People's Hospital — the same institution on
which, as was noted above, three staff psychiatrists had optimistically reported
in 1987:

According to this hospital's statistics, cases of antisocial
political speech and action accounted for 54 percent of all
cases [examined] during the year 1977; currently, the
proportion of such cases has fallen to a level of 6.7 percent.
This shows that the present situation of stability and unity in
China has resulted in a marked fall in the number of cases
arising from such factors.[260]

Remarkably, the Chinese authorities have admitted quite openly that Falun
Gong practitioners are now being admitted to mental hospitals in large numbers.
In an official volume published in late 1999, for example, they stated:

---

[258] See Note 15, above.

[259] The overseas Falun Gong support network stated in its report: "Shi Bei was simply
starved to death." This was unlikely to have been the sole cause of death, however, since
she was reportedly denied food for only a week.

[260] Zhong Xingsheng et al., "A Preliminary Analysis of 210 Cases of Forensic Psychiatric
Medical Assessment,"pp.139-141.

According to doctors at the Beijing University of Medical Science, since 1992 the number of patients with psychiatric disorders caused by practicing "Falun Gong" has increased markedly, accounting for 10.2 percent of all patients suffering from mental disorders caused by practicing various *qigong* exercises. In the first half of this year, the number rose further, accounting for 42.1 percent.[261]

The fact that the Falun Gong sect did not even exist in 1992 (it was formally established in the mid-1990s and grew rapidly only during the last few years) did not deter the book's authors from making this remarkable claim. Another official spokesperson went still further, however, asserting absurdly in September 1999: "Falun Gong practitioners now account for 30 percent of all mental patients in China."[262] In neither case, moreover, was the coincidence between the reportedly very sizeable increase in Falun Gong admissions to mental hospitals in the first half of 1999, and the fact that it was during this same period that the government began preparing its nationwide public crackdown upon the sect, deemed to be worthy of mention.

In October 1999, the Standing Committee of the National People's Congress issued a proclamation stating the following:

> Heretical cult organizations shall be resolutely banned according to law, and all of their criminal activities shall be dealt with severely. Heretical cults, operating under the guise of religion, qigong or other forms, employ various means to disturb social order and jeopardize people's lives and property and economic development, and they must be banned

---

[261] Ji Shi, *Li Hongzhi and His "Falun Gong" — Deceiving the Public and Ruining Lives* (New Star Publishers, Beijing 1999), p.12. Similarly, in a July 1999 report from Xinhua, the official Chinese government news agency, Dr. Zhang Tongling, a psychiatrist at the No. 6 Attached Hospital of the Beijing Medical University, was quoted as saying: "I myself have witnessed a rocketing rate of mental illness among Falun Gong practitioners since 1996." She quoted statistics from the psychiatric departments of two Beijing hospitals as showing that mentally diseased Falun Gong followers now accounted for 42 percent of all mental patients, compared with only 10.01 percent in 1996. "It is an indisputable fact that practicing Falun Gong can lead to many kinds of mental disorders, which however has never been admitted by Falun Gong advocates," said Cai Zhuoji, also a psychiatrist at the Beijing Anding Hospital" ("Medical Scientists Reveal Falun Gong Fallacies," *Xinhua News Reports*, July 24, 1999; reproduced in FBIS, same date).

[262] The claim is made in a video CD-ROM entitled *Falun Gong—Cult of Evil*, issued by the Chinese government in September 1999 as a companion item to Ji Shi, *Li Hongzhi*.

according to law and punished resolutely. People's courts, procuratorates, public security, national security, and judicial and administrative organs shall fulfill their respective duties and join efforts in carrying out these tasks.[263]

Although widely reported overseas as being "a new anti-cult law," this decision in fact merely reinforced an existing set of provisions contained in Article 300 of the 1997 Criminal Law legitimizing the suppression of what the authorities termed "heretical cult organization" (*xie jiao*); the maximum penalty under Article 300 for such crimes is life imprisonment.[264] Since the start of the

---

[263] Decision of the Standing Committee of the National People's Congress on Banning Heretical Cult Organizations and Preventing and Punishing Cult Activities, adopted at the 12th Session of the Standing Committee of the Ninth NPC on October 20, 1999; English translation in *Beijing Review*, no.45 (1999). This Decision, in turn, was essentially a brief public notification of a more complex and detailed set of rules that had been formulated by the Supreme People's Court and Supreme People's Procuracy on October 8, 1999, explaining how Article 300 and other relevant provisions of the Criminal Law were to be applied in the course of the "anti-cult" crackdown. See *Explanations of the Supreme People's Court and Supreme People's Procuracy Concerning Laws Applicable to Handling Cases of Organizing and Employing Heretical Cult Organizations to Commit Crimes*, adopted at the 1079th Meeting of the SPC on October 9, 1999 and at the 47th Meeting of the Ninth Procuratorial Committee of the SPC on October 9, 1999; English translation in *Beijing Review*, no.45 (1999). The latter document is highly reminiscent of a similar set of guidelines issued by the same two bodies in August 1989 explaining how the various Criminal Law statutes on "counterrevolution" were to be applied in practice in the course of the ongoing legal campaign to suppress the nationwide pro-democracy movement of April-June 1989. See *"Zuigao Renmin Fayuan, Zuigao Renmin Jianchayuan Guanyu Banli Fan'geming Baoluan he Zhengzhi Dongluan Zhong Fanzui Anjian Juti Yingyong Falü de Ruogan Wenti de Yijian* (Opinion of the Supreme People's Court and Supreme People's Procuracy on Several Questions Concerning the Specific Application of Law in the Handling of Criminal Cases Committed During the Counterrevolutionary Rebellion and Political Turmoil)," August 1, 1989, in *Sifa Shouce* (*Judicial Handbook*), Vol.6 (People's Court Publishing House, Dec. 1990), pp.100-105.

[264] Harsh as this seems, it actually represented an improvement over the 1979 Criminal Law, Article 99 of which (in conjunction with a September 1983 "anti-crime campaign" decision by the National People's Congress) defined the offense of "organizing and leading a superstitious or reactionary sect or society" (*fandong hui-dao-men*) as being a counterrevolutionary crime punishable, at maximum, by the death penalty. Under this law, literally hundreds of leaders of banned religious and other sects were executed or sentenced to up to life imprisonment in China during the 1980s. Interestingly, the term officially used since March 1997 for banned sectarian activities — *xie jiao* — is a reversion by the authorities to the term traditionally used by the Confucian authorities over the past millennium and more to suppress ideological heterodoxy in Chinese society. For further details of contemporary China's religious sectarian movements and their suppression by the Chinese government, see Robin Munro, ed., "Syncretic Sects and

crackdown, the Chinese authorities have frequently asserted that Falun Gong is an "evil cult" displaying the same abusive and life-threatening organizational characteristics as the Aum Shinrikyo cult in Japan, which released sarin poison gas on the Tokyo subway in 1995, the Branch Davidians cult, dozens of whose members were killed when the U.S. law-enforcement authorities stormed its headquarters in Waco, Texas in 1993, and the Solar Temple cult, many of whose members committed collective suicide in Switzerland in 1994.[265] On this and other implicitly political grounds, the government has further branded the Falun Gong movement as posing a serious "threat to state security."

An additional major justification given for the sect's suppression has been the authorities' claim that the sect tries to prevent its members from seeking proper medical attention when they fall ill. According to officially released data, more than 1,400 Falun Gong practitioners or their family members have died as a result of this malign sectarian doctrine.[266] Sect leaders and members, however,

---

Secret Societies: Revival in the 1980s," *Chinese Sociology and Anthropology*, vol. 21, no. 4 (Summer 1989). For numerous case examples of religious sectarians and members of similar-style groups sentenced in the 1980s under Article 99 of the pre-1997 Criminal Law, see Human Rights Watch, *Detained in China and Tibet: A Directory of Political and Religious Prisoners* (New York: Human Rights Watch, 1994), pp.251-271 and pp.343-350.

[265] See, e.g., "Cults Endanger National Security," *Xinhua News Reports*, September 27, 2000; English translation in FBIS, same date. If comparisons between the Falun Gong and other major sects or cults are to be drawn, then groups such as the Jehovah's Witnesses or (at a stretch) the Church of Scientology would seem to be more apposite and reasonable models of comparison than the very extreme examples of sectarianism raised by the Chinese authorities. One of the best English-language sources of objective information and analysis on the Falun Gong phenomenon is an Internet website assembled by the scholar Barend ter Haar: "Falungong: Evaluation and Further References," available at http://www.let.leidenuniv.nl/bth/falun.htm.

[266] Hundreds of these fatal cases and other alleged tragedies are documented by the authorities in Ji Shi, *Li Hongzhi and His "Falun Gong" — Deceiving the Public and Ruining Lives*. It would be wrong to dismiss these official claims of widespread fatalities as false, but it would be equally inappropriate to accept them as necessarily true — or for that matter, as having the abusive significance ascribed to them by the government — until they have been independently verified and studied, something which has not yet been done. In particular, such an assessment would need to examine whether the number of reported fatalities departed significantly, in either direction, from the normal mortality rate statistics for such a large subgroup of the Chinese population as that accounted for by the Falun Gong (many millions); it is not immediately apparent that it does. And second, the officially claimed causal connection between those deaths and the practice of Falun Gong by those who died would need to be further explored and evaluated by independent medical assessors. Finally, there is no obvious reason to suppose that Falun Gong practitioners are any less susceptible to major mental illnesses, including those of the most florid and potentially dangerous kinds, than is the Chinese population in general; indeed, many if not all of the tragic cases of "Falun Gong-induced" psychopathology

have consistently denied this key government allegation. It is worth noting, however, that for the majority of China's population, the economic market reforms that have been pursued since the late 1970s have made affordable access to Western-style and even to traditional Chinese-style medical treatment become largely a thing of the past. Much of the current popularity among Chinese today of various kinds of "alternative medicine" or "self-treatment" approaches to curing illness can be directly attributed to the severe practical and financial difficulty that many people experience in trying to gain access to more mainstream or professional forms of medical care. Falun Gong practitioners themselves claim that the mental and physical discipline they follow is highly efficacious in helping to maintain good health; the results of two wide-ranging epidemiological surveys and analyses conducted in Beijing in 1998, that is, prior to the government crackdown on the sect, would certainly seem to substantiate this claim.[267] Above all, the question must be asked: why, if Falun Gong has such deleterious effects upon its practitioners as the Chinese government alleges, have there been no reports of similar outbreaks of mental and physical

---

recounted by the Chinese authorities may eventually turn out to have been attributable to this general epidemiological factor, rather than (as is officially claimed) to the practice of Falun Gong.

[267] The first survey examined the cases of 1,449 Beijing residents who practiced Falun Gong, and was conducted by a group of senior physicians in the capital, including Wang Qi, chief physician at the General Hospital for Armed Police; Li Naiyuan, chief physician at the Stomatological Hospital of Beijing Medical University; Zheng Lihua, deputy chief physician at the People's University of China Hospital; Qu Zengqiu, a pharmacist at the same hospital; Tian Xiulan, managing physician at the Beijing Hospital of Nuclear Industry; and Jing Lianhong, a physician at the Dongshi Hospital for Women and Children. The survey addressed a wide range of medical conditions found among the target patients (including diseases or complaints of the cardiovascular, digestive, musculoskeletal, respiratory, urinary, endocrine and nervous systems, as well as gynecological, skin, hematological and ear, nose and throat disorders), and the tabulated results of the study indicated that the practice of Falun Gong led to marked improvements in all these categories of health; only one patient (suffering from a digestive ailment) was reported as showing a deterioration in health (*The Effect of Falun Gong on Healing Illnesses and Keeping Fit: A Survey Among Practitioners in Beijing Zizhuyuan Assistance Center, October 18, 1998* [February 2000], available at http://clearwisdom.net/eng/science_eng/survey98_2eng.htm). The second survey in 1998 examined the health effects of Falun Gong practice on a much larger sample group of practitioners in five districts of Beijing; it was also conducted by numerous highly qualified medical personnel (trained in both Western and traditional Chinese medicine), and its findings were broadly similar to those of the first survey (*Falun Gong Health Effect Survey of Ten Thousand Cases in Beijing*, available at http://clearwisdom.net/eng/science_eng/survey98_1eng.htm).

illness occurring among the numerous and very sizable overseas-based Falun Gong communities in recent years?

Whatever the underlying truth of the matter may be, and while there are no doubt certain aspects of the Falun Gong belief system that many liberal-minded or non-religious people may find to be unacceptable,[268] the fact remains that the Chinese government has thus far presented no plausible evidence to support its central allegation that the sect poses such a threat to national security, or so fundamentally endangers public safety, as to justify, under internationally accepted standards, the imposition of an effective state of emergency requiring the nationwide suspension both of the Falun Gong's constitutional right to exist and also of the fundamental civil liberties of millions of the sect's adherents.[269]

---

[268] Possible examples of the latter include the sect's underlying hostility towards homosexuality and its belief, as taught by Master Li Hongzhi, that human intelligence and civilization were originally brought to planet Earth by aliens from outer space.

[269] The true size and extent of the Falun Gong movement remains open to question, but it is clearly extremely large. The sect itself claims to have around 100 million practitioners worldwide, most of them in China; the Chinese government acknowledges a figure of only several million practitioners inside the country.

The following provides a useful summary of the limits specified under international legal standards on governments' freedom to restrict civil liberties and human rights in the name of national security:

> The International Covenant on Civil and Political Rights provides for the rights of free expression, assembly and association, but qualifies them by allowing restrictions in the interest of protecting national security. Such restrictions, however, are only valid if they are prescribed by law and 'necessary.' The latter requirement means that the restriction must be proportional to its purpose in severity and intensity and the least restrictive means of achieving that purpose. Thus interference with a right must be interpreted narrowly in cases of doubt and not presumed to be the rule. In the case of freedom of association and assembly, a restriction must be 'necessary in a democratic society,' that is it must not only meet the above requirements but must also be respectful of the democratic values of pluralism, tolerance, broad-mindedness and popular participation in the political decision-making process... A threat to national security is not the same as a threat to any given government of the nation, and mere criticism of a governing party or its policies should not be restricted in the name of national security. (Human Rights Watch/Asia and Human Rights in China "Whose Security," pp.4-5.)

See also "Johannesburg Principles on National Security, Freedom of Expression and Access to Information," drafted by an international team of human rights experts, including legal scholars, U.N. rights specialists and diplomats, at a conference in Johannesburg, South Africa, in 1995 convened by the London-based NGO Article 19. The full text of the Johannesburg Principles is available in *The New World Order and*

Certainly, the United Nations' body with primary responsibility for monitoring and enforcing human rights standards around the world has failed to be convinced that any such situation presently exists in China. In a declaration issued in August 1999, the U.N. body stated:

> We are convinced that the banning by the People's Republic of China on 22 July 1999 of the spiritual movement Falun Gong/Falun Dafa and the subsequent arrest of leaders, massive destruction of publications and audio-visual material, and the prohibition of assembly of its practitioners are direct violations of the spirit and provisions of the Declaration on the Elimination of All Forms of Intolerance and of Discrimination Based on Religion or Belief, and of Article 18 of the International Covenant on Civil and Political Rights.[270]

Besides the clear and unambiguous legal proscription of sectarian activities of all kinds in China today, however, the authorities also have at their disposal a medical justification, of sorts, for waging such an intense campaign of persecution against the Falun Gong. Since the late 1980s, the Chinese psychiatric establishment has identified a unique set of mental disorders that it says can arise from the practice of traditional *qigong* forms of exercise and self-cultivation, and also from a more heterogeneous range of thought and behavior broadly termed as "feudal superstitious belief" (*fengjian mixin.*) In 1989, the country's medical authorities formally recorded this category of psychiatric ailments in the Chinese Classification of Mental Disorders (2nd Version, also known as the CCMD-II), under the heading "mental disorders closely related to culture."[271] The international psychiatric community recognizes a range of

---

Human Rights in the Post-Cold War Era: National Security vs. Human Security, papers from the International Conference on National Security Law in the Asia Pacific, November 1995 (Korea Human Rights Network, 1996). According to the Principles, "The peaceful exercise of the right to freedom of expression shall not be considered a threat to national security or subjected to any restrictions or penalties."

[270] *The Banning of the Falun Gong and Subsequent Arrests of Practitioners*, Report of the United Nations Sub-Commission on Prevention of Discrimination and Protection of Minorities, August 4, 1999. For the text of Article 18 of the International Covenant on Civil and Political Rights (ICCPR), see Note 36 above.

[271] The Chinese terms used are "*qigong ban-fa jingshen zhang'ai*" and "*qigong suo zhi jingshen zhang'ai*" (mental disorders associated with or induced by qigong). Detailed clinical and diagnostic discussions of this culture-bound psychiatric condition can be found in the following articles: Shan Huaihai et al., "Clinical Phenomenology of Mental

mental conditions known as "culture bound syndromes,"[272] and there seems to be no reason to suppose that the improper or excessive use of *qigong* may not, in certain circumstances and cases, lead to various forms of mental imbalance or disorder. It is surely remarkable, however, that there so suddenly occurred, according to the official version of events, such a massive epidemiological outbreak of *qigong*-related mental illness across China during the precise period immediately before and after the start of the government's crackdown on Falun Gong in July 1999. Still more puzzling is the fact that, in the Chinese government's main published compilation of evidence concerning the severe psychological damage that the practice of Falun Gong is alleged to induce in its practitioners,[273] the sufferers are, in all recorded cases, said to have contracted an exotic mental disorder known as "dysphrenia" — a condition that is apparently either so rare or so mild that, not only does it not appear in the World Health Organization's ICD-10, it is also entirely absent from the CCMD-II, the Chinese

---

Disorders Caused by Qigong Exercise," *Chinese Medical Journal* (in English), vol. 102, no. 6 (1989), pp.445-448; Shan Huaihai et al., "A Study of the Comparison Between Hysteric-like Episodes Caused by Chinese Qigong (Deep Meditation) and Hysteria with Psychosocial Stress," *Chinese Journal of Nervous and Mental Diseases*, vol. 18, no. 3 (1992), pp.156-158; Xu Shenghan, "Psychophysiological Reactions Associated with Qigong Therapy," *Chinese Medical Journal*, vol. 107, no. 3 (1994), pp.230-233; Shan Huaihai, "*Qigong Suo Zhi Jingshen Zhang'ai de Linchuang Ziliao yu Zhenduan* (Clinical Material and Diagnosis on Mental Disorders Induced by Qigong)," *Chinese Journal of Nervous and Mental Diseases*, no.3 (1999); Yang Desen, "*Qigong Neng Zhiliao Shenjingzheng yu Jingshen Jibing ma?* (Can Qigong Cure Neurosis and Mental Illness?)," *Chinese Journal of Nervous and Mental Diseases*, vol. 26, no. 1 (2000), pp.52-53; He Jiali et al., "*Butong Shiduan Qigong Suo Zhi Jingshen Zhang'ai Linchuang Duizhao Yanjiu Ji Zhenduan Biaozhun Tantao* (A Clinical Comparative Study of, and Diagnostic Criteria for, Qigong-induced Mental Disorders Over Various Periods)," *Chinese Journal of Nervous and Mental Diseases*, vol. 26, no. 2 (2000), pp.116-117; and Zheng Hongbo et al., "*Lian 'Falun Gong' Yinzhi Jingshen Zhang'ai 4 Li Baogao* (A Report on Four Cases of Mental Disorders Induced by 'Falun Gong')," *Chinese Journal of Nervous and Mental Diseases*, vol. 26, no. 3 (2000), pp.142. Finally, a number of individual studies of this type involving cases where criminal charges were brought can be found in Zheng Zhanpei, *Sifa Jingshen Jianding de Yinan Wenti Ji Anli (Thorny Problems and Case Examples in Judicial Psychiatric Appraisal)*, (Shanghai Medical University Press, 1996), pp.275-309.

[272] These include, for example, "*koro*," a type of panic reaction among males, especially in Asia, characterized by intense fear that the penis is shrinking inside the body; "*amok*," a form of violent mass hysteria that is typically found in Malay society; and "*latah*," a condition found in many parts of Africa and characterized by fear that the soul is being taken away from the body. For a detailed discussion of these issues, see Ari Kiev, *Transcultural Psychiatry* (Free Press, 1982).

[273] See Ji Shi, Li Hongzhi and His "Falun Gong."

medical establishment's own official listing of mental disorders.[274] While the legal and psychiatric establishments may not yet be collaborating, therefore, where the official treatment of Falun Gong and other religious sectarians is concerned, in quite so close and systemic a manner as they have for many years been doing with regard to the "political mania" phenomenon, the recent quantitative surge in forced psychiatric committals of Falun Gong activists nonetheless provides a clear indication that law and psychiatry are now working together in ever-closer professional tandem in the fast-growing judicial suppression of proscribed religious heterodoxy.

---

[274] Only a handful of references to "dysphrenia" have been found on the Internet. First, the website of Rick's College, Idaho (an institution run by the Church of Jesus Christ of Latter-Day Saints, or Mormons), contains the following cryptic definition: "Dysphrenic: bad brain" (a literal translation of the original Greek term). Second, an Italian neurological website mentions the term in passing in a brief note on "migraine madness." And third, Amnesty International provided the following information in a recent report on the anti-Falun Gong crackdown in China: "The word 'dysphrenia' is not widely recognized by Western psychiatric professionals and does not appear to be defined in Western medical books. The only references found by AI's expert medical advisor is related to neurological movement disorders which occur as side effects of drug treatment for schizophrenia or a psychopathic disorder of communication — 'psychopathic' meaning a psychiatric illness" (Amnesty International, *People's Republic of China: The Crackdown on Falun Gong and Other So-called "Heretical Organizations,"* March 2000 [ASA 17/011/2000]).

IX. CONCLUSIONS

Excuses and rationales can always be found to explain why doctors become involved in human rights abuses of various kinds, such as in physician-assisted executions,[275] "medical supervision" over torture sessions, the procurement of transplantable organs from executed criminals' bodies,[276] and also politically repressive psychiatry. These range from the claim that expert medical involvement is required, in the case of torture and executions, in order to limit or alleviate the sufferings of the subjects of these procedures; through the more instrumental argument that, in the case of organ transplants and certain types of execution, the procedures themselves are of an inherently medical nature; to the construction of elaborate, pseudo-scientific theories that posit, as in the case of political psychiatry, false medical justifications for the State's enlistment of doctors in the criminal justice and law enforcement process. All these practices entail, however, a fundamental corruption of the basic tenets of medical ethics — notably the principle that medical skills should be deployed only for the improvement of life and health, as summed up in the Hippocratic injunction "Do no harm."

In this article, we have briefly indicated two of the more obvious reasons why Chinese psychiatrists allow themselves to be pressed into the unethical deployment of their skills for State-directed purposes of political and religious repression: first, the professional acculturation process, in which psychiatrists learn from the official medical literature at the outset of their training that certain types of ideologically nonconformist behavior are attributable to severe and dangerous forms of "mental pathology;" and second, the more insidious element of personal and professional fear, inspired by a wider culture involving decades of individual and institutional experience, of the severe negative consequences of departing from the official "political line" laid down by the authorities in such matters. There are surely, in addition to those enumerated above, other more subtle reasons why Chinese psychiatrists become active partners in the political corruption of their profession.

The question remains, however: why do the authorities themselves bother? Indeed, why would any repressive regime go through such elaborate and often

---

[275] For a detailed study of this topic, see *Breach of Trust: Physician Participation in Executions in the United States*, a joint report by the American College of Physicians, Human Rights Watch, the National Coalition to Abolish the Death Penalty, and Physicians for Human Rights (New York, March 1994).

[276] See, for example, Human Rights Watch, *Organ Procurement and Judicial Execution in China* (New York: Human Rights Watch, 1994).

costly steps as adopting coercive psychiatric measures against a certain number
of its political and religious opponents, when other much simpler methods of
neutralizing such troublesome people — for example, execution or lengthy
imprisonment — have always been readily available, and, in the case of both the
Soviet Union and China, were frequently used? One possible reason has to do
with the changed political landscapes that emerged, both in the USSR after the
death of Stalin, and in China after the death of Mao: in these countries, the
former totalitarian solution of the physical liquidation of political enemies was
ended by the emergence of reformist leaderships dedicated to the curtailment of
past policy "excesses." For dissidents of various kinds, this meant that being
arrested by the security police no longer entailed their permanent physical
removal from society, but rather long terms of imprisonment from which they
had a reasonable chance of emerging alive; a sustained dissident network or
movement therefore could, and did, come into being in both these countries after
the deaths of their respective "great dictators." For the successor authorities,
Khrushchev and Deng, however, this represented an unwanted complication of
their new "liberalizing" dispensations, and more elaborate mechanisms of
inducing long-term fear in the ideological enemies of the State thus had to be
found. There are surely few more potent deterrents to dissident activity of any
kind than the threat of permanent or semi-permanent forced removal to an
institution for the criminally insane. A potential Chinese dissident or religious
nonconformist may be prepared to face imprisonment for his or her beliefs, but
indefinite psychiatric custody is probably quite another matter. Additionally,
psychiatric labeling of this kind serves to stigmatize and socially marginalize the
dissident in a way that regular criminal imprisonment, in the present era at least,
often fails to do.

    Another reason why "liberalizing" Communist governments tend to engage
in such practices may derive from the *amour propre*, or self-justificatory vanity,
found in historically repressive regimes of this type when they attempt to
dispense with nakedly terrorist methods of dealing with ideological dissent or
nonconformity. Such phenomena must still, in the official view, be crushed, but
it better serves the government's self-image at such times to adopt more
sophisticated and where possible, scientific means and approaches to the
fulfillment of this task. Thus, the perceived ideological enemies of the regime
are officially said, in some cases, to be merely ill, rather than always or
necessarily ill intentioned. While this general rationale for the use of political
psychiatry may seem to contradict the "deterrent" argument outlined above, in
practice they are not mutually incompatible. Rather, the dissident's fear of being
branded mentally ill and condemned to a lunatic asylum serves as a more subtly

powerful deterrent to any further oppositional belief or activity, while the reforming government, for its part, can rest satisfied in the belief that it is acting more humanely and scientifically than its unreconstructed predecessor ever did.

A closely related reason has to do, no doubt, with the country's international image and prestige. Naked repression as conducted in the old days becomes, in the more forward-looking era of "opening and reform to the outside world," a source of increasing international embarrassment for the government. Hence, the former overtly political crimes of "engaging in counter-revolution" are reborn under the more internationally acceptable rubric of "crimes of endangering state security," while particularly flagrant or uninhibited political protestors, and more recently sample groups of Falun Gong religious detainees, are sent to mental hospitals to be "treated," rather than simply jailed as before. Again, this may appear to be paradoxical or even self-defeating governmental behavior, given the widespread international public awareness that now exists about the malign political uses of psychiatry in the former Soviet Union and certain other countries. But the surprising fact remains that in China there has been, thus far, virtually no public discussion or dissemination of information of any kind concerning the history of psychiatric abuse elsewhere in the world, let alone of the strong reaction to such abuse that has been generated internationally over recent decades. In all the Chinese books and journals on psychiatry that have been consulted for this article, only one explicit and very brief reference to the history of political psychiatric abuse in the former Soviet Union, and none to that of other countries, has been found.[277] In this regard, the Chinese medico-legal authorities may unknowingly have been a victim of the government's longstanding policy of censoring and controlling the flow of sensitive news information from around the world.

All of the above reasons may partly explain the existence of political psychiatric abuse in China today, but they cannot directly account for the fact that such practices existed there long before the inauguration of the Deng Xiaoping "new era" in the late 1970s. Here, both systemic and also more

---

[277] See Jia Yicheng, *Shiyong Sifa Jingshenbingxue*, p.15. The passage referred to the Soviet psychiatric practice of labeling political dissidents as suffering from "sluggish schizophrenia" and incarcerating them in mental hospitals for long periods. It added that this practice had been "severely criticized by representatives from other countries at an international academic conference on psychiatry in 1976." (It is unclear to which conference the author was referring; it was likely a mistaken reference to the WPA's Sixth World Congress at Honolulu in August 1977, the first major international event at which Soviet political psychiatry was exposed to international criticism, and where the historic Declaration of Hawaii [see above, Section II] was passed by the WPA General Assembly.) Significantly, however, the passage in the Jia Yicheng volume itself contained no criticisms of the Soviet practices in question.

contingent factors appear to have played the determinant role. First, there was the fact that Chinese forensic psychiatry largely owed its existence, as a discipline, to the fraternal efforts and advice of Serbski Institute-trained experts from the Soviet Union in the 1950s; Chinese psychiatry thus "benefited" from psychiatric doctrines characteristic of the Khrushchev era, but at a time when China itself was still firmly in the grip of its own unreconstructed Marxist leader. This would clearly explain why the basic doctrines of political psychiatry arose at a seemingly "inappropriate" time in China's political development, and why they continued to hold significant sway in Chinese forensic psychiatry both up to and beyond the death of Mao.

Second, however, there appears to be a deeper and more systemic explanation for the phenomenon, one that has applied almost throughout the history of the People's Republic. In brief, the main underlying reason, observable throughout the official psychiatric literature from the late 1950s onwards, for why some political dissidents and other kinds of ideological nonconformists are singled out – from among the much broader ranks of their prison-bound "counterrevolutionary" or "state security endangering" colleagues – for special treatment in the form of legal-psychiatric diagnosis and forced committal, appears to be that they lack, in the experienced and discerning eyes of the police, the prerequisite hallmark of dissent "street credibility." That is to say, they express their oppositional or contrarian viewpoints openly and with no attempt to disguise their true identities, and when detained by the police on political charges they make no effort to deny their activities or pretend that they weren't really making fundamental criticisms of the regime. As the official literature makes clear, this represents, to China's seasoned enforcers of the "dictatorship of the proletariat," a rarely encountered and inexplicable form of behavior characterized by a perplexing absence of any normal instinct for self-preservation, and thus one that can be perceived only as mentally abnormal. In the authorities' view, "proper" political dissidents and other ideological enemies behave covertly and conspiratorially, because they know the dire penalties for being caught. To act otherwise strikes the authorities, no doubt quite genuinely, as being sheer political lunacy.

This more consistent and longstanding element in the Chinese official conception of criminal-psychiatric deviance or pathology is, in turn, reflective of a fundamental hallmark of Chinese-style Marxism, namely the strong emphasis always placed by Mao upon "correct thinking."[278] In China, even more so than

---

[278] This same emphasis had, of course, much older antecedents, namely the traditional Confucian concern for correct speech and behavior, as expressed for example in the value-concepts of "propriety" (*li*) and "rectification of names" (*zheng ming*).

in Russia, the objective or material Marxian prerequisites for advanced socialism were conspicuously absent in the first half of the twentieth century, and Mao's solution to this revolutionary resource deficit was to transfer the pivotal role away from the economy and towards ideology and other such "superstructural" factors: that is, from being to consciousness, from the objective to the subjective, from the material to the spiritual, and from process to will.[279] The Soviet guardians of the faith, people like chief Party ideologist Mikhail Suslov, decried all this as anti-materialist "voluntarism" on the part of their Chinese colleagues, and even Serbski School-trained forensic psychiatrists might have demurred at the extensive underlying use made by their Chinese counterparts of the basic Soviet medico-legal theory of ideological deviance.

Another important difference, rather ironically, between the two systems was that whereas the Soviets never admitted that psychiatric abuse had been practiced, the Chinese profession acknowledged that it had frequently occurred during the Cultural Revolution. But here again, the Maoist stress on ideological factors meant that the post-1978 reexamination of "past excesses" within the profession was mainly limited to a critique of the categories and specific content of the "politically deluded" ideas that had been identified – wrongly, it was now said – as being symptomatic of criminal mental pathology. No significant challenge was raised to the core notion that thought and speech could constitute crimes, or that in certain cases these could amount also to "political lunacy" in a

---

[279] As Stuart Schram, the leading Western expert on Mao's thought and philosophy, has written:

> Mao's contribution to the theory and practice of revolution is also characterized by an extreme voluntarism. To be sure, "voluntarism," in the sense of an accent on conscious action, is by no means absent from Marx himself. But there is no doubt that it is carried much further in Lenin, and further still in Mao Tse-tung, and in the ideology of the Chinese Communist Party. This voluntarism attained a kind of apotheosis in the theory of the permanent revolution. Consider, for example, a passage such as this (by Mao, 1958):
>
> > "Men are not the slaves of objective reality. Provided only that men's consciousness be in conformity with the objective laws of the development of things, the subjective activity of the popular masses can manifest itself in full measure, overcome all difficulties, create the necessary conditions, and carry forward the revolution. In this sense, *the subjective creates the objective.*"
>
> (Stuart R. Schram, *The Political Thought of Mao Tse-tung* [Harmondsworth: Pelican Books, 1971], pp.135-136 [emphasis added by Schram].)

forensic medical sense. At an important level of official Chinese discourse for the past half century, therefore, there has existed a clear and persistent epistemological identification or elision between, on the one hand, the social concept of correct political thought and action, and on the other, the ascription, in individual cases, of basic mental health and stability. All this represents the deeper and more intractable defining layer or facet of "political psychiatry with Chinese characteristics."

The reality today, however, is that most Chinese, and certainly those of the younger generation, would no sooner think of taking to the streets and staging political protest manifestations — especially in the form of sticking up "big character posters," the most commonly cited symptom of Chinese-style "political lunacy" — than they would think of studying Das Kapital or memorizing the poems of Mao Zedong. The right to engage in street-level politics of this kind, so characteristic of the Maoist era, was excised from the Chinese Constitution in 1982, and there now exists a panoply of legislation that severely criminalizes all such unauthorized forms of political expression by China's citizens; the same is true of all types of unauthorized religious activity. What was formerly a central part of Chinese political culture is now, in the post-Tiananmen era, little more than a folk memory for most people. This fact alone would probably suffice to account for the officially recorded decline, since the 1980s, in "cases of a political nature" in Chinese forensic psychiatry.[280]

One important issue should be raised in this connection, however. The official statistics on this question never included, and still today omit, a range of other activities that are elsewhere generally seen as being quite civic-minded or at least socially permissible in nature: persistent petitioners and complainants of various kinds (the so-called litigious maniacs), people who seek to expose corruption or malfeasance in the workplace and in government administration (the "whistleblowers," or those with so-called paranoid delusions), and also

---

[280] This decline in the official social acceptability of the "big character wallposter" culture in China may also, however, make it even more likely that those who still persist in such activities and behavior will be viewed by the authorities as being mentally disturbed in some way, and thus liable for forensic psychiatric examination and committal. A further important point concerns the current rapid increase in China of all types of forensic psychiatric appraisal cases; with the passage (as described above) of a series of relevant countrywide rules and regulations in recent years and the concomitant institutional build up of the legal-psychiatric appraisals system, the absolute number of such cases is now multiplying annually in China. A decline in the percentage incidence of "political" and other such cases does not necessarily mean, therefore, that fewer actual cases of these types are being dealt with under the system. The overall trend may even be in the other direction.

nonconformist religious or spiritual practitioners of various kinds, such as the *Falun Gong* (the so-called dysphrenics). As China continues to develop and expand both its legal system and the overall principle of rule by law, and as a greater degree of rights consciousness correspondingly takes hold among the populace as a whole, examples of the former kinds of behavior are bound to increase dramatically; thus far, however, there has been no reported decrease in the numbers of such cases dealt with as constituting crimes by the mentally ill. Similarly, although for somewhat different reasons, religious sectarianism or spiritual nonconformism is now rapidly on the rise in most parts of the country, and the authorities' recent extension of the "mental pathology" model to significant numbers of *Falun Gong* adherents thus further lengthens the shadow over any hopes or optimism that political psychiatry may be destined soon to disappear from the Chinese law-enforcement scene.

In conclusion, we return to the question of whether or not those dealt with in China as being dangerously mentally-disordered political or religious offenders really are, as the authorities claim, suffering in significant numbers from any recognizable form of mental illness. Ultimately, this is an irrelevant question to be asking in the ostensible context of the practice of forensic psychiatry, since the acts in question are not only absent from the internationally accepted definition of crime, but also specifically protected under international law as clear examples of the exercise of the right to freedom of expression. Indeed, it is this that defines the Chinese authorities' practices in this general area as constituting a fundamental abuse of human rights. If for the sake of argument, however, one suspends all disbelief, takes the official case reports and statistics at face value and accepts that all of those dealt with in this way were in fact seriously mentally ill, then another conclusion arises: that Chinese-style "political lunacy" represents a genuinely new, post-1949 "culture-bound syndrome" of considerable size and extent, and one that therefore deserves formal recognition in the country's official classification of acknowledged mental disorders. It is certainly true that the incessant mass political campaigns waged by the Chinese Communist Party over the past fifty years has claimed countless lives and driven large numbers of people insane. It may well also be true that the deeper cultural effects of this longstanding history of political witch-hunts and persecution have caused many of those suffering from genuine mental illness to exhibit their disorders in the form of politically colored language, thought, and behavior.[281] For China's medico-legal authorities to

---

[281] In the case of the Soviet Union, when Western psychiatric delegations were finally, in 1989 and 1990, allowed access to alleged mentally ill dissidents held in psychiatric custody, a minority of those examined were found to be suffering from some form of mental disorder or other. In most such cases, however, these were deemed by the Western

charge psychiatrically disturbed individuals of this kind with committing serious offenses and then send them to institutes for the criminally insane, however, is clearly to add insult to injury.

The challenge for the international psychiatric community now is to find ways of exerting its influence to ensure that China's secretive Ankang system and other custodial psychiatric facilities around the country can no longer be used by the security authorities as a long-term dumping ground for political and religious nonconformists who, for one reason or another, they find it awkward or inconvenient to bring to criminal trial. As an indispensable first step towards this goal, both the World Psychiatric Association and its constituent national professional bodies should begin seeking direct access to the Ankang network and other places of psychiatric custody in China, with a view to independently monitoring conditions and practices therein.[282] Advocacy efforts by local and international psychiatric bodies would also greatly assist in encouraging individual Western governments and the European Union to take up the issue, notably by placing the issue of political psychiatric abuse in China on the formal agenda of the various bilateral human-rights dialogue sessions that have become, in recent years, a central and regular feature of Sino-Western relations.

---

experts to be little more than harmless borderline conditions, and of a kind that should not have occasioned even civil psychiatric committal, let alone compulsory forensic-style custody. For details of the findings of one of these expert delegations, see Bonnie and Polubinskaya, "Unraveling Soviet Psychiatry," pp.279-298; see also Richard J. Bonnie, "Soviet Psychiatry and Human Rights: Reflections on the Report of the U.S. Delegation," *Law, Medicine and Health Care*, vol. 18 (1990), pp.123-131.

[282] Initial steps have already been taken in this direction. In May 2000, for example, the American Psychiatric Association's Committee on the Abuse of Psychiatry and Psychiatrists passed a resolution at the APA's annual conference in Chicago "recommending that the World Psychiatric Association investigate the alleged wrongful detention of Falun Gong practitioners in psychiatric hospitals" ("APA Committee Calls for Investigation of Chinese Psychiatric Abuses," *Psychiatric News*, June 16, 2000, available at http://www.psych.org/pnews/00-06-16/chinese.html). According to a subsequent report, "The Board [of APA Trustees] also referred this matter to the APA Commission on International Psychiatry and the Committee on Misuse and Abuse of Psychiatry for monitoring the progress of the WPA's investigation" (*Psychiatric News*, June 16, 2000, available at http://www.psych.org/pnews/00-08-04/board.html). Additionally, when an APA delegation of sixty-five American psychiatrists attended the Second Sino-American Conference on Psychiatry in Beijing in April 2000, "[The U.S. psychiatrists] Herbert Peyser, [Allan] Tasman, [Jeffrey] Geller and other psychiatrists met with Chinese Society of Psychiatry leaders informally to convey their concerns about Falun Gong practitioners being allegedly detained involuntarily in psychiatric hospitals and injected with harmful medications for political reasons" (*Psychiatric News*, June 16, 2000, available at http://www.psych.org/pnews/00-06-16/china.html).

Appendices

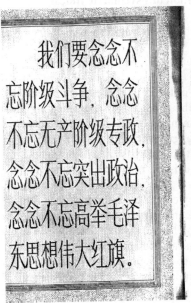

"We must think constantly about the class struggle and the dictatorship of the proletariat, give full prominence to politics at all times, and remember always to raise high the great red banner of Mao Zedong Thought."

This slogan, printed in one inch-high Chinese characters, occupied the entire inside cover of the April 1966 issue of the *Chinese Journal of Neurology and Psychiatry*, appearing directly before a long article titled "Raise High the Great Red Banner of Mao Zedong Thought and Actively Participate in the Socialist Cultural Revolution." It was to be the last issue of the *Chinese Journal of Neurology and Psychiatry* and most other psychiatric journals in China for more than ten years.

APPENDIX I: THE CULTURAL REVOLUTION AND LATE 1970s

DOCUMENT 1[283]: **Give Full Prominence to Politics and Follow China's Own Path Toward the Cure and Prevention of Psychiatric Illness**[284]

Editorial Board of the *Chinese Journal of Neurology and Psychiatry*

April 1966

After Liberation, under the leadership of the Party and especially since the Great Leap Forward of 1958, all parts of the country have been making great efforts towards the cure and prevention of mental illness, and definite successes have been achieved. However, we are still lagging sharply behind in this area, as compared with the excellent overall situation that has arisen throughout the country as a whole. Many problems still exist in our work, foremost among them being that some psychiatric workers are still quite heavily influenced and affected by bourgeois medical ideology: they emphasize treatment and cure, but not disease prevention; they are concerned only with the situation inside their hospitals and ignore the situation beyond the hospital walls; they use too many drugs and pharmaceuticals to treat patients and fail to mobilize the positive factors within the patients themselves, and so end up treating the illness rather than the person; they rely in their work upon a small number of specialized personnel and not upon the broad masses of the people; they one-sidedly stress objective factors and conditions and are afraid of difficulties; and their ideology is lacking in the self-consciously revolutionary spirit of self-reliance, of hard work and thriftiness, and of wholeheartedly serving the people.

For the past year and more, medical health workers throughout China have been resolutely implementing the directives of the Party Central Committee and Chairman Mao by taking part in the Three Great Revolutionary Movements;[285] large numbers of doctors and pharmacists have been going "up to the mountains and down to the villages" in order to relieve the peasant masses of their pains and illnesses; and while healthcare work has been greatly reinforced in the

---

[283] All translations of the following documents are by Robin Munro; article titles and subheadings are as they appear in the original documents.

[284] "*Tuchu Zhengzhi, Zou Woguo Jingshenbing Fangzhi Gongzuo Ziji de Lu,*" Chinese Journal of Neurology and Psychiatry, vol. 10, no. 2 (1966), pp.95-97.

[285] In Maoist parlance, these are: the struggle for production, the class struggle, and scientific experimentation.

countryside, a revolution has been taking place in the urban healthcare field. Most important of all, an ardent high tide in the universal study of Chairman Mao's works has been unleashed, allowing us to raise our level of ideological awareness, to give full prominence to politics, and to criticize and condemn the bourgeois ideological preference for working in isolation from politics, the masses and reality. [...]

As regards work on the treatment and prevention of schizophrenia, our medical personnel, after profoundly studying and learning from the works of Chairman Mao, have become imbued with the spirit of serving the people wholeheartedly and of conquering the academic viewpoints of subjective idealism and metaphysics that previously filled their minds.[286] As a result, a whole new situation has arisen, and they have smashed through the old mindset of treating mental illnesses solely by means of insulin coma therapy, electroconvulsive treatment and psycho-pharmaceuticals. Now, at the same time as using drugs and so forth, they also stress mobilizing the positive factors within the patients themselves. Many work units have organized the patients into groups to study Chairman Mao's teachings on the treatment and cure of disease, and this has fortified the patients in their resolve to do battle with their illnesses and relieved them of all kinds of psychological burdens, thereby benefiting their recovery.... In Beijing's Anding Hospital, for example, the relapse rate among schizophrenics has fallen from a previous level of 60 percent to a mere 20 percent. [...]

In Chengdu in March of this year, at a national symposium to exchange research-work experiences in the fields of psychiatry and neurology, the question of the content and essential nature of "psychotherapy" (*xinli zhiliao*) was quite extensively discussed. In the view of the conference, China's "psychotherapy" is fundamentally different in nature from the old-style "psychotherapy" found elsewhere. The main difference is that it has a clear and distinctive class nature: it employs a variety of means to help the patients strengthen their resolve to fight their illnesses for the sake of the revolution, and to do so self-confidently; and it firmly opposes the subjective-idealist ideological standpoints adopted by the bourgeois schools of psychoanalysis and psychobiology. The second difference is that it emphasizes the importance of mobilizing the patient's inner subjective dynamism[287] during the treatment

---

[286] In Maoist political philosophy, the terms "metaphysics" and "idealism" are generally used as terms of abuse to denote any viewpoints or policies that are officially deemed to be diametrically opposed to, respectively, the Marxist theories of "dialectics" and "materialism."

[287] The concept of "subjective dynamism" (*zhuguan nengdongxing*) was a prominent strand in radical Maoist thought from the early 1960s onward; it reflected Mao's belief

process... "Psychotherapy" is therefore a kind of ideological re-education, the essence of which is to instill in the patients a revolutionary worldview and outlook on life... Although for the meantime we are using the term "psychotherapy" to denote this treatment method, it may well turn out to be a rather inappropriate term. We will need to reconsider what name to use for it in the light of subsequent practical experience...

---

that China under socialism could develop at a much faster rate than the backward material and economic conditions of the country would otherwise allow, provided the population fully believed in and utilized the transformative powers of human subjective will. In a colloquial sense, it amounted to a kind of "mind over matter" belief system, the principal target or adversary of which was the orthodox (Soviet) Marxist doctrine of "economic determinism."

DOCUMENT 2: Give Full Prominence to Politics and Revolutionize the Clinical Management of Mental Illness[288]

Tianshui Mental Hospital, Gansu Province

April 1966

Whether we do a good or a bad job in managing mental illness is a crucial issue that affects both the quality of the medical treatment provided and also the recovery rate among the mentally ill. Here we would like to describe the efforts made by this hospital over the past few years to revolutionize our clinical management work.

In the early period after the founding of our hospital, we lacked experience in clinical management and so tried to study and emulate the experiences of other local hospitals. But we basically continued to follow the capitalist managerial model, with patients being confined in isolation, spending long periods in a boring and depressing environment and undergoing a gradual mental decline. In the course of the 1957 Anti-Rightist Movement and the struggle to annihilate capitalism and assert the proletarian worldview,[289] however, the level of ideological awareness among our medical personnel rose greatly and we made initial progress in critiquing the bourgeois viewpoint that "mental illness is protracted and incurable" and so nothing much can be done about it. [...]

In line with the gradual unfolding and deepening of the Great Socialist Education Movement,[290] we have been conducting a major campaign to study the works of Chairman Mao, to learn from the People's Liberation Army and to promote the excellent situation of "Upholding the Four Firsts,"[291] and we have been greatly educated and inspired by this. Getting clinical management work right is essentially a complex human relations project. Every human activity has an ideological basis, and the mentally ill are no different in this regard. Where

---

[288] *"Tuchu Zhengzhi, Cujin Jingshenbing Linchuang Guanli Gongzuo Geminghua,"* Chinese Journal of Neurology and Psychiatry, vol. 10, no. 2 (1966), pp.107-108.

[289] *"fan youpai, xing-wu mie-zi de douzheng"*

[290] The Socialist Education Movement began in the early 1960s, first in the countryside and then later in the cities, and was the immediate forerunner of the Cultural Revolution.

[291] *"jianchi sige diyi,"* namely, "the priority of men over weapons, of political work over other work, of ideological work over routine political work, and of living ideology over ideas from books"; see Stuart R. Schram, ed., *Mao Tse-tung Unrehearsed – Talks and Letters: 1956-71* (Harmondsworth: Pelican Books, 1974), p.246 and p.339 (Note 6).

problems of an ideological category are concerned, it is no use just relying on giving medicine and injections. What we really have to focus on is helping mental patients to give full prominence to politics, raise their levels of class-consciousness, and embrace the ideology of becoming well for the sake of the revolution and of waging conscious battle against their illnesses. While following the medical principle of curing both the sickness and the sufferer, and at the same time as unfolding "psychotherapy" work, we have set up an "administrative ward inspection system" whereby every Saturday morning the Party secretary, the hospital director and all the various department heads carry out a comprehensive and thoroughgoing inspection of the sick wards, holding conversations with the patients and discovering and solving any problems.

Among the patients themselves, depending on their individual circumstances, we have set up groups for the living study and living application of Chairman Mao's works, organized newspaper-reading classes, and held education sessions on current political affairs and on the advanced example set by the heroes of the revolution. Moreover, especially among the long-term inmates, we have compiled textbooks that take account of their particular mental conditions and which we use for purposes of re-educating them. The mental patients have found these very interesting, and when used in combination with psychotherapy and appropriate clinical management they have proven to be quite effective. In addition, we have purposefully arranged for the patients to view films such as "Be Eternally Loyal to the Party" and "The Spark of Life," to visit exhibitions on political class education, to take part in "recalling past bitterness and remembering present happiness"[292] sessions, and to hold group classes where they enthusiastically sing revolutionary songs, and all of this has helped release the patients' subjective positivity and has imbued them with a spirit of revolutionary optimism. In short, the everyday atmosphere in the sick wards is increasingly brisk, lively and dynamic. One mental patient, for example, wrote to us after being discharged from hospital: "My stay in hospital this time was just like being in a school of politics – you cured both my physical illness and also my ideological sickness. I want to thank the Party for all the warmth and concern it has shown me."[293] [...]

---

[292] "*Yi ku si tian*": political consciousness-raising sessions in which people would hear tales from the elderly about how harsh and exploitative life had been before 1949 and then dwell upon all the ways in which life had improved under Communism. These sessions were a regular feature of daily life in China from the early 1950s until the late 1970s.

[293] Elsewhere in the same issue of the journal, another patient was reported as saying: "In the past, when the doctor told me that 'to cure your sickness you must be guided by

DOCUMENT 3: **Analysis of a Survey of 250 Cases of Mental Illness**[294]

Chenzhou District Mental Hospital, Hunan Province;
Medical Group of the Mental Clinic of PLA Hospital No.165

August 1972

(*Editor's Note*: The history of mankind's understanding of mental illness and of the development of psychiatry is at the same time a history of struggle between idealism and materialism. Since the start of the Great Proletarian Cultural Revolution, China's revolutionary medical workers, guided by Chairman Mao's revolutionary line on medical healthcare and with Chairman Mao's philosophical thoughts as their compass, have carried out new explorations in the field of mental illness and have achieved many gladdening results. The following article provides an object example of this. Mental illness is a very complex phenomenon, especially as regards its fundamental nature and how one should categorize the various types of illness, and diverse views and opinions exist on these matters. The authors of the article have based their views on the practical experiences gained in their own work units, and we hope that our readers, in accordance with Chairman Mao's policy of "letting a hundred flowers bloom and a hundred schools of thought contend," will study and discuss it. We believe that such a discussion will be of great benefit to China's creation and development of a new-style psychiatry.)

Guided by Chairman Mao's revolutionary line, under the correct leadership and concern of our superior Party committee, and in accordance with our great leader Chairman Mao's instructions to "stress investigation and research" and "conscientiously summarize experience," our work units conducted, from the

---

correct ideology," I felt quite upset and offended. How could correcting one's ideology ever make one recover from mental illness? Would this not mean that actually I had an ideological sickness? Now that I've gained an understanding of the dialectical relationship between ideology and illness, however, I know why the medicine I used to take had no effect and I've become confident of being able to cure myself" (*Chinese Journal of Neuropsychiatry*, vol. 10, no. 2 [1966], p.114).

[294] *Xin Yixue – Shenjing Xitong Jibing Fukan (New Medicine – Supplementary Series on Diseases of the Nervous System)*, no.8 (1972), pp.12-16. This journal was published on a monthly basis "for internal use only" (*neibu faxing*) by the Zhongshan Medical College in Guangzhou and was one of only a tiny handful of medical journals produced in China during the Cultural Revolution.

standpoint of "class struggle," "one divides into two"[295] and "practice first," a home-visits follow-up survey of 250 mental patients (from altogether five counties, three municipalities, one town and eight factories and mines) who had been discharged from hospital during the period since May 1959. After combining this with a rough analysis of the relevant clinical materials, we reached the following findings:

General Situation

1. Gender distribution: 135 males, accounting for 54.0 percent of the cases studied; and 115 females, accounting for 46.0 percent of the cases.

2. Age at onset of illness: One person of nine years of age (0.4 percent); ten people in the 10-15 years age range (4.0 percent); 127 people in the 16-25 years age range (50.8 percent); 72 people in the 26-35 years age range (28.8 percent); 27 people in the 36-45 years age range (10.8 percent); eleven people in the 46-60 years age range (4.4 percent); and two people aged 61 years or more (0.8 percent.)

3. Family history of mental illness: among the 250 cases, 45 people (or 18 percent) were found to have a family history of mental illness.

Survey Of The Causes Of Mental Illness

Concerning the causal factors that led to mental illness in these 250 cases, our survey found:

---

[295] The proposition "one divides into two" (*yi fen wei er*) is a key tenet of Maoist dialectics and epistemology and stresses the primacy of contradiction and struggle in human affairs. It was given great prominence by Mao before and during the Cultural Revolution, as a means of combating both the early 1960s Khrushchevite doctrine of "peaceful coexistence" between the Communist world and the United States and also the increasing elite support within China at that time for the alternative Marxist philosophical proposition "two combine into one" (*he er er yi*); the latter sought to downplay, among other things, the centrality of class struggle in China's post-capitalist development.

1. In 219 of the cases (87.6 percent), mental illness arose as a result of certain objective things that were reflected within the person's mind but which he or she was unable to deal with properly. (See Table 1.) For details of the personality characteristics of these people, see Table 2.

Table 1   Statistics on the Various Psychological Factors Leading to Mental Illness

Category	Number of Cases	Percentage
Inability to deal with criticism correctly	50	20.0
Family disharmony	49	19.5
Inability to deal with family upsets correctly	33	13.2
Romantic disappointment	31	12.4
Inability to subordinate personal interests to the interests of the Party	15	6.0
Failure to unite with others	14	5.6
Non-fulfillment of personal desires	11	4.4
Inability to deal correctly with difficulties at work	7	2.8
Being frightened or receiving a shock	6	2.4
Dissatisfaction with the policies of the Party owing to erroneous standpoint	3	1.2

Table 2 Statistics on Personality Characteristics

Category	Number of Cases	Percentage
Fragile and delicate	8	3.2
Arrogant and conceited	8	3.2
Lively and energetic	19	7.6
Solitary and withdrawn	45	18.4
Narrow-minded and intolerant	110	44.0
Ordinary type	59	23.6

As Chairman Mao teaches us: **"The fundamental cause of the development of a thing is not external but internal; it lies in the**

contradictoriness within the thing.[296] As can be seen from Tables 1 and 2, because people live in society, objective facts or things are reflected within their minds, and these [mental reflections] in turn engender different ideologies. When certain objective things are reflected within the minds of people whose worldview has not been properly reformed and in whose thinking the word 'private' is playing havoc,[297] or because their ideological methodology for the handling of contradictions is incorrect, an intensified struggle arises among the various contradictions in their mind, thereby leading to an imbalance in the biological functioning of certain parts of the brain and hence to the emergence of a whole series of psychiatric symptoms – namely, mental illness. Mental illness is therefore not, as the bourgeois scholars would have us believe, a "supra-class, solely biological phenomenon," but rather something that is inextricably linked with the class struggle and with the clash between the two major worldviews.[298] Human personality is mainly acquired, not innate, and is a reflection of one's overall worldview. With people who are relatively heavily imbued with bourgeois ideology, we generally find that their personalities are narrow-minded, intolerant, solitary and withdrawn, or else show a mixture of fragility and arrogance. Unless people like this diligently and earnestly study Marxism-Leninism and Mao Zedong Thought and conscientiously reform their own worldviews, they will usually become obsessed with thoughts of personal gain or loss and fail to apply the methodology of "one divides into two" in dealing with problems, and instead end up making nit-picking self-justifications and putting their own personal interests in first place. Under the socialist system, a clash will inevitably develop between the concept "public" and their own preoccupation with the concept "private," engendering a contradiction within their minds between these two things. And unless this contradiction can be correctly resolved, the ideological struggle within their minds will intensify and may produce partial imbalances in the functioning of their cerebral cortexes; so people like this can very easily develop mental illnesses.

---

[296] Mao Zedong, "On Contradiction," *Selected Works of Chairman Mao*, pp.289-291. NB: Until the late 1970s, any quotations from the works of Mao in the published writings of others were always highlighted in bold text; we have preserved this convention in the translated documents presented here.

[297] "*si' zi zuo guai*," i.e., they still retain "selfish" ideas that conflict with the Communist or socialist values of public ownership and communal living.

[298] i.e., the proletarian worldview and the capitalist or bourgeois worldview.

2. Mental illness arose in fifteen of the cases, or 6.0 percent of the total, as a result of external injury, infection or similar causes. These included six cases of external injury (2.4 percent), five of poisoning (2.0 percent), one of infection (0.4 percent) and three of post-natal complications (1.2 percent.)

The mental impairments resulting from these various factors were successfully cured after appropriate treatment. In eleven of the cases, mental factors led to the reemergence of the impairments later on; and in the remaining four cases (two of external injury, one of poisoning and one of post-natal complications), the reasons for relapse were not identified.

3. The causes of mental illness could not be ascertained in sixteen of the cases (6.4 percent.)

Clinical Manifestations And Illness Categorization
Controversy still exists over the question of how to categorize mental illnesses. In our own clinical practice in treating the mentally ill, we find that while the precise causal factors may vary in each case, the patients' clinical signs and treatments nonetheless show common features. Using the combined methodology of clinical symptoms and treatment, therefore, we have roughly categorized the 250 mentally ill persons' conditions as follows:

1. Manic type: 111 cases (or 44.4 percent.) Clinical symptoms: onset of illness was generally acute, and those afflicted showed a prior tendency toward irritability and irascibility; after falling ill, they mostly slept and ate very little or else ate food randomly and suffered from insomnia; and they became argumentative or started singing and dancing around, talking incessantly and in a decadent manner running around all over the place, taking off their clothes and going around naked, beating and injuring people, and sometimes even inflicting self-harm or attempting to commit suicide.

2. Depressive type: 76 cases (or 30.4 percent.) Clinical symptoms: in general, onset of illness was fairly slow and there was a pre-illness tendency toward low mood and emotional distress; after falling ill, the patients became dull and morose, confused of speech, prone to bouts of abnormal crying and laughing or to periods of prolonged silence, stopped eating or moving, lay on their beds all day long, became stiff of movement and blank of facial expression, or incontinent and unable to control their bowels.

3. Hallucinatory and delusional type: 55 cases (or 22.0 percent.) Clinical symptoms: slow onset of illness, with a marked prior tendency toward suspiciousness and mistrust; after falling ill, the patients became dysthymic and suffered visual and auditory hallucinations, delusions of grandeur and delusions of persecution, and these notions were deep-seated and unmovable.

4. Chronic type: eight cases (or 3.2 percent.) Clinical symptoms: lengthy duration of illness (three to five years or more), with little or no response to prolonged treatment and showing progressive mental decline.

Accord Mao Zedong Thought The Commanding Role At Each And Every Stage In The Process Of Treating Mental Illness
In our clinical practice, we emphasized resolving the relationship between "internal factors and external factors," between "commonality and particularity" and between the "principal contradiction and secondary contradictions," and by arming the patients' minds with the weapon of Mao Zedong Thought we were able fully to mobilize their own internal [curative] factors; after then, on this basis, applying a supplementary combination of new-style acupuncture, Chinese herbal medicine and a small therapeutic dosage of wintermin,[299] we succeeded in turning around and resolving the patients' inner contradictions. In all, we managed to cure 198 of the patients and substantially improve the condition of a further forty-nine, resulting in a complete recovery rate of 79.2 percent and an effective cure rate of 98.8 percent; the average course of treatment was forty-six days.

I. Using Mao Zedong Thought to re-educate and reform the mentally ill.
In firmly seizing the fundamental task of using Mao Zedong Thought to re-educate and reform the mentally ill, we persisted in organizing the patients into groups to study the works of Chairman Mao, held frequent and numerous lecture meetings and mass criticism sessions, exchanged experiences among ourselves, unfolded mutual assistance programs and conducted one-on-one discussions with the patients. Throughout this, we comprehensively educated them on the following four main topics:

---

[299] *"Dongmian ling"*: a herbal preparation used in traditional Chinese medicine; see also (on its uses in "deep sleep therapy" in China) Note 75, above.

a. *Political class education.* When applying class education, we focused on "recalling past bitterness and remembering present happiness" and on "recalling past bitterness and remembering our present empowerment,"[300] and by so doing we were able to raise the patients' level of class consciousness and make them bear firmly and constantly in mind that their personal emancipation has been entirely due to the Communist Party and that they have Chairman Mao to thank for all of their present happiness and good fortune.

b. *Education on political line.* We frequently lectured the patients on the history of the two-line struggle [within the Party] and held profound sessions of revolutionary criticism and denunciation, during which we purged the patients' minds of the residual poisonous influence of the traitor Liu Shaoqi and his black "six theories," while at the same time raising their level of awareness of the political-line struggle and of the need to self-consciously defend Chairman Mao's revolutionary line and to take the initiative in doing battle with all kinds of undesirable ideological tendencies.

c. *Education on the current situation.* Focusing on major events within China and abroad, we gave the patients frequent and extensive lectures on the excellent nature of the overall current situation, thereby making them pay attention to national affairs and the world situation and arousing their revolutionary spirit and ardor.

d. *Education on worldview.* We organized the patients repeatedly to study articles by Chairman Mao such as "Serve the People," and thereby, taking the "three glorious examples" as a model,[301] encouraged them to take a correct outlook on matters of life and death, happiness and suffering, love and marriage and so forth, to struggle consciously against capitalism and revisionism, and to implant within themselves the proletarian worldview.

---

[300] "*yi ku si quan*"

[301] Namely, the Canadian doctor Norman Bethune, a Red Army soldier named Zhang Side and the "Foolish Old Man of North Mountain," about whom Mao wrote, respectively, in his celebrated three articles titled "In Memory of Norman Bethune" (1939), "Serve the People" (1944) and "The Foolish Old Man Who Removed the Mountains" (1945). These three articles were at the core of all Communist Party educational efforts in China after 1949.

e. *Education on the theory of dialectics.* In addition, we organized the patients to study Chairman Mao's glorious philosophical thinking by repeatedly doing a good job of both studying and applying the fundamental principles of "one divides into two," "practice first," "the relationship between internal causal factors and external ones" and "the turning around and resolving of contradictions," and thereby eliminating idealism and metaphysics and upholding the theory of materialist dialectics.

f. *Education on doing battle with one's illness.* In accordance with the different ideological realities of the individual patients, we organized them to take part in a variety of study groups in which we explained to them the causes of their mental illnesses and helped them to properly identify the principal contradictions in their thinking; by this means, we fully mobilized their inner subjective dynamism and enabled them to dig out the real roots of their illnesses by eradicating "private" thoughts and implanting the concept "public" in its place, thereby reinforcing their sense of self-confidence in waging battle with their illnesses.

II. Using Mao Zedong Thought to manage the mental patients.

Here, we made a decisive break with the previous management methods of "confining, tying down, and suppressing" mental patients, and in their place mobilized the "two enthusiasms"[302] and set up a new management system covering both work and rest:

a. We organized the patients into Red Health Squads (*hong-jian-lian*) and let them manage themselves.

b. We widely lauded model individuals and events as a way of arousing the patients' positivity.

c. We implemented open-door treatment and, in accordance with the specific nature of their illnesses, organized the patients to take part in manual labor, cultural and sports activities, physical exercises or to go for walks.

d. We set up some rough and ready sickbeds in the outpatient section, as a means of fully mobilizing the enthusiasm of the [patients'] partners and

---

[302] The meaning of this term is unclear.

allowing them to play an active role in the job of improving the patients' ideology and assisting in the management and treatment work.

III. Combining Western and Chinese medicine

At the same time as persisting in the use of Mao Zedong Thought to re-educate and reform the mentally ill, thereby removing the causes of illness at the fundamental level, we also had to provide a supplementary combination of Western and Chinese medical treatment in order to help restore the biological functioning of the patients' brains. The details of the treatment courses appear in Table 3.

Table 3 Statistics on Treatment Outcome by Group

	New-style acupuncture	New-style acupuncture + wintermin	Herbal medicine + new-style acupuncture + wintermin
Total number of cases	89	152	9
Complete recovery	51	103	4
Near recovery	19	19	2
Condition improved	18	29	2
No change	1	1	1

[Section omitted][303]

On The Problem Of Illness Recurrence

In our home visitation survey, we found that among the 198 patients who had been cured (either complete or near cure) and discharged from hospital, recurrence of illness had occurred in 40 cases, or 20.2 percent of the total, while there was no recurrence in 158 of the cases, or 79.8 percent of the total. There appeared to be four main reasons for the relapses that occurred. First, after being discharged, the patients did not show a high level of self-awareness in studying Mao Zedong Thought and had insufficiently emphasized the task of self-reform.

---

[303] The section omitted here contained around half a page of medical details on the dosages of herbal remedies and the combinations of acupuncture points used in the treatments summarized in Table 3.

Second, in certain work units, timely and appropriate arrangements to look after and manage the discharged patients were not made, and also the patients themselves had failed to deal correctly with this situation. Third, a small portion of the populace had continued to treat them like ill people and used colorful or derogatory language toward them. And fourth, some patients were hospitalized for too short a period of time, so the roots of their illnesses had not been properly dug out and there was poor recovery of function.

In socialist society, there are still classes, class contradictions and the class struggle. The reformation of people's ideology will never be fully completed. As soon as one contradiction is resolved, a new contradiction arises in its place. Mentally ill people are no exception to this rule, and so the recurrence [of mental illness] and the struggle to avoid such relapse is absolute. We consider that, in practice, the following steps must be taken in order to consolidate cure and forestall any recurrence of illness:

1. During hospitalization, persist in using Mao Zedong Thought to re-educate and reform the mentally ill, thereby helping them to dig out the roots of their illnesses and self-consciously replace their selfish "private" ideas with the new "public" ones. Prior to being discharged, patients should be placed in study groups to help them understand the causal pattern of their illnesses and also to teach them the methodology of turning around and resolving contradictions, and treatment should be reinforced.

2. At the time of discharge, take the opportunity of accompanying the patients home to explain to their work units and families both the reasons why they became mentally ill and also the methodology of turning [contradictions] around; and stress to them the importance of looking after the patients' political welfare, as well as the need to help them resolve the practical problems of daily life.

3. Go out into society to publicize widely Chairman Mao's great directive, **"All people in the revolutionary ranks must care for each other, must love and help each other,"**[304] in order to change past erroneous attitudes toward the mentally ill, mobilize the masses to show them warm assistance, and jointly implement a mass-based approach to prevent their illnesses recurring

---

[304] Mao Zedong, "Serve the People," September 8, 1944.

4. Through correspondence or home visits, keep in frequent contact with the patients, their families and work units, and find out about their situations in a timely manner so that recommendations on preventing any recurrence of illness can be made when needed.

Typical Cases

Case 1: Wu XX, male, 29 years old, a worker at a factory in Changsha. The patient graduated from a vocational middle school in 1963, had high hopes of becoming a technician and then eventually an engineer, and he also wanted to find himself a "pretty" wife. After meeting with disappointment in these goals (he was assigned a job as a lathe operator), he became extremely unhappy and increasingly despondent; he couldn't sleep at all and started talking all the time about how he wanted to "become an engineer and marry a pretty wife." He was hospitalized three times and given numerous courses of "electroconvulsive therapy," but all to no apparent effect; and November 25, 1969 he was admitted to our hospital.

Diagnosis: psychosis, hallucinatory-delusional type.

Hospital treatment: Since the patient's mental illness resulted from his unfulfilled desires, we held numerous sessions with him to study and re-study "Serve the People," "In Memory of Norman Bethune" and "The Foolish Old Man Who Removed the Mountains." In addition, we held revolutionary mass criticism sessions to denounce the "six theories" of Liu Shaoqi, so that he could gradually acquire a more correct understanding of such matters. And we combined this with new-acupuncture therapy (applying needles once a day at the *tailing*, *anmian* and *baihui* pressure points) and, when he had trouble sleeping, a daily dosage of 250 mg wintermin taken orally. The symptoms basically disappeared and he was discharged from hospital on July 19, 1970.

Follow-up situation: The patient returned to work after leaving hospital and remained in average condition thereafter.

Case 2: Huang XX, male, 66 years old, a worker at a Chenzhou bean curd factory. He was previously always diligent and responsible in his job, but on November 19, 1969, a fellow worker with whom he was preparing a pot of bean curd juice accidentally spoiled the pot, and later the same day he also damaged a sheet of muslin used for straining the bean curd. Huang then became extremely anxious and couldn't sleep all night long; the following day, he started muttering incessantly to himself, saying things like: "It's all over now, someone's going to roast me for sure," and "I have to be vigilant because they're going to start catching bad people again." Eventually a fight broke out and he was admitted to hospital on November 21, 1969.

> Diagnosis: psychosis, hallucinatory-delusional type.

> Hospital treatment: The patient's mental illness was caused by his incorrect ideological methodology in dealing with problems, so during his time in hospital we studied together with him the doctrines of "serve the people" and "one divides into two," and we praised him for eschewing negligence and taking a responsible attitude towards revolutionary work. We then inspired him to correctly use the method of "one divides into two" in dealing with the incident at work, thereby lancing his ideological "boil," and we followed up with some new-acupuncture therapy (applying needles once a day at the *tailing, zusanli* and *anmian* pressure points) and a daily dosage of 100 mg wintermin. On December 1, 1969 he regained his health and was discharged from hospital.

> Follow-up situation: The patient displayed an enthusiastic and responsible attitude at work, was able to deal correctly with any incidents that occurred and was praised by everyone.

Case 3: Li XX, female, 18 years old, a member of a county-level commune in Guiyang. In early December 1968, the patient's fiancé was assigned to work as a cook; considering this to be an inglorious occupation, she became moody, depressed and insomniac. Later she became overly loquacious and would often weep and create disturbances and run around all over the place; eventually she started taking off her clothes, breaking things and getting into fights with people, and became unable to look after herself properly. On January 10, 1969 she was admitted to hospital; her father, elder sister and elder brother all had histories of mental illness.

> Diagnosis: psychosis, manic type.

Hospital treatment: Although the patient's family had a history of mental illness, the direct cause of her mental illness was still her problematic worldview. After being hospitalized, she was given both electroconvulsive therapy and large dosages of wintermin; this relieved her symptoms somewhat, but the improvement was not stable and so the above-mentioned symptoms repeatedly reemerged. In April 1969, we made her participate in the hospital's "First Study Group on Mao Zedong Thought." In the course of the study group, we read together with her "Serve the People" and other articles by Chairman Mao, and also, in line with the realities of her ideological situation, repeatedly propagated to her Chairman Mao's great teaching that "everyone is a functionary of the people, irrespective of the high or low status of their job." At the same time, we carried out careful and patient ideological work to make her realize that there is no social hierarchy within the revolution, only a division of labor, and that no matter what one's job may be, one is always serving the people. Thereupon, her mood gradually returned to normal again. We also supplemented this with some new-style acupuncture: from April 18 to 25, we applied needles once a day to the *tailing*, *zusanli* and *neiguan* pressure points, which basically removed her psychiatric symptoms; and we followed this up with a daily stimulation of the *taodao* and *neiguan* pressure points. By May 17, she had completely recovered and was then discharged from hospital.

Follow-up situation: After leaving hospital, the patient enthusiastically participated in collective production work and took the lead in studying Mao Zedong Thought. When her husband requested a divorce on the grounds that she had been mentally ill, she dealt with this personal difficulty in a correct manner. Moreover, she mobilized the other women to plough the fields and build a reservoir and was then selected as leader of the women's production team. In 1970, she gloriously participated in the Guiyang County Activists' Conference for the Study of Mao Zedong Thought.

Conclusion
Our findings from this survey analysis of 250 cases of mental illness were as follows:

1. Mao Zedong Thought and Chairman Mao's glorious philosophical thinking is the powerful ideological weapon that guides and directs our

understanding, treatment and prevention of mental illnesses. The decisive factor in treating and curing mental illness is to mobilize the "two enthusiasms" and employ Mao Zedong Thought to re-educate and reform the patients.

2. The reason why most patients become mentally ill is connected to the class struggle, and the fundamental causal factor in the majority of cases is that the patients still retain a bourgeois worldview and methodology.

3. On the basis of clinical symptoms and treatment, mental illnesses can be divided into four main categories (manic type, depressive type, hallucinatory-delusional type and chronic type).

4. The main prerequisites for successfully treating and curing mental illnesses are: to deal correctly with the relationships between "commonality and particularity" and "internal causation and external causation"; to break with the former management practices of "confining, tying down and suppressing" the mental patients; to comprehensively break with the "three great treasures" (electroconvulsive treatment, insulin coma therapy and high-dosage wintermin medication), all of which destroy the patients' health; and to adopt new medical treatment methods based on a combination of Western and Chinese medicine.

5. Using Chairman Mao's "mass line" standpoint, make contact and liaise with the work units and families of the patients after their discharge from hospital and mobilize everyone to do a good job of consolidating the patients' recoveries.

Our level of study of Mao Zedong Thought and Chairman Mao's philosophical works is far from sufficient, our level of awareness of the political line is not high enough, and our survey data is rather incomplete. As a result, many problems still exist in our practical understanding of mental illness and in our attempts to treat it, and we invite readers to point out and correct any shortcomings or errors in our survey analysis.

Appendix I: New-style acupuncture pressure points [– omitted]
Appendix II: Herbal medicines [– omitted]

DOCUMENT 4: Study and Discussion Notes on "Analysis of a Survey of 250 Cases of Mental Illness"[305]

Yichun District Mental Hospital, Jiangxi Province

March 1973

We have recently been studying the article that appeared in issue No.8 of *New Medicine*, titled "Analysis of a Survey of 250 Cases of Mental Illness" (hereafter referred to as *Analysis of a Survey*). Guided by Chairman Mao's instruction to "let a hundred flowers bloom and a hundred schools of thought contend," we have discussed this article thoroughly among ourselves and now offer our views on it.

First of all, we all agree that the trail blazed by the comrades of Chenzhou Mental Hospital – their spirit of daring to think and act fearlessly; their conscientious work style of careful investigation and research; the great efforts they have made in deploying Mao Zedong Thought to re-educate, reform and manage the mentally ill; their resolute pursuit of the path of combining Chinese and Western medicine in the treatment of mentally ill people; and their policy of going outside the hospital and into society in order wholeheartedly to serve the workers, peasants and soldiers – is one that has achieved outstanding results and is eminently deserving of our emulation. Indeed, our own efforts are orientated in the same direction.

On the basis of our experience in clinical practice, however, my colleagues and I wish to express several views and opinions that are at variance with those given in *Analysis of a Survey*.

1. On The Causal Factors Of Mental Illness

As a wealth of facts demonstrate, whether in the pre-illness period, during the illness or after clinical recovery, certain problems can always be identified in the mental patient's worldview and methodology; that is to say, contradictions exist between objective reality and their ideological awareness. In view of this, we ourselves at all times persist in using Mao Zedong Thought to re-educate, reform and manage the mentally ill, and practice has shown us that doing this task well always has a positive effect on their treatment and management and

---

[305] *Xin Yixue (New Medicine)*, vol. 4, no. 3 (1973), pp.176-178; cover date March 15, 1973.

helps to prevent their illnesses from recurring. In studying and learning from the Chenzhou experience, we have gained an even deeper understanding of these matters.

From the point of view of psychiatry as a branch of science, however, we feel it is inappropriate to regard problems of worldview and methodology as being the fundamental causal factor in the emergence of mental illness as a whole. According to *Analysis of a Survey,*

> Since the worldview [of those afflicted] has not been properly reformed and the word "private" is playing havoc in their minds, or because their ideological methodology for the handling of contradictions is incorrect, an intensified struggle arises among the various contradictions in their mind, thereby leading to an imbalance in the biological functioning of certain parts of the brain and hence to the emergence of a whole series of psychiatric symptoms – namely, mental illness.

If this were indeed the case, then the majority of ordinary people would also be likely to develop mental illness, since at the present stage of social development a very large section of the population still cleaves to the word "private" and has an improperly reformed worldview; but why, then, is the rate of mental illness among China's population still running at the level of only several people per thousand? Pursuing this logic further, if the word "private" [and associated thinking] serves as the "hotbed" of mental illness and if reactionary ideology lies at the root of all such illnesses, then people whose thinking is most heavily larded with the concept "private" – namely, those whose worldview is basically bourgeois or capitalist in nature – should all surely become mentally ill. But in actual practice, we discover no such rule or regularity as this.

In our view, problems relating to worldview and methodology can only partially explain the emergence of mental illnesses and cannot be regarded as the primary causal factors behind mental illness as a whole; nor should they be seen as the principle reason for the emergence of schizophrenia, a very common illness, for to do so would hinder our further investigations into the true reasons for this illness and impede the search for an effective somatic cure. According to the current findings of research into schizophrenia, people with this illness have certain protein and glucose-related metabolic disorders, so continued efforts should be made to investigate and understand these disorders.

2. On Clinical Manifestations And The Categorization Of Illness

We find the ideas and proposals put forward in *Analysis of a Survey* to be simple and clear, easy to grasp and suitable for wider dissemination, and we regard them as having a certain practical significance in the field of disease prevention work. From the more specialized scientific point of view, however, attempting to identify illnesses and their subtypes solely on the basis of clinical manifestations is a highly inadequate and incomplete way of proceeding. A much more appropriate methodology is to start by investigating the causes of illness, and then to identify particular categories of illness by finding out which factors are most conducive to their cure and prevention, to the goals of scientific research, to the assessment of prognosis, and to clinical practice. For example, in the case of organic psychosis, one would never be able to prescribe an appropriate cure for the sufferer's symptoms by focusing solely on the clinical manifestations of the illness. And certain other illnesses (for example, neurotic functional disorder) are in no way amenable to categorization under the kind of typology presented in *Analysis of a Survey*. For these reasons, we continue to favor adhering to the "Draft Classification of Mental Diseases," as formulated in 1958 by the First National Conference on the Cure and Prevention of Mental Illness.

3. On The Treatment And Cure Of Mental Illness

Studying the Chenzhou experience has further strengthened our determination to employ Mao Zedong Thought as a means of re-educating and reforming the mentally ill, and we have now begun pursuing this task in a variety of different ways. Practice has shown that when we do a good job in this area, the political atmosphere in the wards becomes rich and all-pervasive, the mental patients' thinking and ideology undergo a total transformation, and an orderly and well-structured climate for treatment and cure is created. At the same time, we have achieved heartening results by making extensive use of Chinese herbal medicine and new-style acupuncture therapy. In the case of Ms. Gan, for example, a schizophrenia sufferer who had been hospitalized for over eight months and had received – all to no avail – large doses of chlorpromazine and extensive insulin coma treatment and electroconvulsive therapy, we eventually cured her by using a compound of herbal remedies, and her health continued to be good after two years of follow-up visits. The combined use, in the treatment of mental illness, of Chinese herbal medicine and new-style acupuncture (electric acupuncture) on the one hand, and tranquilizer drugs on the other, has achieved fairly good therapeutic results and has also allowed us to reduce the amount of tranquilizers given. Electric acupuncture has also proven to be fairly efficacious in reducing over-excitement and bodily agitation.

In short, our achievements in practice have made us all the more resolute in perceiving the need to continue along the path of combining Chinese and Western medicine. But in applying the new medical therapeutic methods, we have also encountered many mental patients whose conditions fail to respond to the new treatments that are currently available. In accordance with Chairman Mao's instruction to "Make foreign things serve China," by using, in such cases, an appropriate quantity of the "three major therapies,"[306] we have managed to restore the health of certain people whose mental illnesses had hitherto proved intractable. A schizophrenic named Huang and a compulsive neurotic named Li, for example, both failed to improve after more than a year of combined treatment with Chinese and Western medicine, new acupuncture therapy and electric acupuncture, but they were eventually cured by a course of insulin coma treatment. For this reason, we feel that the "three major therapies" should be viewed and understood in the light of historical materialism and dialectical materialism, and that we should preserve what is best in them while discarding what is bad, in order that they may more effectively serve the cause of the people's health; simply rejecting them across the board is not, in our view, an appropriate or advisable course of action.

4. On The Question Of Preventing Recurrences

We concur with the various proposals put forward in *Analysis of a Survey* on "the measures required for consolidating the cure and guarding against a relapse." In addition, in the course of our own clinical practice and follow-up observations, we have found that in the case of the commonest form of recurrent mental illness, schizophrenia, the maintenance of tranquilizer therapy over a fairly long period is an effective way of preventing recurrence.

---

[306] "*San da liao fa*," namely, chlorpromazine (or other antipsychotic medications), insulin coma therapy, and electroconvulsive treatment.

DOCUMENT 5: Mental Disease Cannot be Regarded as an Ideological Defect
– An Opinion on the Essential Nature of Mental Illness[307]

Yang Desen
No.2 Affiliate Hospital, Hunan Medical College

August 1976

Mental activity is a function of the human brain; it is the inner reflection of objective reality.

Mental illness is a disease of the brain, and it is expressed primarily in abnormalities of mental activity.

Mental abnormalities manifest themselves, in cognitive terms, in the form of distorted reflections of objective reality, and on the practical level these are expressed in the form of disordered speech and behavior.

Distorted reflections of objective reality can be found in normal people's thinking as well as in the minds of the mentally ill. In the latter case, this is caused by the presence of disease in the brain, and one of the ways it expresses itself is through mentally pathological thoughts. In the former case, the brain itself is not defective, and the various manifestations – such as erroneous thoughts and ideology, the presence of [philosophically] idealist theory, religious superstitions, and prejudiced and one-sided notions of various kinds – are all rooted in the question of [political] class and epistemology. When erroneous ideas emerge in the minds of normal people, they can usually be resolved in the course of social practice and through persuasion and re-education. But mentally pathological thoughts and ideas are produced by illness, arising in train with the development of the disease and then duly disappearing once the illness has been cured; so they do not amount to a simple question of epistemological error, and the two situations are essentially different. While in general terms one can say that mentally pathological thoughts also fall under the heading of incorrect cognition and understanding, it is nonetheless quite wrong to lump them together with [the erroneous ideas of mentally normal people].

What points of commonality and difference exist, then, between the pathological thoughts of the mentally ill (for example, hallucinatory and

---

[307] Yang Desen, *Xin Yixue – Jingshen Xitong Jibing Fukan* (*New Medicine – Supplementary Series on Diseases of the Nervous System*), vol. 2, no. 3 (1976), pp.187-189. NB: This article was published only one month before the death of Chairman Mao and at the height of power of the ultraleftist "Gang of Four."

delusional content) and the erroneous ideology of normal people? This question has not yet been openly discussed in China. Comrade Stalin gave an explication of this issue in his writings on the relationship between Marxism and linguistics, and in China in the 1960s, when our philosophers discussed the question of the unity between thought and [social] existence, the majority viewpoint held that erroneous thoughts and existence also occur in unity. All this provides a source of enlightenment for us in the present discussion. The pathological thoughts of the mentally ill do not simply fall from the skies, any more than do the erroneous thoughts and ideology of normal people, and neither are they something fixed or eternal in the minds of the mentally ill (different people suffering from the same mental illness, for example, often express similar thoughts and ideas). They too represent a distorted reflection of objective reality. The dialectical-materialist and historical-materialist principle that existence determines consciousness, and that social existence determines social consciousness, is a universal truth and one that is equally applicable when interpreting the pathological thoughts of the mentally ill.

One point should first of all be clarified: the ideological speech and behavior of a mentally ill person can by no means be viewed as being entirely, one hundred percent abnormal. Usually, a certain portion of his or her ideological speech and behavior will remain normal in character, and this represents a direct continuation of the person's pre-illness ideological consciousness and expression; whatever the ideological tendency displayed, such speech and behavior should still be seen as normal, and certainly not as something pathological. This is true not just during the illness but also prior to the onset of illness: no fundamental distinction should be drawn here, and hence there is no need to dwell further on this point.

What needs to be clarified here is that the pathological thoughts of mentally ill people still constitute a distorted reflection of objective reality. This is a fundamental question relating to our continued staunch adherence, in the field of psychiatry, to the materialist theory of reflection.[308] The content of the delusions in the minds of the mentally ill has a clear social nature and a clear class nature. With delusions of grandeur, for example, a person's belief that he or she is an emperor, prime minister or general would be a reflection of the feudal social consciousness; while in the case of those believing themselves to be model workers, it would serve to reflect the social consciousness of the

---

[308] "*weiwuzhuyi fanyinglun*": the Marxist epistemological doctrine whereby all human mental activity is seen as being rooted in, and ultimately reflective of, events and circumstances occurring in the "material" realm.

socialist system. Similarly, a [mentally ill] person's belief that he or she was a landlord or a capitalist would, under the psychiatric symptomatology of the old [i.e. pre-1949] society, have manifested itself as a delusion of grandeur accompanied by a sense of elation; whereas the same belief in the new society would serve to express something quite different: namely a delusion of guilt or culpability, accompanied by feelings of depression. In the case of delusions of influence, moreover, we typically see a shift in the content of such delusions, away from the idea that the sufferer is being possessed by spirits and ghosts, and toward the idea that he or she is being controlled by some remote electronic device; or in the case of delusions of invention, from believing they have invented airplanes or tanks toward the imagined invention of ballistic missiles, satellites and so forth.

All this shows us that the content of mental delusions changes over time and in accordance with the trends of social change and development, and that such content is entirely a transplanted and distorted reflection of objective reality. And this is true not only of the content of delusions, but also of the particular forms they assume (delusions of grandeur, self-guilt, persecution, jealousy and so forth): these various forms are also distorted expressions of human social relations. Delusions of so-called grandeur or self-guilt are undoubtedly concepts involving an individual's social self-evaluation, and if the person were to be removed from his or social context, for example by being placed on a desert island, then the notions of grandeur or self-guilt would lose all grounds for existence; similarly, delusions of persecution no doubt serve to reflect the "dog-eat-dog" social mentality found in the exploitative social systems; and it is very hard to conceive of delusions of jealousy arising within, for example, the polygamous systems of primitive societies. To sum up: neither the content nor the form of mental delusions should be regarded as something eternally unchanging and divorced from real social existence. The speech and behavior of the mentally ill is a reflection of their diseased mental reality. In class society, the pathological thoughts of the mentally ill are also clearly stamped with the mark of class.

We should now consider the further question: what is the nature of the interrelationship between the pathological thoughts and ideology of the mentally ill and the normal thoughts and ideology they had prior to falling ill?

Some people maintain that pathological thoughts are simply a continuation of the normal thoughts found prior to the onset of illness, and that if any changes occur, these can only be quantitative and not qualitative in nature. Putting the matter bluntly, they maintain that the pathological thoughts provide a naked, wholesale revelation of the true thoughts and ideology that the mental patients had prior to falling ill. And they attribute the fact that the patients concerned did not express such thoughts before they fell ill, and that they hastily try to repudiate such thoughts after recovering their mental health, to mere phony and disingenuous attempts by the patients to conceal their true thoughts. They then conclude that the patients' expression of pathological thoughts provides the clearest possible indication of the essential nature of their underlying ideology. According to this line of analysis, patients who develop delusions of grandeur were from the outset prone to self-aggrandizement and overestimation of self; those who develop delusions of self-guilt have all along been resigned to their own backwardness and given themselves up as hopeless; those with delusions of persecution have always been conspiratorial and manipulative by nature; those suffering from delusions of loss have only become so because of their consistently self-interested and selfish dispositions; those with hypochondriac delusions are that way because they have been deeply influenced by the philosophy of survival preached by the modern revisionists;[309] the shallow and frivolous sexual behavior of patients suffering from manic disorder is merely an expression of their corrupt and degenerate ideology; the underlying pessimism and attempted suicides of those suffering from depression is the outcome of their atrophied revolutionary willpowers; the sudden mood swings of those with manic-depressive illness is but a typical expression of the constant shift between [political] fanaticism and dejection characteristic of the petty-bourgeois ideological mindset; and so on and so forth. According to this general perspective, all the symptoms of mental illness are fundamentally rooted in the patient's pre-illness ideological and political-class background, and moreover a positive identification of the patient's ideological awareness and character can be made on the basis of these symptoms.

While this general viewpoint is not entirely unjustified as a means of analyzing the symptomatic manifestations of certain psychogenic mental illness, for example psychogenic delusions, the majority of professional psychiatric workers would regard it as being of little practical use as a way of interpreting the symptoms of organic psychosis (for example, poliomyelitis-induced imbecility, or delusions of grandeur caused by a tumor of the prefrontal cortex) – indeed, a wealth of practical clinical experience flatly contradicts any such simplistic and mechanistic theory of causation as this. In addition, a great many of the pathological thoughts found among those suffering from the most common form of severe mental illness, schizophrenia, cannot be explained at all

---

[309] *"huoming zhexue"*: expanded English translation above taken from *The Pinyin Chinese-English Dictionary* (Beijing, 1990); the author's implicit reference to the "modern revisionists" who allegedly spout this philosophy means, in the context of late Maoist thought, the USSR and the Communist Party of the Soviet Union.

on the basis of this theory: for example, a schizophrenic from a stable and harmonious family background who starts suspecting that his mother or spouse is trying to poison him or that his infant son is keeping him under surveillance; or the case of a revolutionary cadre who, because of his mentally disordered condition, starts claiming that he has committed major crimes of counterrevolution. In these cases, no causal interconnection whatsoever can be found between the patient's pre-illness thoughts and ideas and those that arise after the onset of illness; the latter are diametrically opposed to the former, and the patients themselves, once recovered, see them as absurd and ridiculous. Another example is that of a schizophrenic who suffered from auditory hallucinations in which he heard his neighbor swearing and cursing at him. In reality, the neighbor was a bad person, but the patient's psychiatric symptoms then assumed the form of a determination on his part to do battle against all bad people and things. Eventually he moved house, but the auditory hallucinations then began to contain the voice of his new neighbor – who happened to be a leading official in his work unit. The patient's mental symptoms took the form of making frequent complaints and bizarre statements [about the leading cadre], and in the end they escalated to the level of an outright and open confrontation between him and the entire organizational leadership. As an indicator of his [political] ideological awareness, therefore, the psychiatric symptoms of the very same patient were transformed, in essence, into their own diametrical opposite. At times, the two sets of antagonistic thoughts may also become mixed up together, giving rise to coercive or compulsive thinking that goes against the patient's own subjective wishes and desires. It is hard to connect or reconcile any of these kinds of phenomena with the pre-illness ideological realities of those concerned.

By indiscriminately and matter-of-factly applying the methodology of analyzing normal people's thinking to the task of analyzing the pathological thoughts of the mentally ill, and in the process equating the latter with the erroneous ideological tendencies of normal people and overestimating the role played by mental factors in the genesis of different types of mental illness, it becomes very easy to start seeing mental illness itself as constituting an "ideological defect." The absurd content of the pathological thoughts generally eludes and evades any kind of strict ideological source analysis, and attempts to extrapolate from these pathological thoughts the nature of the patient's pre-illness ideological consciousness can therefore easily give rise to an extremely superficial conclusion: namely, that all mental illness is caused by the extreme and unchecked development of individualism.[310] Public opinion in general, and

---

[310] *"jingshenbing dou shi gerenzhuyi jiduan fazhen de jieguo"*

also people who have done no serious investigation or systematic observation of the essential nature of mental illness, are all too ready to accept and give credence to this kind of conclusion. This in turn easily creates a public mindset whereby mentally ill people are universally looked down upon and discriminated against, to the point even where certain individuals try to prosecute and hold mentally ill people legally responsible in all kinds of ways for their pathological speech and behavior (although they have no capacity to bear such responsibility).

Mental disease cannot be equated with defective ideology. Severe mental illness can result in death or long-term disablement, and what the patients urgently need is medication and treatment. There is a world of difference between this situation and that of normal people who display ideological defects, and the two simply cannot be put on a par. While we cannot say that pathological thoughts have absolutely no connection to the patient's pre-illness thinking, there is certainly no direct or necessary relationship of cause and effect to be found between them. Hence, the viewpoint described above cannot be said to be fully grounded in scientific fact, and it undeniably contains elements of subjective conjecture. Since it is not grounded in the concrete analysis of concrete contradictions,[311] it cannot be seen as being in complete conformity with the principles of Marxism.

Precisely because mentally ill people still retain a certain amount of normal brain activity, they are able, just like normal people, to benefit from re-education based on Marxism and Mao Zedong Thought; their inner subjective dynamism can be mobilized and they can engage in battle against their illnesses. Psychotherapy is very important, [but] it neither precludes nor can totally substitute for pharmaceutical medications. The speech and behavior of mentally ill people may well have adverse influence and effects upon society, and all erroneous things should of course be subjected to appropriate criticism and must not be permitted to spread unchecked or to threaten public order and stability. [Such people] should be subjected to compulsory treatment and we should reinforce management over them; this is essential for purposes of safeguarding both the interests of society and also the personal interests of the mentally ill.

The opinions expressed above are not necessarily correct and I would be glad to receive any criticisms or corrections.

---

[311] See below, Note 316.

DOCUMENT 6: More on the Essential Nature of Mental Illness[312]

Jia Rubao

Employees' Hospital of the Huashan Metallurgy and
Vehicle Repair Plant, Huayin, Shaanxi Province

April 1977

The history both of mankind's understanding of mental illness and of the development of psychiatry itself is one of a battle between materialism and idealism. Within the psychiatric domain, many idealist and metaphysical viewpoints continue to persist even today. For example, attempts to use psychology to arbitrarily construe the changes that occur in the minds of the mentally ill – stuff like "sexual urges being repressed since childhood," "inequilibrium of the personality" and "lack of adaptation to the environment" – all fall under the headings of idealism and mind–body dualism. In addition, there is the school of experimental research that studies mental phenomena in isolation from their social context, repudiates the class nature of mental activity, denies the counteractive force of mind upon matter (the brain), ignores the distinction between humans and animals, and carries out certain anatomical, physiological and biochemical work that is independent of human society. This is all a reflection, within the field of psychiatric research, of the one-sided and mechanistic doctrine of mechanical materialism,[313] and bears no relation at all to objective reality.

I agree with Yang Desen's basic propositions: "Mental activity is a function of the human brain, a reflection of objective reality," and "Mental illnesses are diseases of the brain that primarily manifest themselves in

---

[312] *Xin Yixue – Shenjing Xitong Jibing Fukan (New Medicine – Supplementary Series on Diseases of the Nervous System)*, vol. 3, no. 2 (1977), pp.142-143. It is clear from this article that the author, Jia Rubao, was also one of the authors of Document 3, above: "Analysis of a Survey of 250 Cases of Mental Illness."

[313] "Mechanical materialism" was the pejorative term used by Marx to describe the system of thought of the German philosopher Ludwig Feuerbach (see, for example, Marx's famous 1845 essay, "Ten Theses on Feuerbach," and also his 1886 article "Ludwig Feuerbach and the End of Classical German Philosophy"). Marx claimed to have "redeemed" Feuerbach's materialism by removing the "mechanistic" aspects and replacing them with a (similarly cleansed) version of Hegel's theory of dialectics; Marx called the resultant theory "dialectical materialism."

abnormalities of mental activity." This is because mental activity is a reflection within the human brain of things that exist in objective reality; it is certainly not something permanently fixed in the brain, and neither is it something subjectively generated within the brain from nowhere. The content of mental activity originates from within social practice – that is, from the struggle for production, from the class struggle and from scientific experimentation[314] – which is why infants and small children very rarely suffer from non-organic psychosis. It is social existence that determines people's consciousness and the realities of the class struggle that determine people's ideology and emotions. **"In class society everyone lives as a member of a particular class, and every kind of thinking, without exception, is stamped with the brand of a class."** (Chairman Mao, "On Practice," [1937] *Selected Works of Mao Zedong*, p.272.) For this reason, the content of the psychiatric symptoms of the mentally ill (their thoughts, emotions, behavior and also the imbalance between these things and the environment) is all closely bound up with the reality of the three great revolutionary struggles[315]; that is to say, [these symptoms] are a reflection of the different ideologies, cultures, customs and beliefs, emotions and sentiments of different societies (classes.) In its essential nature, mental illness is a disease intimately connected to worldview. The following are the points on which Comrade Yang and I disagree:

Mental illnesses (aside from those caused by organic changes in the brain resulting from external injury, poisoning or infection) are non-organic diseases involving imbalances in the functioning of the brain. Since they are diseases, they cannot simply be defined as defects of ideology; however, this still misses the essential nature of the problem. **"People's knowledge and understanding of things, phenomena, processes and so forth consists of a constantly deepening [cognitive] progression, one that goes from phenomenology to essence and from less profound levels of essential nature to more profound levels."** (Lenin, "Extracts from Hegel's *Logic*," Collected Works of Lenin, Vol.38, p.239.) This is a core tenet of dialectics. Similarly, **"practice is the sole criterion of truth"** is a fundamental principle of Marxist philosophy; and **"carrying out concrete analysis of concrete conditions"** is the living soul of Marxism.[316] Guided by the philosophical thought of Chairman Mao, when we

---

[314] These three things are often referred to, in Maoist political discourse, as the "three great revolutionary movements" (*san-da geming yundong*).

[315] See preceding Note.

[316] The last two quotes are taken from Mao Zedong's writings. The *locus classicus* of the proposition "practice is the sole criterion of truth," which in 1978 became Deng

thoroughly investigate and conscientiously analyze the disease-causing factors and the mental activity of mentally ill people, we can readily observe that mental illness is intimately connected to the question of worldview, and that the pathological thoughts and ideas [of the mentally ill] are closely interconnected with the normal thoughts and ideas they had prior to becoming mentally ill. Quantitative increase [in such thoughts and ideas] leads to qualitative change (i.e. cause and outcome), leading to mental illnesses caused by unchecked and uncontrollable imbalances in the functioning of the brain. In seeking to treat and cure mental illnesses, therefore, we must accord Mao Zedong Thought the commanding role at each and every stage of the psychotherapeutic process, and if we do so, outstanding results will be guaranteed.

Using the epistemological method of dialectical materialism, we carried out an extensive survey analysis of several hundred mental patients in order to identify the causal factors that had made them mentally ill. We found that the overwhelming proportion (94 percent) had fallen ill as a result of external psychological blows, such as family disputes, romantic disappointment, inability correctly to deal with criticism, or accidents and natural disasters, or as a result of objective [sic] factors such as getting a fright or shock, not uniting with others (*bu tuanjie*), being afraid of difficulties, putting self first-ism (*geren diyizhuyi*) or having unfulfilled selfish desires. That is to say, when certain objective factors (things) are reflected in people's minds, and if those concerned do not apply the dialectical materialist viewpoint in order to deal with them correctly, then these factors or things will turn into adverse psychological pressures or stimuli leading to mental illness.

As we know, however, not everyone who encounters these kinds of disease-causing factors (things) in his or her mental world falls mentally ill. As Chairman Mao taught us: **"The fundamental cause of the development of a thing is not external but internal; it lies in the contradictoriness within the thing"**; and **"Materialist dialectics...holds that external causes are the condition of change and internal causes are the basis of change, and that external causes become operative through internal causes." ("On Contradiction,"** *Selected Works of Chairman Mao*, **pp.289-291.)** In our

---

Xiaoping's battle cry in his decisive struggle against the residual ultraleftists in the Chinese Communist Party, is Mao's famous article of July 1937, "On Practice." The main source for the Maoist variant of the phrase "the concrete analysis of concrete conditions" is Mao's equally famous August 1937 article, "On Contradictions." (Mao himself borrowed the phrase from Lenin's article, "Communism," in which Lenin, criticizing the Hungarian Communist Bela Kun, said that he "gives up the most essential thing in Marxism, the living soul of Marxism, the concrete analysis of concrete conditions" [see *Collected Works of Lenin*, Russian edition, Moscow, vol. 31 (1950), p.143].)

survey, we found that the overwhelming majority (92 percent) of the mental patients had shy and solitary dispositions, were narrow-minded and intolerant, and also vain and arrogant. Personality and character is acquired, not innate, and it is an expression of one's worldview. When these sorts of people are faced with the persistent presence in their minds of certain objective things, because they have failed to reform their worldviews properly and have used incorrect ideology in dealing with contradictions, the contradictory struggles within them only intensify; and since they are unable to rid themselves of the constant pressure and stimulus arising from these intensified contradictory struggles, the external factors (objective things) then act through the internal factors (worldview and methodology) to produce partial imbalances in the biological functioning of the brain and hence a whole series of psychiatric symptoms.

Mental illness, therefore, is not, as the bourgeoisie would have us believe, a "supra-class, solely biological phenomenon," but rather something that is inextricably linked with the class struggle and with the clash between the two major worldviews. Indeed, the pathological thoughts are simply a continuation of the normal thoughts that existed prior to the onset of illness. As we know from their own post-recovery accounts, the mentally ill are often people who previously were obsessed with considerations of personal gain and loss, were backward and had no desire to make progress in life, had failed to employ the methodology of "one divides into two" in dealing with their problems and resorted instead to mere hair-splitting and self-justification, and who were drowning fast in the sea of individualism. They paid no attention to the advice of others and so the struggle between contradictions became more and more intense in their minds, leaving them in a constant state of agitation and insomnia, with no interest in food, and increasingly withdrawn and isolated. The process goes exactly like this: under the socialist system, it is impossible for these people to satisfy their selfish desires and so the "boil" cannot be lanced; at first, the normal thoughts and the pathological thoughts coexist side by side, but as the pathological thoughts steadily gain the ascendant in their minds, they begin to sing, dance and run around aimlessly, tearing off their clothes and going around naked, and sometimes injuring or killing people – that is, they become mentally ill. We see, therefore, that bourgeois worldview and methodology are the fundamental causal factors in the emergence of mental illness; indeed this is the essential nature of mental illness. Some people will ask the question: in capitalist society, then, is mental illness more commonly found among the bourgeois class? Yes, there are certainly more mentally ill people from this class background than elsewhere. But since the bourgeois scholars absolutely never try to study or analyze the problem in this light, the only set of treatments that the mentally ill ever receive [in capitalist societies] is: "Lock them up, tie them down, suppress them, give them electroshock therapy and drug them up to the gills."[317]

Our own approach, by contrast, is: "Examine the symptoms, find the causes, and treat the illness at its source." [In practice this means:] combining Chinese and Western medicine; persisting in using Mao Zedong Thought to re-educate and reform the mentally ill and also arming their minds with the weapon of Mao Zedong Thought; fully mobilizing within them the positive role of subjective dynamism;[318] emphasizing, in clinical practice, the correct handling of the relationship between internal and external causal factors, while carefully analyzing and actively removing the external ones; making a diligent analysis of both the general and the specific character of the problem (i.e. its universality and particularity) and then focusing upon the primary contradiction, using the method of "opening a lock with the appropriate key"; using class education and political-line education to profoundly re-educate the mentally ill in the proletarian worldview, and thereby implant within them a correct conception of human destiny, romantic love, and personal pleasure and hardship; hooking them up with reality by educating them about both the current [political] situation and the principles of dialectical materialism, and by raising their awareness of the class struggle, the struggle over political line, and the necessity of continuing the revolution under the dictatorship of the proletariat; digging out the roots of mental illness by overthrowing the concept of private ownership and establishing the principle of public ownership, waging a stubborn battle against disease by engendering the lofty and far-sighted ideals of Communism and convincing [the patients] of the inevitability of victory; while at the same time, on this overall basis, applying a supplementary combination of Chinese herbal medication, new acupuncture therapy, an appropriate amount of sedatives and tranquilizers, thereby correcting the imbalances in the functioning of the brain; and finally, under certain specific conditions, organizing the mental patients to take part in recreational visits, manual labor, and sporting and cultural activities. If we do all these things well, then the overwhelming majority (90 percent) of mentally ill people can be completely cured.

In order to consolidate the curative effect and to forestall any recurrence of illness, we must also pay close attention to the need for the patients work units, families and neighbors to persist in sincerely and actively giving them ideological reassurance that they will not be discriminated against or abused and

---

[317] It is unclear why this passage appears in quotation marks in the original text; it is probably a quotation from some ultraleftist Chinese "authority" on psychiatry.

[318] See Note 287, above.

ill-treated, as a means of combating erroneous past attitudes toward the mentally ill. In particular, we must help mentally ill people to acquire both a firm understanding of the patterns of origin of their illness and also the methodology of spontaneously trying to resolve their own inner contradictions. It should be stressed that the process of reforming and raising one's ideological level is a never-ending one; as soon as old contradictions are resolved, new ones will keep on emerging. Therefore the recurrence [of mental illness] and the attempt to avoid such relapses is absolute. But as the socialist revolution deepens over time, and as the new-style medical science of combining Chinese and Western medicine unfolds and develops, not only will a broad new vista emerge on the mental illness preventative front in China, but also the non-organic mental illnesses will become more and more rare and will eventually disappear altogether.

DOCUMENT 7: **Subjective Conjecture is No Substitute for Scientific Research**[319]

(A Summary of Readers' Views)

Yang Desen, August 1978

(*Editor's note*: Since issue No.3, 1976, this journal has given space to an academic debate on the question of the essential character and nature of mental illness. This debate has attracted the widespread support and attention of our readership and many people have sent us manuscripts expressing their viewpoints. All this became possible only after the smashing of the "Gang of Four" by our brilliant leader, Chairman Hua Guofeng, and the Party Central Committee and as a result of their promotion of the policy of "letting a hundred flowers bloom and a hundred schools of thought contend."

In the course of the development of psychiatry, there have been numerous controversies over the issue of the essential nature of mental illness. This is one of the fundamental questions in psychiatry. Up to the present day, however, owing to the limitations of scientific development and research methodology, a definitive resolution of this issue has still not been reached. In fundamental terms, we have not yet identified the factors causing specific mental illnesses. A thorough exposition of the essential nature of mental illness would affect not only the kinds of attitude we adopt toward mental illness and the mentally ill, and the ways in which we deal with them, but also the orientation of our overall research work in the field of psychiatry, and would thus be beneficial to the development of our preventative work in the mental health field.

The following is a summary digest of eleven articles we have received expressing similar viewpoints on this question. For reasons of space, among other things, we shall now impose a temporary moratorium on further discussion of the topic. This journal intends to reopen the discussion at a suitable future date. In our view, where academic questions are concerned, provided the "hundred schools of thought" policy is respected and people adhere to facts and rational argument, the full and untrammeled expression of different opinions is the only effective way of enlivening the academic atmosphere and advancing the cause of science.)

---

[319] *Xin Yixue– Shenjing Xitong Jibing Fukan* (New Medicine – Supplementary Series on Diseases of the Nervous System), vol. 4, no. 5-6 (1978) (cover date August 20, 1978), pp.329-332.

The article by Comrade Yang Desen in Issue No.3, 1976 of this journal and the article by Comrade Jia Rubao in Issue No.2, 1977 presented fundamentally opposite views on the question of the essential nature of mental illness.[320] Both these viewpoints are quite influential both within domestic social opinion as a whole and among medical personnel in the psychiatric field. The debate has attracted strong interest and support from everyone and has been closely followed, understandably enough, by many mentally ill people and their families. We have received eleven separate articles supporting Yang's position, and since for reasons of space we cannot publish these articles in their entirety, we have instead put together a summary digest of the main points and arguments.

1. First of all, we must define more narrowly the real scope of this debate; otherwise the controversy will remain diffuse and unfocused. [Manuscripts 1 & 2.]
Apart from the neuroses and mental retardation, mental illnesses generally fall into one of three main categories, and opinions were basically unanimous on the first two of these categories, with controversy being focused mainly on the last category. First, there are the organic and symptomatic mental illnesses, caused by infection, poisoning, external injury or somatic disease; opinions were unanimous and no conflict of views arose with regard to this category of illness. Second, there are the psychogenic and reactive psychoses, which appear in susceptible individuals as a result of intense psychological pressures and stimuli; cases of this type are few in number, with such reactions being much more commonly found among neurosis sufferers, and again opinions were pretty much united in regard to this category. And third, there is the major category known as the endogenous mental illnesses, foremost among which is schizophrenia, whose causal factors still remain to be discovered; the controversy was centered primarily on this category of mental illness.
On the one hand, while some outstanding research discoveries have been made in the fields of psycho-biochemistry, genetics, neuropathology, psychopharmacology and experimental psychiatry, these have still not produced any affirmative conclusions on the question in hand. On the other hand, only in certain specific cases [of schizophrenia] can we observe, prior to the onset of illness, the presence of any clear and conspicuous elements of psychological pressure or stimulus. Thus far, [schizophrenia] has always been known as a

---

[320] See Documents 5 and 6, above.

"functional" psychosis; some scholars, however, both at home and abroad, now regard it as being similar in nature to idiopathic epilepsy, that is to say, they see it as being an organic brain disorder caused by certain as yet unknown genetic defects or metabolic disorders. The controversy over the nature of the factors causing schizophrenia has therefore centered upon two main issues: first, the question of how to assess the role played by psychological pressure or stimuli in the genesis of the disease; and second, the question of the connection between the formation of mental illness and the nature of the sufferer's worldview and methodology.

2. Mental illness is a common disease that afflicts the ordinary working populace; it has always existed and can be found both in China and all other countries. Just as in the case of high blood pressure-induced ulcers or other disorders, mental illness knows no class boundaries or divisions. [Manuscripts 3 & 4.]
Comrade Jia maintains that in capitalist societies "there are certainly more" mentally ill people from within the bourgeois classes than from elsewhere in society. Some people questioned whether any actual survey data exists to support this view, while others maintained that the exact opposite is true: that since there is usually a direct link between poverty and illness, it is by no means clear that the working people of capitalist societies – given the oppression and exploitation they are under, the psychological distress and practical difficulties they experience in daily life, and also their lack of access to medical treatment – are at all less likely than others to be afflicted by mental illness. According to surveys by certain foreign scholars, the incidence of mental illness (including mental retardation) among the population has been found to be inversely proportional to family income and standard of living, that is, it occurs more frequently among the impoverished social classes, and it would be wrong for us to discount these findings as having no basis in fact. Seen in this light, mental illness is somewhat like tuberculosis, in that, whether in the old society or the new, it strikes disproportionately against the working population.
We cannot, therefore, in disregard of the plight of large numbers of working people who suffer from mental illness and in the absence of any compelling scientific evidence, simply claim that mental illness is a disease of the bourgeoisie, a disease of capitalist society. In our own view, within the field of health and hygiene, the superiority of the socialist system lies mainly in the fact that socialism seeks, by universally expanding disease prevention work and the social welfare system, to reduce the incidence of diseases of all kinds among the working population and to wipe out the serious infectious illnesses. In the case, however, of certain illnesses whose causes are still unknown – for example

cancer, cardiovascular disease and schizophrenia – thus far, and irrespective of
national boundaries, the disease incidence rates have shown no sign of
declining; to the contrary, as mortality rates fall, they have been steadily rising.
The objective existence of schizophrenia, therefore, cannot be explained away as
being the product of any particular social system; indeed, there is a much more
conspicuous causal connection to be seen between certain organic mental
illnesses, such as those induced by syphilis, alcoholism and narcotic addiction,
and the particular nature of the social system. Under the superior kind of social
system that we live in today, what we ought to be doing is widely to publicize a
correct understanding of the essential nature of mental illness and diligently to
pursue the tasks of disease prevention and cure. What we should not do is either
to commit the error of thinking that by acknowledging the objective existence of
mental illness in our society we will somehow be harming China's reputation, or
to prematurely set ourselves the goal and task of eliminating all mental illness,
in the belief that it is somehow incompatible with our [superior] social system.
Neither of these approaches is at all conducive to a fact-based resolution of the
problems.

*3. We cannot accept that bourgeois worldview and methodology is the main and
fundamental factor causing mental illness. [Manuscripts 1-11.]*
      The contributors were unanimous in rejecting Comrade Jia's contention that
"A bourgeois worldview and methodology are the fundamental causal factors in
the emergence of mental illness; indeed this is the essential nature of mental
illness." They opposed this viewpoint from a range of angles and on various
different grounds, which may be summarized broadly as follows:

> a. The character of a mentally ill person, prior to the onset of illness,
> may display certain weaknesses or defects, such as having a shy and
> solitary disposition or being narrow-minded and intolerant, but these
> are not necessarily all attributable to the "vanity and arrogance" and
> "putting self first-ism" (*geren diyizhuyi*) found in the bourgeois
> worldview. A person's character or disposition cannot be equated with
> his or her worldview, for within a given social class, one comes across
> many people who share the same worldview but whose characters are
> quite different. There are only two basic worldviews, the proletarian
> and the bourgeois, but individual character comes in endless shapes and
> sizes: for example, the brave or timid types, the frugal or spendthrift
> types, the profound or superficial types, and the well-adjusted or over-
> solitary types. Furthermore, given that all of us need to reform our

worldviews and that no one is in a position to say they have finally succeeded in this task, the claim that mental illness is the consequence of a failure to properly reform one's worldview could plausibly be applied to everyone who has ever been afflicted by any kind of mental illness, and is therefore devoid of any specific meaning or significance. Trying to understand and explain the particularity of a given contradiction by considering only its universal aspect, as, for example, in the attempts of some people to explain the mental activity of the brain by reference to the contradictory motion of atoms, is at once the most economical of approaches and also the one least likely to produce a solution to specific problems.

We often say that one important reason why people make mistakes is that they have not done a good enough job of reforming their worldview, so if we now also identify this problem as being the reason why people become mentally ill, it becomes all too easy to start equating becoming mentally ill with making mistakes, and to start seeing mental illness itself as constituting an "ideological defect" (*sixiang maobing*); at the very least, the distinction between these things becomes blurred and vague. None of this tallies with what we actually observe in the course of clinical psychiatric practice. To stick the accusatory labels of "putting self first-ism" and "improperly reformed worldview" onto large numbers of mentally ill workers, peasants and soldiers is neither fair nor just. People with widely divergent worldviews and all different levels of political consciousness fall victim to schizophrenia. In our clinics and sick wards, we come across numerous workers, peasants and soldiers, and also many cadres and intellectuals, who suffer from this disease, among them Party officials, model workers and other advanced individuals of various kinds, and both during their illnesses and afterwards, they all show warm love and affection for the Party, an enthusiasm for laboring on behalf of socialism, the qualities of loyalty and reliability, and a willingness to help others; while at the same time, we come across some patients whose minds are filled with selfish ideas of all kinds and in whom individualism is running relatively unchecked. Both situations exist side by side, and we must not take a one-sided view of things or seek to characterize the whole on the basis of a part, far less try to draw any blithe theoretical generalizations.

b. During the initial onset of illness and also prior to any relapses, many schizophrenia sufferers show no conspicuous signs of being under adverse psychological pressure or stimuli, or of having been caught up in any obvious clash or conflict of personal interest; the attribution by others, after the onset of illness, of so-called psychogenic factors in their cases is often quite forced and arbitrary. Even going by Comrade Jia's own statistics, we see that not all of his cases showed psychogenic causal factors; and even if those that didn't amounted to only a few percent of the total, how then can he explain either the reasons for these people becoming mentally ill or the essential nature of their mental illnesses? In children, schizophrenia can emerge before the age of ten, and at this early age, strictly speaking, they cannot yet be said to have formed any particular worldview. Simple schizophrenia can also strike suddenly and without warning in childhood or early youth and then progress slowly thereafter. Countless numbers of chronic schizophrenics are left disabled for many years by the disease, unable to take care of themselves and more or less completely isolated from the outside world, but no pre-existent adverse psychological pressures or stimuli can be found in their cases. And in those cases where psychogenic factors were identified at the onset of illness, such factors have mostly long since disappeared from the scene. In all such cases, the chronic course of the illness is remarkably similar to that of the organic diseases, and it is very hard to explain such an outcome by reference either to psychogenic factors or to the nature of the sufferer's worldview.

c. In many cases of schizophrenia, prior to the sufferers being hospitalized and with a view to resolving any ideological contradictions or unfulfilled desires that may be present in their minds, the work units, colleagues, families and friends of those afflicted have often made extensive efforts to educate, persuade, comfort and reassure them, and also to improve their living environments, but the effect and outcome of all this work is generally quite minimal; the illness continues to develop as before, and eventually those afflicted have to be sent to mental hospitals for treatment. Once in hospital, they can get relief from their symptoms only if given drug therapy; or if that too fails, they will be discharged as incurable. In all countries around the world, large numbers of schizophrenia sufferers improve as a result of drug therapy alone, and after recovery their individual worldviews remain, as one would only expect, entirely the same as before. Truth knows no boundaries and is equally valid everywhere, so a correct theory of medical treatment must be equally applicable to patients overseas and those living in China. While not denying the importance and significance of ideological re-education and psychotherapy (*jingshen zhiliao*),[321] we do not believe that bourgeois worldview and methodology is the universal and fundamental causal factor leading to onset of the endogenous mental illnesses.

4. The case findings from numerous other medical surveys conducted in China [Manuscripts 1, 2, 3 & 9] do not support the "overwhelming majority" conclusions derived by Comrade Jia from his survey.

In his article, Comrade Jia says that his survey of several hundred cases of mental illness established that there were "three overwhelming majorities," namely, that in an overwhelming majority (94 percent) of the cases he studied, the cause of illness was adverse psychological pressure or stimuli; that in an overwhelming majority of cases (92 percent), the sufferers had "failed to reform their worldviews properly and used incorrect ideology in dealing with contradictions"; and that the overwhelming majority of mentally ill people (90 percent) can be completely cured. And Comrade Jia also states: "The pathological thoughts are simply a continuation of the normal thoughts that existed prior to the onset of illness." Our various contributors put forward the following set of dissenting opinions on these points:

a. Comrade Jia overestimates the role played by psychological pressures and stimuli prior to the onset of illness, and also the extent to which these factors actually exist. Without contradictions there would be no world, and inasmuch as mental contradictions are a reaction to the contradictory existence of objective matter, we can all be said to have mental contradictions. These naturally exist also before people fall mentally ill, but a large proportion of them do not directly cause the illness, and indeed may have no causal connection with the illness whatsoever. But Comrade Jia's survey stresses the key role played by psychogenic causal factors, so whenever such factors appear, he

---

[321] Somewhat confusingly, given the generally positive image of psychotherapy in the West, in China "*jingshen zhiliao*" was introduced by the Maoist ultraleftists in the mid-1960s and was essentially a process whereby the mentally ill were subjected to compulsory political and ideological re-education. To' some extent, the term "psychotherapy" retains these negative connotations in China even today. (See also the final paragraph of Document 1, above.)

adamantly and confidently ascribes to them the decisive role in the illness's overall genesis.

b. Under the special circumstances [of China's recent past], "when evildoers are in power, the good people suffer"; but even when those evildoers' worldviews were of the most extremely reactionary kind, they themselves did not become mentally ill. Many good people, on the other hand, were attacked, persecuted, killed or driven insane by them. By what kind of bizarre logic are we now supposed to ask those who became mentally ill as a result of all this to start "re-examining their worldviews" in an effort to find the "causes" of their illnesses, not to mention the absurdity of attributing their mental problems to "putting self first-ism"? The pathological factors leading to mental illness include, among other things, being so grief-struck at the death of a family member through accident or natural disaster that one falls seriously ill. Are we supposed also to lump this kind of mental illness under the heading of "improperly reformed worldview"? Just what kind of a theory is this?

c. The results obtained to date in the treatment of schizophrenia, both at home and abroad, are very far from satisfactory. In the case of those with acute or short-term illnesses, the rate of recovery or near-recovery is no more than around 70 percent; and in the case of chronic sufferers whose illnesses have been going on for a long time it is less than 20 percent. Claims that the overwhelming majority of sufferers can be cured of the illness are generally based on loose and inaccurate diagnostic criteria (for example, including hysteria sufferers in the sample group) or on excessively broad criteria for identifying recovery (for example, the inclusion of sufferers who have improved to the extent merely of having their excitement states brought under control), and they simply ignore any residual negative symptoms or impairments of self-awareness that may exist; and usually, no follow-up examinations of the patients have been carried out either.

d. Among mental patients we find those who, because of delusions of jealousy, kill their own wives and children; those whose delusions of self-guilt drive them either to refuse all food or to eat their own excrement; people who, because of their shallowness of emotion, stand muttering and laughing in front of their dead mother's body; others whose conflictual auditory hallucinations drive them to curse and swear into the empty air; and still others who – in Comrade Jia's own words – "sing, dance and run around aimlessly, tearing off their clothes and going around naked, and sometimes injuring or killing people." In none of these cases, however, would it be plausible to assert, "The pathological thoughts are simply a continuation of the normal thoughts that existed prior to the onset of illness." It is unimaginable that all such abnormal and pathological thoughts, statements and actions as those just mentioned were prefigured by, or existed in, the normal thinking of those concerned prior to the onset of their illnesses, or that there was any kind of systematic connection between their eventual pathological behavior and their initially normal mentality.

5. Marxism-Leninism and Mao Zedong Thought can only be a guide to psychiatric research; it cannot be a substitute for it.

a. To regard mental illness as being an ideological defect, and hence to substitute ideological reeducation work based on Marxism-Leninism and Mao Zedong Thought in place of pharmaceutical drug therapy; to substitute the philosophical concepts of internal and external causality in place of the medical theory whereby specific internal and external causal factors are sought within the various mechanisms leading to each different disease; to regard psychiatry itself as being a social science rather than a branch of medical science; and to repudiate the biological basis of mental illness, and hence deny the validity of natural-scientific research in this field – none of these approaches accords, in any way at all, with the principles of Marxism-Leninism and Mao Zedong Thought.

b. Comrade Jia writes,

> In addition, there is the school of experimental research that studies mental phenomena in isolation from their social context, repudiates the class nature of mental activity, denies the counteractive force of mind upon matter (the brain)…and carries out certain anatomical, physiological and biochemical work that is independent of human society. This is all a reflection, within the field of psychiatric research, of the one-sided and mechanistic doctrine of mechanical

materialism, and it bears no relation at all to objective
reality.[322]

Comrade Jia correctly emphasizes here the social nature and class
nature of mental phenomena; the latter cannot be "reduced" simply to
physiological or biochemical phenomena. But two further points need
to be made in this connection. First, the "counteractive force of mind
upon matter" means, in philosophical terms, that mental or spiritual
factors can become transformed, in the course of practice, into physical
or material factors; in other words, it signifies the real counteraction of
the spiritual world upon the material world. It does not, however, mean
"the counteractive force of mind upon matter (the brain)"; mental
activity is a function of the brain itself, and therefore can exist neither
in isolation from the brain nor in opposition to it. Second, mental
illness is the consequence of pathological changes occurring in the
physical matter that makes up the brain, so it is vital that dissections,
physiological and biochemical studies and other forms of scientific
research be carried out on the brain; there is simply no substitute for
this. Provided the research findings are properly construed and
understood, there is no grounds for dismissing such work as
"mechanical materialism."

c. In Comrade Jia's view: "The process of reforming and raising one's
ideological level is a never-ending one; as soon as old contradictions
are resolved, new ones will keep on emerging. Therefore the recurrence
[of mental illness] and the attempt to avoid such relapses is absolute."
But he then goes on to say, "the non-organic mental illnesses will
become more and more rare [as socialism advances] and will
eventually disappear altogether." As several contributors to the
discussion pointed out, these two statements are self-contradictory:
according to the former, the task of reforming and raising one's
ideological level (i.e. the struggle between contradictions) is eternal;
while in the latter, it is predicted that the non-organic psychoses will
eventually become extinct (i.e. the struggle between contradictions will
cease, or at least will never again flare up or intensify.)

---

[322] For an explanation of the term "mechanical materialism," see Note 313, above.

d.   According to Comrade Jia's understanding, every recurrence (relapse) of a mental illness is due to the emergence of a new contradiction, and each time a recurrence of illness is cured, it is because the contradiction has been resolved. The question of the recurrence and remission of mental illness becomes, therefore, one of a struggle between contradictions in the realm of ideology, or rather a reflection of the ongoing struggle between the two major worldviews. This kind of attempt to use philosophical concepts to explain the natural course of illnesses, such as the remission and recurrence of schizophrenia and mania, is hardly very plausible or convincing. Even in the case of episodic hysteria, there will not necessarily be any psychogenic factors in evidence; somatic illness, pain in the internal organs, or just excessive work can also spark off the condition.

Compiler's Postscript
The question of the correct understanding of the essential nature of mental illness is something that has direct relevance both for the treatment of millions of mentally ill people and also for the future development of our profession, and the present debate has been an important struggle between truth and fallacy in this arena. Moreover, this is a debate that has been going on since ancient times, and it continues to this day all over the world. In the past, when mental illness was believed to be the result of possession by ghosts or spirits, people used to scorch the flesh of the mentally ill with burning sulfur in an attempt to purge them of evil, or would lash them with peach branches until their bodies were a mass of bleeding wounds. Subsequently, when mental illness was believed to result from unfulfilled erotic urges, the mentally ill would be tricked or forced into sudden arranged marriages, thereby making their lives even more unmanageable, with children left destitute and uncared for, and creating an even greater burden for society. Our ignorance about the essential nature of mental illness has resulted in endless forms of random and harmful treatment being applied, including starvation, bloodletting, anacarthsis [forced vomiting] and the use of drastic abdominal purgatives, with the sufferers often being left on the verge of death. At other times, techniques of fear and intimidation were employed, for example, firing guns in the air, submerging the sufferers in water, or spinning them around in mid-air until they were almost unconscious from shock. And then along came other treatments, such as artificially raising the patient's body temperature, applying electric shocks to their brains and surgically removing parts of the frontal lobe. In short, the impotence of science has exacerbated the sufferings of the mentally ill in manifold ways.

After the founding of New China, the Party and the People's Government made great efforts to improve the health of the population and actively pursued all kinds of disease prevention work, especially in regard to tuberculosis, leprosy and mental illness. Large numbers of hospitals, convalescent homes and reception centers were set up, many new medical staff and specialists were educated and trained, and numerous medical journals and publications were established. In universities and colleges, courses in psychiatric medicine were set up and, guided by Chairman Mao's revolutionary line in healthcare, enormous progress was made in this field, as in other branches of medical science in China.

After Lin Biao and, especially, the Gang of Four started to peddle their reactionary political line – a line that was "left" in form but right in essence – the country was plunged into deep disaster. Every aspect of official life in China suffered the noxious consequences of their doctrines, and the damage wrought in the field of psychiatry was certainly no less serious and profound than elsewhere. They threw people's thinking into complete chaos, and metaphysics and idealism became rampant. As part of their nakedly careerist plan to seize political power within the Party and the government, they even, at one point, instigated mental patients to "rise up in rebellion," and those who did so were then lauded as being "madmen of the new era." They claimed that mental patients were being "persecuted" in our socialist hospitals, and they vilified the broad mass of revolutionary medical workers by accusing them of exercising "bourgeois dictatorship" over mental patients. They characterized all the currently effective, though far from ideal, forms of treatment and therapy used for mental illness in China and the rest of the world as being "instruments of torture designed to destroy patients' health." They even laid down a "class line of demarcation" in respect of the dosages of medication that could be prescribed. Old therapies would be suddenly banned, and new ones imposed, solely by administrative fiat. As a result of all this, in the worst hit mental hospitals, recovery rates and sickbed rotation rates began to decline and medical staff became so demoralized that they left psychiatry altogether.

Eventually, [the ultraleftists] claimed that the real reason people became mentally ill was that their heads were filled with an "excess of selfish ideas and personal concerns" and that mental illness was the product of "an extreme development of individualism." Simplistic techniques of ideological re-education then became the principal form of treatment and cure for mental illness in China. Mentally ill people were made to undergo re-education at the hands of the medical staff and ordered to dig out, from within their own minds, the "ideological roots" of their illnesses. In some mental hospitals, patients who uttered banned thoughts or engaged in banned forms of behavior because of their illnesses were held criminally responsible, and even their families were wrongfully implicated. This conception of mental illness as being an ideological sickness and a disease of the bourgeoisie, the belief that it is a product of the capitalist social system, holds in lofty disdain the sufferings of countless numbers of working-class mentally ill people and has served to consign psychiatry to the distant margins of public health work in our country. Is it not now incumbent upon us, therefore, to expose and criticize to the fullest extent possible all these absurd theories and pernicious policies of the Gang of Four, these perversions of medicine that have inflicted such harm and damage upon the mentally ill and upon the great majority of those working in our profession?

As Chairman Mao taught us,

> Idealism and metaphysics are the easiest things in the world, because people can talk as much nonsense as they like without basing it on objective reality or having it tested against reality. Materialism and dialectics, on the other hand, need effort. They must be based on and tested by objective reality. Unless one makes the effort, one is liable to slip into idealism and metaphysics.[323]

No matter what the circumstances, we must always have the courage to uphold the truth, rectify our mistakes, seek truth from facts and study with humility. Only thus will we be able to contribute to the cause of socialist reconstruction by realizing the Four Modernizations, including the modernization of science and of psychiatric medicine.

Index of manuscripts cited above:

1. Zhu Xixi, "My Views on the Question of the Essential Nature of Mental Illness."
2. Yu Zhanfei, "Some Rough Opinions on the Causes and Treatment of Mental Illness."
3. Liu Hengwen, "A Discussion of the Causal Factors Leading to Mental Illness."

---

[323] Introductory note to "Material on the Hu Feng Counterrevolutionary Clique" (May 1955); translation taken from *Quotations from Chairman Mao Tse-tung*, (Peking: Peking Foreign Languages Press, 1966).

4. Long Yaxian, "Reflections Upon Reading [Jia Rubao's] 'More on the Essential Nature of Mental Illness'."
5. Sun Ru, "Taking Issue with Comrade Jia Rubao on the Question of the Essential Nature of Mental Illness."
6. He Xingqing, "Subjective Conjecture is No Substitute for Scientific Research."
7. Zhang Jiejie, "Mental Illness is Not an 'Ideological defect'."
8. Ding Qinzhang, "Do 'Ideological Problems' Play the Leading Role in the Causation of Mental Illness?"
9. Cao Songyao, "Marxist Philosophy Provides a Compass for Understanding the Essential Nature of Mental Illness."
10. Yan Shengmei, "The Study of Dialectics is the Guide to Medical Practice."
11. Lu Lizhao, "Taking Issue with Comrade Jia Rubao."

(Compiled by Yang Desen)

Wang Wanxing, a dissident held at the Beijing Ankang institute since June 1992 for unfurling a pro-democracy banner in Tiananmen Square. For more details on Wang's case, see page 36.

**DOCUMENT 8: Summary and Analysis of Papers Submitted to the
First National Academic Conference on Forensic Psychiatry**

Jia Yicheng
Psychiatric Teaching and Research Group of the
Shanghai Railways Medical College[324]

September 1987

From June 16 to 20, 1987, the First National Academic Conference on Forensic Psychiatry took place in the city of Hangzhou, and more than 100 scholarly articles were submitted to the conference from all over China. The following is a preliminary summary and analysis of these various articles, presented here for reference and information purposes.[325]

The papers can be grouped according to theme and content under the following main headings:

1) The organizational and institutional framework of forensic-psychiatric appraisals work, the appraisals procedure, and the qualifications and accreditation of appraisers (altogether three articles.)
2) Theoretical studies on the capacity for legal responsibility of mentally ill persons (15 articles.
3) Comprehensive analyses of specific cases of forensic psychiatric appraisal (12 articles.)
4) Empirical summaries of the forensic psychiatric appraisal of each main type of psychiatric illness (34 articles.)
5) Analyses of the various categories of dangerous behavior displayed (11 articles.)
6) Other headings, including: the psychological testing of mentally ill people who create disastrous incidents (3 articles); the question of suicide (3 articles); an investigation into the use of narcotics as a means

---

[324] Jia Yicheng, *Shanghai Archives of Psychiatry* (*Shanghai Jingshen Yixue*), no.3 (1987) p.118.

[325] The author notes elsewhere that the following analysis was based on fifty-seven of the articles presented at the 1987 conference.

of questioning suspects (1 article);[326] several articles on other related topics; and three articles concerning the draft legislation on forensic psychiatric appraisals (i.e. the fifth draft of the *PRC Law on Mental Health*, the discussion draft of the *Regulations on the Work of the Forensic Psychiatric Appraisal of Mental Illnesses*, and the discussion draft of the *Zhejiang Provincial Regulations on the Work of Forensic Psychiatric Appraisals*).

I.

Among the twelve articles that provided comprehensive analyses of forensic psychiatric appraisal cases, two gave no recommendatory opinions on [the examinees'] capacity for criminal responsibility, and another contained no indication of the types of mental illness involved. Despite the incomplete nature of the information supplied in some of the articles, however, taken as a whole they provide a useful overview of the current general state of forensic psychiatric appraisals work in China.

1) Altogether, the twelve articles discussed a total of 7,699 criminal cases, in which the main varieties of dangerous behavior displayed were as follows:

   a. 1,772 cases of murder (23.03 percent) and 392 cases of injury (5.09 percent). One article dealt with these categories under the composite heading of "murder and injury", resulting in a combined figure of 2,288 cases (or 29.72 percent).

   b. 590 cases of rape (7.67 percent). In one article, the three categories of murder, rape and injury were dealt with under the composite heading of "violations of the person"; [the number of rapes] was given as 308, resulting in a total figure of 3,186 (or 41.38 percent).

   c. 340 cases involving other sex offenses and acts of hooliganism (4.42 percent).

   d. 770 cases of crimes against public or private property, including theft, fraud, looting and corruption (10 percent).

   e. 1,621 cases of reactionary or counterrevolutionary behavior (21.05 percent).

---

[326] The Chinese term used is *mazui fenxi* (drug analysis): this refers to the police practice of drugging criminal suspects before questioning and interrogation, as a means of lowering their level of self-vigilance and inhibition and making them freely "confess." (See also Note 88, above.)

f.   326 cases of disturbing social order (4.23 percent).
g.   187 cases of arson and sabotage (2.43 percent).
h.   371 cases involving various other types of dangerous behavior (4.81 percent).
i.   898 cases involving the sexual molestation or violation of mentally ill women (11.66 percent).

2) According to the statistical data supplied, the total number of forensic psychiatric appraisals covered in these studies amounted to 7,862. (Besides the criminal cases, a number of civil cases and other types were also included.) Among these, altogether 6,880 of those examined were diagnosed as suffering from mental illness (87.51 percent). Of the remaining 982 cases (or 12.49 percent), 932 persons were diagnosed as having no mental illness (11.85 percent), and 45 were determined to be malingerers [i.e. as having feigned mental illness] (0.57 percent).

Regarding the 6,880 persons diagnosed as suffering from mental illness:

a. Schizophrenia was the principal diagnosis, accounting for altogether 3,488 cases (or 44.37 percent of all those appraised);
b. there were 1,570 cases of mental retardation (19.97 percent); and
c. 287 cases of neurosis, mainly hysteria (3.65 percent);
d. 282 cases of epilepsy (3.59 percent);
e. 185 cases of reactive psychosis (2.35 percent);
f.   160 cases of personality disorder (2.04 percent);
g. 125 cases of affective illness (1.59 percent);
h. 89 cases of organic psychotic disorder;
i.   79 cases of paranoid psychosis;
j.   52 cases of sexual perversion;
k. 30 cases of prison psychosis;
l.   27 cases of alcoholic poisoning;
m. 7 cases of grafted psychosis
n. 499 cases of other mental disorders (6.35 percent).

3) In the above-mentioned 10 articles,[327] opinions on the question of [the examinees'] capacity for criminal responsibility were provided in altogether 3,505 cases: findings of total absence of legal responsibility were made in 1,365 cases (38.94 percent); findings of partial or limited legal responsibility were made in 972 cases (27.73 percent); and findings of full legal responsibility were made in 1,168 cases (33.33 percent).

4) Issues requiring further comment:

a. As can be seen from the statistical data provided in the 12 articles, altogether 1,621 (or 21.05 percent) of the 7,699 criminal cases under examination involved reactionary or counterrevolutionary speech or action (*fandong huo fan'geming yan-xing*), placing this category in a high second position on the overall statistical list of dangerous behaviors. However, when viewed from a periodic perspective, a very clear distinction emerges. Six of the articles contained statistical data on appraisals carried out during the post-Cultural Revolution period of 1981-86, and among the 2,019 criminal defendants who were appraised during this period, only 59 (or 3.12 percent) had engaged in counterrevolutionary speech or action. The other six articles contained statistical data from the period beginning in the 1950s and ending in 1976, and among the 5,680 criminal defendants appraised during this period, the relevant figure was 1,562 persons, or as much as 27.5 percent. This was clearly a product of the Cultural Revolution period and of the ultraleftist ideological trend that preceded it.

b. Altogether 898 of the cases (or 11.66 percent) involved the forensic examination of mentally ill women who had been sexually abused, placing this category of offense in third most frequent position after murder/injury and counterrevolution. This category [of offense] is still rapidly on the increase at present, and given the dramatic fall in the number of forensic appraisals of counterrevolutionary speech and action that has occurred since the 1980s, it has probably now risen to second place in the frequency ranking of forensic

---

[327] This figure appears to be a misprint; it seems to refer to the twelve articles containing comprehensive analyses of actual cases, but since the matter is unclear the original figure has been left unaltered here.

psychiatric appraisals in criminal cases. This situation ought to arouse substantial concern and attention on our part.

c. As regards the distribution of mental illnesses by [diagnostic] category, several of the articles reported the incidence of schizophrenia among those forensically appraised as having been, variously, as high as 75.45 percent, 60 percent and 56.7 percent, with the lowest reported incidence of the illness being 17.8 percent; the average rate of schizophrenia derived from the overall statistics found in 11 of the articles came to 44.37 percent. It is noteworthy that in the two articles describing the situation in Beijing and Shanghai, both of which covered relatively large numbers of forensic appraisals (1,259 cases and 708 cases respectively), the incidence of schizophrenia was reported as being 26.45 percent (Beijing) and 20.76 percent (Shanghai). Very clear discrepancies can be seen, therefore, among the relevant figures provided in the various articles. Aside from the objective differences found in the individual targets of appraisal, the most important reasons for this were probably the divergent levels of rigor and precision applied in diagnosing schizophrenia, together with a tendency toward over-broad diagnosis of the condition and a lack of uniformity in the criteria used. [Case example: omitted in this translation.] Henceforth, therefore, it is vital that any diagnoses of schizophrenia made in the course of forensic psychiatric appraisals should be strictly based upon the diagnostic criteria for this condition as laid down by the Chinese Medical Association in 1984, in order to avoid the bias toward artificially amplifying the scope of schizophrenia diagnosis.

d. There were also fairly large discrepancies between the figures given in the various articles for the proportion of those found to be not suffering from mental illness; in two of the eleven articles [that addressed this issue], the figure was said to be 0 percent, which clearly did not accord with the objective reality. Could it be that these authors simply assumed that the people being appraised must all be suffering from some mental illness or other, causing them to disregard issues and factors of common criminal psychology, so that they became unconsciously enmeshed in the "pan-psychiatrism" perspective? This is a problem that merits our further attention. The lowest figure given for the diagnosis of absence of mental illness was 0 percent, the highest figures were 26.32 percent and 33.33 percent (Inner Mongolia and Shanghai, respectively), and the total average figure derived was 11.85 percent.

e. The discrepancies among the statistical proportions for those found to be feigning mental illness were also quite substantial. Seven of the articles gave a figure of 0 percent on this count, but several of the authors had placed the cases of malingering they observed under the heading of "absence of mental illness" (e.g. Beijing and Shanghai). In four other articles, the proportions given for malingering were 0.63 percent, 0.71 percent, 1.79 percent and 4.26 percent (17/399); this last figure seems to be artificially high. Altogether 45 cases of malingering were identified in the 11 articles, accounting for 0.57 percent of the total number of criminal cases forensically appraised. It is clear from this that cases of feigning mental illness are in fact very rare, and therefore that special caution must be exercised, and solid evidence adduced, before making this diagnosis.

f. As regards the appraisal of capacity for criminal responsibility, again, substantial discrepancies and variations were found to exist. The highest proportion given for those found to bear full legal responsibility [for their criminal actions] was 51.6 percent, the lowest figure given was 12.22 percent, and the average proportion derived from ten of the articles on this count was 33.32 percent. The statistic for Beijing stood at 32.1 percent, and that for Shanghai at 48.9 percent. (All these figures included persons found to be not suffering from any mental illness.) By contrast, the proportions given for those found to bear no legal responsibility for their actions ranged from a high point of 73.33 percent, to the low levels of 27.5 percent (Beijing) and 29.6 percent (Shanghai), the two latter figures being fairly close together.

As the present author has discovered: in cases where the proportion of those under appraisal who were deemed to bear no legal responsibility is high, and where also the proportion of those deemed to bear full legal responsibility is mostly low, one finds, at the same time, that the relative incidence of the diagnosis of schizophrenia has also been high. That is to say, there is a definite interconnection between these three factors. In one of the articles, for example the proportion given for those found to bear full legal responsibility was 12.22 percent (the lowest value), while those deemed to have no legal responsibility accounted for 73.33 percent (the highest value); at the same time, the proportion diagnosed as suffering from schizophrenia also stood at the high level of 56.7 percent. (This was the third highest finding on schizophrenia among all the articles; two other articles gave even higher figures on this count – 75.45 percent and 60 percent – but neither article contained any analytical data on the apportionment of legal responsibility.) For this reason, in order to avoid excessive disagreements in future among colleagues from different parts of the country over the question of how to evaluate and apportion the capacity for legal responsibility, it has now become a matter of the utmost importance that we should not only adhere strictly to the agreed criteria for the diagnosis of schizophrenia, but also that we should further proceed to formulate a set of differential criteria for deciding upon the correct levels of legal responsibility that should be assigned, in view of the divergent mental states involved, in every one of the main categories of mental illness (including schizophrenia, mental retardation, epilepsy, hysteria, psychopathic personality, sexual perversion, and alcoholism).

II.

Thirty-four of the articles dealt with the forensic appraisal of each different type of mental illness; the following is a comprehensive analysis of these articles.

1) Six articles on schizophrenia: three of the articles contained insufficient data, so we will focus here on the data reported in the three articles on Shanghai, Nanjing and Guizhou.

   The total number of appraisals where schizophrenia was identified came to 489, of which 434 were male and 55 were female. The ratio of males to females was roughly 8:1, which approximates to the male-female ratio found among normal criminal offenders.

   Clinical typology: 273 cases of paranoid schizophrenia were diagnosed (55.83 percent of the whole); 41 cases of hebephrenic schizophrenia (8.38 percent); ten cases of catatonic schizophrenia (2.04 percent); five cases of simple schizophrenia (1.02 percent); 81 cases of indeterminate or composite schizophrenia (16.56 percent); 53 cases of chronic schizophrenia (10.84 percent); 23 cases of residual or remittent schizophrenia (4.78 percent); and three cases of other schizophrenic variants (0.16 percent). The paranoid, indeterminate (or composite) and chronic types were the most common, with – most strikingly – the paranoid variant accounting for over one half of the cases.

Ranked in order of frequency, the various forms of dangerous behavior [carried out by schizophrenics] were as follows:

a. 206 cases of murder (42.13 percent) and 64 cases of injury (13.09 percent); the combined figure for both types of dangerous behavior was 270 cases (or 55.22 percent), making this the most frequent category. Among the data from Shanghai and Nanjing, 177 persons committed acts of murder and injury, killing 122 persons and injuring 83, making a total of 204 victims. Of these, 165 were known by the perpetrators and 39 were strangers. Among the known group, 82 were relatives of the perpetrators, while the remaining 83 were neighbors, friends or colleagues. Hence, it is vital that relatives and friends of mentally ill people, and especially the close relatives, should increase their levels of vigilance and avoid upsetting or provoking them in any way.

b. 38 cases of rape (7.78 percent);

c. 29 cases involving other sex offenses or acts of hooliganism (5.93 percent);

d. 49 cases of disturbing social order or disrupting traffic and production (10.02 percent);

e. 41 cases of reactionary or counterrevolutionary speech and action (8.38 percent);

f. 28 cases of theft, looting and corruption (5.73 percent);

g. 23 cases of arson and sabotage (4.70 percent);

h. seven cases involving other types of dangerous behavior (1.43 percent); and

i. four cases of sexual molestation (0.82 percent).

The two most frequent types of dangerous behavior, therefore, were murder and disturbing social order.

2) Five articles on mental retardation: these contained a total of 231 cases, of whom129 were male and 102 were female, giving a broadly equal gender ratio. The cases can be grouped under the following two headings:

a. 95 cases involved the forensic appraisal of female victims, accounting for a very high percentage of the total (95/231 = 41.13 percent). Intelligence testing and evaluation of capacity for self-defense were performed in only 40 of these cases of mentally retarded women who had been sexually abused. Minor mental retardation or lower was identified in ten of the cases, moderate retardation in 16 cases, and severe retardation or higher in 14 cases. Capacity for self-defense was evaluated in 25 cases (or 62.5 percent of the whole): 14 women were found to have partial capacity for self-defense (35 percent), and one woman was found to have full such capacity (2.5 percent).

b. 136 cases of appraisal of criminal defendants were carried out, of whom 129 were male and seven were female, giving a gender ratio of 18.4:1. Intelligence testing was performed in 97 of these cases; moderate mental retardation was identified in 20 cases, and minor mental retardation or lower was identified in 87 cases.[328] Among the 136 cases were also found eight persons who underwent psychotic episodes or were suffering from grafted psychoses.

The forms of dangerous behavior [engaged in by these mentally-retarded criminal defendants] were as follows:

    i.   42 cases of rape (30.88 percent);
    ii.   31 cases involving acts of indecency or hooliganism (22.79 percent);
    iii.   24 cases of theft and looting (17.65 percent);
    iv.   21 cases of murder (15.44 percent) and five of injury (3.68 percent);
    v.   nine cases of arson and sabotage (6.62 percent);
    vi.   five cases of reactionary speech or action (3.68 percent); and
    vii.   one case of prostitution (0.74 percent).

---

[328] Figures as given in the original text; one of the three figures appearing in this sentence seems to be a misprint.

Among the 136 defendants, capacity for legal responsibility was evaluated in 107 cases; of these, 37 persons (or 34.58 percent) were found to have no legal responsibility for their acts, 47 (or 43.92 percent) were found to bear partial or limited legal responsibility, and 23 (or 21.50 percent) were found to bear full legal responsibility.

3) Five articles on sexual perversion: these dealt with a total of 18 cases, among which there were six cases of exhibitionism; four cases of voyeurism or scopophilia; three cases of fetishism; three cases of homosexuality (two males, and one woman who committed a lesbian-related "murder of passion"); one case of polymorphous sexual perversion (involving exhibitionism, voyeurism, *frottage* and incest); and one rarely-seen case of complex necrophilia (involving necrophilic intercourse, dismemberment of the female corpse, and the removal of sex organs and other body parts and their concealment on the perpetrator's body). Partial capacity for legal responsibility was established in six of these cases (including two exhibitionism cases, two fetishism cases, one case of voyeurism and the case of polymorphous sexual perversity); full legal responsibility was established in three cases (one case of exhibitionism, one of fetishism, and also the lesbian case); and no evaluation of legal responsibility was made in the remaining nine cases.

In addition, three of the articles dealt with the question of personality disorders, but these were mainly theoretical discussions about this aspect of forensic psychiatry and did not contain specific case examples or analysis. Also, a few writers either assigned cases of homosexuality or necrophilia to the category of psychopathic personality disorder or else saw them as "borderline states," and some evaluated those with psychopathic personality disorders of the merciless (anti-social) type as having partial capacity for legal responsibility.[329] All these matters merit further investigation.

---

[329] In most national jurisdictions, personality disorders are not viewed as sufficient grounds for findings of legal non-imputability in criminal cases; the author's implication here is probably that the detainees in question should have been found fully capable of bearing legal responsibility for their offenses.

4) Four articles on cases of epilepsy: the data in one of these articles was fragmentary, but the remaining three dealt with a total of 97 cases, of whom 89 were male and eight were female, giving a gender ratio of 11:1. Based on clinical investigations of the mental states of those concerned at the time the crimes were committed, the cases can be grouped as follows:

a. 49 cases of epileptic personality disorder (50.52 percent);
b. 20 cases involving epileptic disturbances of consciousness (20.62 percent);
c. 10 cases of schizophreniform epileptic psychosis (10.31 percent);
d. four cases of epileptic psychomotor seizure (4.12 percent);
e. three cases of epileptic paroxysmal dysthymia;
f. two cases of epileptic impairment of intelligence;
g. one case of epileptic sleep-walking;
h. three cases involving other mental impairments; and
i. five cases where crimes were committed during the intermission between *grand mal* epileptic seizures.

The following varieties of dangerous behavior occurred:

a. 34 cases of murder (35.05 percent) and 23 cases of injury (23.71 percent), giving a combined figure of 57 cases (58.76 percent); the crimes committed were often extremely cruel and vicious in nature, resulting in numerous injuries and very severe consequences;
b. 22 cases of disturbing public order (22.69 percent);
c. six cases of reactionary speech and action;
d. five cases of theft and looting;
e. three cases of rape;
f. two cases of hooligan behavior; and
g, two cases of arson and sabotage.

Another article supplied opinions on the capacity for legal responsibility of 59 of the afflicted persons: six were found to bear full legal responsibility (10.35 percent); nine were found to have partial legal responsibility (13.90 percent); and 44 were found to have no legal responsibility for their actions (75.95 percent). Of the six persons who bore full legal responsibility, five committed their crimes during intermissions between *grand mal* seizures and while mentally normal;

and the other had a minor epileptic personality disorder and committed his crime while mentally normal, during a fit of intense anger brought on by a practical setback. Among the 44 persons who were found to bear no legal responsibility, 16 had epileptic personality disorders accompanied by outbursts of pathological excitement; 13 had post-*grand mal* disturbances of consciousness and one had pre-*grand mal* disturbance of consciousness; nine had schizophreniform epileptic psychosis; three had epileptic psychomotor seizures; two suffered from severe epileptic impairments of intelligence; and another suffered from epileptic sleep-walking.

5)   Four articles on cases of alcoholic poisoning: [section omitted here]

Other categories: Two other articles focused on the issues of hysterical spirit-possession, sorcery and witchcraft, and the dangers posed by superstitious activity in general. They also contained two vivid and complex case studies of this kind, which aroused great interest among all those at the conference and produced a unanimous feeling that this was a topic of practical significance that deserved further research and investigation. In addition, a writer from Tianjin reported on two cases of pathological postdormitum state; Beijing's Anding Hospital reported on a case of "social compliance syndrome"; and a writer from Jiangxi Province reported on 42 cases of labor-reform inmates who suffered from "prison psychosis disorder." All of these reports aroused considerable interest at the conference.[330]

---

[330] The final section of this article has been omitted here for reasons of space; it explored in greater detail the questions of murder, injury and sexual offenses by the mentally ill.

DOCUMENT 9: A Survey of the Current State of China's Ankang Hospitals

Tang Xiaofeng, Li Shenlu and Zhao Bencheng,[331]
Ankang Hospital of the Hangzhou Municipal Public Security Bureau

Spring 1996

Overview

Objective: an understanding of the current state of the national Ankang hospital system. Methodology: a survey carried out by draft questionnaire to ascertain the current situation in China's Public Security system-affiliated institutions for the custody and treatment of mentally ill people in the various provinces and municipalities.

Findings: At the end of 1993, China had altogether 20 Ankang hospitals (mental hospitals run by the Public Security system), comprised of 5,090 beds, 559 doctors and 991 nurses.

Key Words: Mental hospital, Public Security system.

For a long time now, the Ankang hospital system has been shrouded in mystery for most people, and there has been very little information available about its function and purposes, its size and distribution, and its current situation and inner workings. In order to give our colleagues throughout the country a more complete picture of the Ankang hospital system, in October-December 1993 we drew up a questionnaire titled "Survey of the Current State of China's Ankang Hospital System" and distributed it to all 20 Ankang hospitals in the country.

Survey Results

1. Distribution and personnel:

As of the end of 1993, there were a total of 20 Ankang hospitals nationwide, and apart from the one in Inner Mongolia, which for various reasons had not yet formally opened, all were operating normally. As can be seen from

---

[331] *Shanghai Archives of Psychiatry*, vol. (New) 8, no.1 (1996), pp.24-25.

the attached Table,[332] the regional distribution and numbers of beds of the various Ankang hospitals was very uneven, with the largest number (four) being located in Zhejiang Province, in the cities of Hangzhou, Ningbo, Jinhua and Shaoxing. The Ankang hospital network had a total capacity of 5,090 beds, the greatest density of which was in Beijing, Tianjin and Hangzhou, accounting for 47.54 percent of the whole. The Beijing and Tianjin facilities each had a capacity of 1,000 beds, but half of the remaining Ankang hospitals had no more than 100 beds. Fifteen of the hospitals, or 75 percent, were built since the start of the 1980s, all of which shows that China's Ankang enterprise is currently still at the fledgling stage of development.

Across the national Ankang network, there were 559 specialized doctors (*zhuanke yisheng*) and 991 nurses. The ration of beds to doctors was 1: 0.11, while that of beds to nurses was 1: 0.19 (the national statistical average was somewhat lower than that reported by Zhejiang Province). As regards the composition by professional and cultural ranking, there were altogether 42 senior-level physicians (7.51 percent), 183 medium-level physicians (33.45 percent) and 330 basic-level physicians (59.03 percent). One hundred and one of the doctors, or 18.7 percent, were university graduates; 139, or 24.87 percent, were college (*da-zhuan*) graduates; 286 were technical secondary school (*zhong-zhuan*) graduates; and 44, or 7.87 percent, had received an informal professional training. Of the nursing staff, 69 were senior nurses, 343 were middle-ranking nurses, and 579 were basic nurses. In all but a few of the Ankang hospitals, there were insufficient numbers of doctors and nurses, and the shortfall was especially severe at middle and senior professional levels. The cultural level of the staff was also uniformly low.

2.   State of operations:

The total number of mentally ill people being detained for treatment within the Ankang system nationwide was 4,637. According to incomplete data, altogether 1,907 of the patients (or 41.13 percent) had created disastrous incidents of various kinds within society, including 1,045 persons (or 22.54 percent) who committed murder or injury. The length of stay for patients of this kind is usually quite long, and even if they recover and become cured, many patients cannot easily be discharged and have to spend the rest of their lives within the [Ankang] system. For all kinds of reasons, specialized hospitals [of other types] around the country are unwilling either to admit or to treat patients

---

[332] For some reason, the article as published did not include the table referred to by the authors.

of this category. So again, we can see the urgent need for more Ankang hospitals to be established. The majority of those detained for treatment within the Ankang network have been involved in acts of behavior that pose a definite threat to society, and hospital staff members are thus correspondingly likely to meet with sudden or violent assaults by these patients. Incomplete figures show that during 1993, staff members were assaulted 343 times by patients, resulting in minor injuries or less to 105 of the victims. The degree of hardship experienced by Ankang staff is readily apparent and naturally deserves the support and understanding of people at all levels of society.

The most frequent type of mental illness found among Ankang patients is schizophrenia, accounting for 74.12 percent of the total. The next commonest categories are affective mental disorder, mental retardation and epilepsy. These four categories combined account for 89.51 percent of all those hospitalized.

At present, 13 of the Ankang hospitals conduct forensic [psychiatric] appraisals. Apart from a few institutions, most of these hospitals have only recently begun doing this kind of work. Some of them also invite experts and professors from outside the Ankang system to take part jointly in the forensic appraisals. So far, forensic appraisals of over 10,000 cases of all types have been carried out, and this has greatly reduced the [country's] previous difficulties in getting such appraisals done, while at the same time greatly assisting the ability of our political and law-enforcement personnel (*zheng-fa renyuan*) to deal with cases rapidly.

In addition, seven Ankang hospitals have in recent years set up detoxification wards for drug addicts and people with other pharmaceutical dependencies; more than 1,000 addicts have so far been cured in these wards. The detoxification process relies on a combination of voluntary and coercive measures, in order to guarantee smooth results. Since drug abuse has been continually increasing and spreading in certain parts of China, it is important that Ankang hospitals in all areas should collaborate with the work of the Public Security departments in banning drugs.

As regards the question of patient expenses, all Ankang hospitals currently levy rather low charges. The monthly cost per patient ranges from 200 to 800 yuan, averaging out at 447.33 yuan, which is far lower than the amount charged by other specialized hospitals. This undoubtedly benefits those patients who come from the economically backward rural areas, as well as those suffering from chronic illnesses who require lengthy hospitalization. From the long-term perspective, however, such low charges leave most Ankang hospitals in danger of being economically unviable; moreover, they exert a negative influence on the hospitals' prospects for institutional expansion, their ability to attract new talent, improve the living conditions of both the staff and the patients, and so forth.

3. Academic and research achievements:

In 1988, the journal *Research in Public Security [Psychiatric] Custody and Treatment* (*Gong'an Guan-Zhi Yanjiu*) was founded; for internal circulation only, it appears annually and so far five issues have been published. In the same year, a National Ankang Hospitals Coordinating Group was set up to provide unified coordination of scientific research work, exchange of information and data, and other tasks, throughout the Ankang network. It was also decided that a national academic exchange conference on Public Security custody and treatment work should be convened every two years. According to preliminary figures, a total of 1,024 research articles have been written and produced within the Ankang hospitals network since its founding; of these, 185 have been published in national scholarly journals, 241 in provincial-level journals, and 598 have been circulated on an internal-use-only basis. Progress in this area has still been uneven, however; the general level of the articles has left much to be desired, and a minority of Ankang hospitals is still not using quantitative evaluation tables or psychological testing procedures such as WAIS and MMPI.[333] In addition, the Ankang facilities have few academic exchanges and vocational links with other specialized hospitals, and only seven of them periodically invite outside experts to come in and carry out ward inspections, deliver lectures and perform forensic appraisals. Fourteen Ankang hospitals have sporadically taken part in some of the academic activities of the local specialized hospitals, but it is clear that increasing the level of exchanges of this type and promoting further vocational contacts with the specialized hospital network is vital if the Ankang hospitals are to raise their standards of medical treatment.

Discussion
The target groups for custody and treatment in the Ankang hospital network, which was uniformly designated as such by the Ministry of Public Security in 1988, have been clearly stipulated to be those mentally ill persons who: 1) commit acts of murder, arson, rape and explosions; 2) seriously disrupt the work either of Party, government or army offices, or of commercial and service enterprises; 3) seriously disturb public order, disrupt traffic, or endanger

---

[333] MMPI: the Minnesota Multiphasic Personality Inventory test; WAIS: the Wechsler Adult Intelligence Scale.

public safety; 4) make an exhibition of themselves in public and threaten public morals; or 5) adversely affect social stability, where serious consequences ensue.[334] As these regulations by the Ministry of Public Security show, Ankang hospitals are not just purely managerial institutions, but rather are meant to be specialized hospitals that serve the goals of public order by taking in and treating mentally ill people who create disastrous incidents of various kinds. As the Ministry of Public Security calculated in 1993, there are approximately 12 million severely mentally ill people in China, more than 1.3 million of whom pose a serious danger to public order; it is therefore essential that every province in China should establish its own Ankang hospital. At present, the distribution of Ankang facilities around China is very uneven, and the great majority of provinces in the southern and north-western parts of the country have as yet not set up any such facilities. The locations of those that do exist are far from ideal, with more than half being currently situated far away from the urban districts and having poor transport links; this greatly hinders the proper treatment of the patients and engenders many practical living difficulties for the staff. Both historical factors and current resource limitations mean that the majority of Ankang hospitals suffer, to varying degrees, from an insufficiency of doctors and nurses, a severe shortfall in the numbers of highly skilled staff, a generally low quality of specialized expertise, not enough contact and exchange with outside professionals, and a dearth of research capacity and resources. All these problems urgently need attention and solutions.

---

[334] According to the *China Encyclopedia of Public Security* (1990), the complete list of official police targets for Ankang psychiatric custody also includes the following category of "mentally ill offenders": "Persons who shout reactionary slogans, or who stick up or distribute reactionary banners and leaflets, thereby exerting an undesirable political influence." (See above Notes 187-188 and accompanying text.)

DOCUMENT 10: An Analysis of Forty-One Mentally Ill People Involved in Cases of a Political Nature

Luo Jiming, Li Shenlu and Tang Xiaofeng,
Hangzhou Ankang Municipal Hospital[335]

December 1996

Instances whereby mental illness sufferers, owing to the severe weakening or outright loss of their powers of recognition and control, become involved in [criminal] cases of a political nature are by no means rare. After committing these crimes, once ascertained in the course of forensic-psychiatric evaluation as being not legally responsible for their actions, the majority of such people are committed to Ankang hospitals. During the period 1978-89, the Hangzhou Ankang hospital admitted 41 patients of this kind, accounting for 7.8 percent of all admissions. The largest numbers were admitted in 1978 and 1989, when they accounted for 17.1 percent and 14.6 percent of total admissions respectively – markedly higher than in other years (P<0.01). Our findings on these cases were as follows:

Analysis of data: Of the 41 cases, 30 were male (73.2 percent) and 11 were female (26.8 percent). Their ages ranged from 21 to 65 years, averaging 41.3 years (± 8.6). Fourteen were married (34.1 percent), 17 were single (41.5 percent) and 10 were divorced (24.4 percent). Educational status: 18 were educated to lower-middle school level (43.9 percent), 7 to upper-middle school level (17.1 percent), and 4 to university or college level (9.8 percent). Professional status: 7 were peasants (17.1 percent), 18 were workers (43.9 percent), 9 were cadres (21.9 percent), and 7 were from other working backgrounds (17.1 percent.) Seven persons (17.1 percent) had positive family histories [of mental illness], while 26 persons (63.4 percent) themselves had previous histories of mental illness.

Clinical diagnoses: 30 cases of paranoid schizophrenia (73.2 percent), three cases of paranoid psychosis (7.3 percent), two cases of depression (4.9 percent), two cases of mania (4.9 percent), three cases of psychogenic mental disorder (7.3 percent), and one case of mild mental retardation (2.4 percent).

---

[335] Journal of Clinical Psychological Medicine (*Linchuang Jingshen Yixue Zazhi*), vol. 6, no. 6 (1996), pp.356-357.

Criminal case categories: (see Table 1.) In all cases, the commission of the crimes was directly related to the persons' mental symptoms. Fifteen cases arose from delusions of persecution, three from delusions of reference, two from delusions of grandeur, two from delusions of non-blood [non-parentage] relationship, one from delusions of physical influence, eight from auditory hallucinations, five from impairments of thought and logic, two from emotional depression, two from disturbance of consciousness, and one from pathological lying.

Table 1 Clinical Diagnoses and Types of Crime in Forty-one Political Cases

Type of crime	Sending reactionary letters	Writing reactionary slogans	Petitioning and litigation	Shouting reactionary slogans	Spreading rumors to delude the masses	Total
Schizophrenia (paranoid type)	15	8	4	3		30
Paranoid psychosis			3			3
Depressive illness	1		1			2
Mania				1	1	2
Psychogenic mental disorder	2			1		3
Mental retardation					1	1
Total	18	8	8	5	2	41

Discussion: According to reports in the Chinese literature, the proportion of mentally ill persons subjected to expert judicial appraisal who have committed political offenses is between 15.7 percent and 20.5 percent (see reference notes 1 and 2); this is second only to cases of murder and injury, although there has been a marked decrease in such cases since the 1980s. The majority of those in the case group had schizophrenia, but unlike the situation in other kinds of criminal cases, they were all suffering from the paranoid variety. This shows that paranoid schizophrenics tend to commit "anti-government" activities much more readily than those suffering from other variants of the disease, probably as a result of their delusions of persecution, delusions of reference, and delusions of grandeur, as well as their impaired thought processes. Three of the paranoid schizophrenics were dominated by systematic delusions that led them to make ceaseless complaints and accusations against their so-called "persecutors." In the cases of the two people suffering from depression, getting themselves punished was the actual aim of their criminal activities. The two mania sufferers committed their crimes as a result of a severe impairment of their powers of self-control. Of [the three persons] suffering from psychogenic mental disorders, two wrote letters to enemy intelligence organizations after encountering frequent setbacks in life, as a way of trying to extricate themselves from their difficulties, and compared with the other mentally ill [offenders of this type] they showed a higher degree of premeditation and also a greater sense of self-preservation; the other person shouted reactionary slogans while undergoing an acute episode accompanied by disturbance of consciousness.

As regards the modus operandi of the various offenses, in the overwhelming majority of cases – whether it was sending letters or writing reactionary slogans – the methods employed were all relatively simple, stupid, or self-contradictory and inconsistent. For example, one sufferer who sent a signed letter to members of the central [Party] leadership began by writing "Dear Comrade So-and-so," then went on to say "I'm determined to bring about your downfall" and other such things. Another sufferer wrote to a newspaper saying that he planned to hijack an airplane and go to Taiwan; he explained his reasons for doing so and then wrote down his real name and work unit at the end of the letter. A minority of the sufferers wrote long screeds that went on for thousands of words, but these documents were vague, general and repetitive in content, and lacking in any clear or purposeful sense of logic. As for the "reactionary slogan" writers, most used cigarette packets or other pieces of scrap paper to write down their thoughts on, so the pathological nature of their activities was obvious to others, and clearly different from most other cases of counterrevolutionary crime. Among the eight cases of petitioning and litigation, the majority involved people who kept barging into [government] offices and ceaselessly quibbling and arguing, in an indiscriminate and directionless manner that took no account of whether or not they were talking to the appropriate official and if they were having the desired effect; this again was markedly different from petitioning and litigation by normal people. Of the cases of mentally-ill crime under study, all were committed by single persons rather than groups of people; none of the offenders had considered the likely consequences of their actions beforehand, and afterwards they all actively confessed and showed no sense of concealment or fear.

The greatest numbers of sufferers from the group in question were admitted to hospital in 1978 and 1989, and this seemed to be distinctly related to the wider background and climate of those two years.[336] In all successive periods of large-scale social change and political campaigns, it can be seen that a number of mentally ill people "respond promptly to the call" by coming out to add further fuel to the flames; for example, the manic illness sufferers who go around making speeches all over the place, inflaming public sentiment, setting up road blocks, shouting slogans, and generally exerting a highly pernicious influence in society. For example, the mildly retarded person in the group under study had expressed a horrifying political rumor to a large group of onlookers, and taken much pleasure in doing so. This prompts us to the need to exercise even greater control and management over mentally ill people during periods of social turmoil and change. Cases of political crime created by the mentally ill usually exert a highly negative influence in society and have extensive ramifications. They take up large amounts of human and material [police] resources and pose a definite disruptive threat to the normal functioning of state offices and to the political stability of the country. An examination of the specific hallmarks of this type of crime thus has considerable practical importance.

(Article received on March 11, 1996.)

References:

1. Jia Yicheng, "Summary and Analysis of Papers Submitted to the 1st National Academic Conference on Forensic Psychiatry," *Shanghai Archives of Psychiatry*, 1981, No. 3, p.118.[337]
2. Shen Muci, "An Analysis of 654 Cases of Forensic Psychiatric Evaluation," *Chinese Journal of Nervous and Mental Diseases*, 1988, No.2, p.167.

---

[336] The year 1978 saw the emergence of China's first modern dissident groups, focused on the Beijing's "Democracy Wall"; and 1989 was the year of the Tiananmen Square protest movement and the June 4 massacre of peaceful student and worker demonstrators in Beijing.

[337] As given in original text; the actual year of publication for this article was 1987, not 1981 as stated. (See Document 8, above.)

DOCUMENT 11: On Negative Political Speech and Action

Liu Baiju[338]

August 2000

Overview

Acts that endanger the nation and threaten the social system can, when severe in nature, constitute crimes. Offenses of this type are customarily referred to as political crimes. The criminal codes of all countries, past and present, have contained stipulations on political crime, and these offenses have always been subject to even more severe punishments than those laid down for other types of crime. The only differences have been in the specific names that are given to these offenses, in their differing class implications, and in the range of required criteria for the constitution of such crimes. In the past in China, according to both the 1951 Regulations for the Punishment of Counterrevolutionaries and the 1979 Criminal Law, acts carried out with the aim of overthrowing the dictatorship of the proletariat (the people's democratic dictatorship) and the social system, or acts endangering the People's Republic of China, all constituted "crimes of counterrevolution." In the 1997 Criminal Law, in accordance with changes that had taken place in China's political, social and economic situation, "crimes of counterrevolution" were redesignated as "crimes of endangering state security," and fairly substantial changes were made to the content of these provisions.

Mentally ill people, owing to the pathological factors that beset them, may also engage in behavior that endangers the state and the social system, and the most commonly seen forms of such behavior are the writing of banners, distributing leaflets and flyers, sending letters, making speeches, and shouting out slogans. However, even if we discount the mental state of those concerned, and only consider the nature and degree of the threat posed by such actions, it is clear that the majority of acts of this type carried by mentally ill people do not fulfill the relevant criteria of the Criminal Law for the constitution of crimes. The question therefore arises of how to characterize, from an overall perspective, the commission of acts by the mentally ill that endanger the state

---

[338] Liu Baiju, *Jingshen Zhang'ai Yu Fanzui* (Mental Disorders and Crime), (Beijing: *Shehui Kexue Wenxian Chubanshe* [Social Sciences Documentary Publishing House], August 2000); the present document is a translation of most of Chapter 7 ("*Xiaoji Zhengzhi Yan-Xing*") of this recent 857-page, two-volume work. The author, Liu Baiju, is a Researcher at the Chinese Academy of Social Sciences' Bureau of Scientific Research, and a graduate of the law department of Chinese People's University.

and the social system. To describe it as "counterrevolutionary behavior" or as "behavior that endangers state security" would obviously be "inappropriate." To call it "reactionary behavior" would also not be good, since the term "reactionary" has excessively vague connotations. In the end, this writer has decided to use the term "negative political speech and action" to denote such behavior.

A review of the literature on forensic-psychiatric medical appraisals shows us that while the expression of negative political speech and action by the mentally ill is hardly a common occurrence, it is also by no means rare.

- In a report by Zhong Xingsheng *et al* on 210 cases of forensic appraisal that were carried out during 1981-84, fourteen out of the 181 crimes at issue (or 7.73 percent) were ones of anti-social speech and action.
- In a report by Shen Muci *et al* on 654 cases of forensic appraisal conducted during 1973-86, out of a total of 566 crimes, 103 were cases of a political nature, or 18.2 percent. (Eighty of these cases dated from 1980 or earlier.)
- Xu Shenghan, in a report on 708 cases of forensic appraisal carried out during 1982-86, found that 32 of the 638 offenses committed (or 5.02 percent) were crimes of counterrevolutionary behavior.
- In a report by Liu Guangyu *et al* on 931 forensic appraisal cases dating from 1979-90, among a total of 667 offenses committed, 27 (or 4.05 percent) were identified as being political cases.

Among these various studies, the one by Shen Muci *et al* showed the highest proportion of such cases, at 18.2 percent, while in the other reports the proportion of cases that were political in nature averaged out at 5.6 percent. It should be stressed here that Shen Muci's report was the only one that included cases from the 1970s (and in his report, political cases were the second most frequent category after cases of murder and injury). We see from this that there was a marked drop, among the total number of forensic psychiatric appraisals, in the percentage of cases of a political nature during the 1980s as compared to the 1970s. In addition, as experts familiar with the situation regarding psychiatric appraisals in the 1950s and 1960s have pointed out, the proportion of political-style cases was also extremely high during those two periods.

This decline in the incidence of cases of a political nature affords much food for thought. Tracing the matter to the source, and leaving other issues to one side, one major factor at least has been the change in the political climate. After the conclusion of the Cultural Revolution, and particularly since the start of [China's] opening up and reform, there has been a gradual relaxation in the political environment, and some acts that were previously seen as being "counterrevolutionary crimes" are no longer regarded as such, and may even not be viewed as crimes at all; having the Criminal Law available as a yardstick by which to ascertain "crimes of counterrevolution" has allowed us to avoid the [former] problem of the arbitrary amplification of the scope of these crimes. We can also anticipate that, following the redefinition of "counterrevolutionary crimes" as "crimes of endangering state security," the number of political cases will inevitably decline still further as a proportion of all crimes committed. Naturally, however, an incidence rate of 5.6 percent is by no means something that we can afford to ignore, and it fully justifies treating acts of negative speech and action by the mentally ill as being a problem requiring special study and attention.

Politics and Mental Disorders

Politics is something that intimately involves each and every person; everyone is affected by politics, even if they seek to stay as far away from it as possible. Indeed, politics can even become a direct causal factor or circumstance in the development of certain mental illnesses, for example schizophrenia, reactive psychosis, and neurosis. In China, politically stressful events have always been recognized as a major causal factor in mental disturbances. Using their "Inventory Table for the Assessment of Factors Leading to Mental Disturbance," Zheng Yanping and Yang Desen have produced a hierarchy of forty-three such factors, and the third most common causal element they identified in their study – after death of a spouse, and death of the main family member – was "being attacked in the course of political movements."[339] Similarly, in the "Inventory for the Assessment of Life Events" formulated by Zhang Mingyuan et al, "coming under political attack" ranked high on the list of relevant life events, closely preceded only by such events as the loss of a spouse, death of children or parents, and divorce.[340]

Especially during the periods when politics was all encompassing and the political atmosphere had descended to an especially vicious level, the role played by political factors [in generating mental illness] was even more pronounced. At those times, some people were unable to withstand the

[339] Zheng Yanping and Yang Desen, "Life Events, Mental Anxiety and Neurosis," *Chinese Journal of Nervous and Mental Diseases*, no. 2 (1983).

[340] Zhang Mingyuan et al., "An Inventory for the Assessment of Life Events: Some Common-Pattern Outcomes," *Chinese Journal of Nervous and Mental Diseases*, no. 2 (1987).

politically-induced mental stresses they experienced after coming under political persecution and attack; others could not adapt to the psychological pressures they had to endure as a result of the cruel and harsh political environment; still others were unable to deal with the psychological blow of being discovered to have "political problems"; and others again were incapable of adapting to or dealing with the sudden dramatic changes that so often occurred in the political climate. As a result, they either suffered from short-term mental-abnormality reaction states or else developed full-blown mental disorders.

The writer Hu Feng was one such example. As Hu's son, Zhang Xiaoshan, has revealed, after the Cultural Revolution, while he was lying in hospital recovering from the long-term political persecution he had endured, and longing for news of his rehabilitation by the Central Committee, Hu became mentally abnormal:

> The quiet hospital room in no way served to calm father's nerves. One morning, sitting on the sofa and with eyes staring fixedly ahead, he told me he had received a message through the air saying that Vice Premier Deng [Xiaoping] had delivered a speech calling for several people to be punished, and that five people had been stripped of their Party membership and taken away in handcuffs. News of this event would shortly be appearing in the newspapers: 3,890,000 copies had already been printed and had sold out immediately... That afternoon, he said he had received another message through the air, telling him to take a helicopter and leave right away; he began to put on his overcoat and tried to go out to board the helicopter, and despite all our efforts we were unable to prevent him from going outside.

> Some days later, his mental condition had still not improved. He slept only very rarely and so we took turns to watch over him constantly. On one occasion when I'd locked the door, he kept demanding that I open it, and father and son ended up having a pitched fight over the matter. He said that a political coup had taken place within the Central Committee, that someone had seized power from Deng Xiaoping and that the Central Committee had sent someone over to try and save him... One night, while mother was standing watch over him,

father was suddenly overcome by an indefinable sense of fear
and dread, and he began trying to jump out of the third-floor
window. When mother struggled to prevent him doing this, he
lashed out at her with his stick, breaking the glass in the door
to his room. At 2.00 AM that night, father was finally admitted
to the psychiatric wing of the Beijing No.3 Hospital.

Father was far from being the only person to become mentally
deranged as a result of the 1955 affair (i.e. the false branding
of Hu Feng and others as being a "counterrevolutionary
clique." [L.B.])[341] Many more such incidents also occurred
during the Cultural Revolution, when the psychiatric wing of
the Beijing No.3 Hospital alone was filled with untold
numbers of prominent senior Party cadres.[342]

Moreover, mental illness can also influence people's political behavior. In
contemporary society, every mentally normal person has his or her own political
beliefs and political consciousness, and may engage, at appropriate times, in
certain types of political action and behavior on the basis of these beliefs and
consciousness. So, can the same be said of those suffering from mental
disorders? It is quite hard to give a general answer to this question. Mentally ill
people who do not suffer from impairments of thought, consciousness and
intellect, or those who, despite having such impairments, still retain relatively
good powers of recognition and discrimination[343] and also the capacity for
political consciousness and political behavior, are able to participate in political
activities. The situation of mentally ill people who suffer from severe
impairments of thought, consciousness and intellect, however, is quite different.
Their capacity to receive and understand political information, and their ability
to make judgments about political issues and engage in political behavior, are all
relatively severely impaired; since their capacity for political consciousness and
political activity has either been weakened or entirely lost, they are incapable of

---

[341] For a detailed account of the political persecution of one of Hu's closest associates,
the writer Lu Ling, see above, "Judicial Psychiatry in China and its Political Abuses,"
Section III.B.

[342] Zhang Xiaoshan, "A Fragmentary Reminiscence: In Commemoration of the Fifth
Anniversary of the Death of My Father, Hu Feng (*Pianduan de Huiyi: Jinian Fuqin Hu
Feng Shishi Wu Zhounian*)," in *Historical Materials on the New Literature (Xin Wenxue
Shiliao)*, no. 4 (1990).

[343] "*bianren nengli.*"

fitting in with [existing] political life. When their illnesses are exceptionally severe, then the political rights that they enjoy as citizens may be restricted according to law. For example, Article 23, paragraph 2 of China's "Law on Elections" stipulates: "If a mentally ill person is incapable of exercising his or her electoral rights, then upon confirmation of this by the Electoral Commission, he or she shall not be listed on the roll of electors."

However, to say that a mentally ill person's capacity for political consciousness and political activity has either been weakened or entirely lost is only true in terms of the substantive meaning of that statement, and it by no means implies that mentally ill people of this kind are fundamentally incapable of forming views of a certain political coloration, of uttering language of a certain political coloration, or of engaging in behavior of a certain political coloration. The reason for this, primarily, is that these mentally ill people have already, prior to becoming ill, doubtless been in receipt of all kinds of political information and influences, and these influences may persist after they become ill and may also make themselves manifest. Secondly, mentally ill people of this type, after they fall ill, may receive all kinds of [new] items of political information and may react to them, even though they may now perhaps fail to correctly understand the nature of the political information and may be incapable of reacting to it in an appropriate manner. This was all the more true during previous eras in China when politics was the main topic on the national agenda.[344] For example, during the decades when "politics came first" [zhengzhi diyi], politics formed the single most important aspect of daily life and everyday language was filled with political terminology of all kinds; everyone talked non-stop about politics and even small children became infected with the habit, so how could mentally ill people living in the same social environment manage to completely avoid such influences? In those times, politics even penetrated into the symptomatology of mental illness. For example, some sufferers would walk only on the left-hand side of the road, believing that this would prove they were "leftists"; others developed delusions of guilt that they were agents or spies; and others would have auditory hallucinations in which they heard messages to them from the central Party leadership. [...]345

---

[344] *"Zai neizhong da jiang zhengzhi de shiqi jiu geng shi ruci."*

[345] *Four pages omitted here*: Accounts of "mad national leaders" in history, e.g. Liu Xin (a famous homosexual emperor of the Han Dynasty), Hong Xiuquan (leader of the Taiping Rebellion), Caligula, Nero, Emperor Charles VI of France, and Adolf Hitler; also, a discussion of the Western analytical schools of psychohistory (Erich Fromm, Lloyd DeMause) and pathography.

Negative Political Speech and Action by the Mentally Ill

The first issue that needs to be explored here is, why do mentally ill people sometimes engage in negative political speech and action? On this question, we must again distinguish between different categories of the mentally ill. If those who do not suffer from impairments of thought, consciousness and intellect engage in negative political speech and action, or if those still retaining relatively good powers of discrimination despite having such impairments do so, then it is usually on account of some real and authentic reason, and so cannot be attributed merely to the fact that they are suffering from mental illness. In the case, however, of those mentally ill persons who have entirely or basically lost their powers of recognition and discrimination, the question of quite why they should engage in negative political speech and action is very hard to explain. Here, we can only put forward a series of hypotheses.

First, it may be a consequence of the mentally ill person's own history prior to their falling ill. If the mentally ill person was actively concerned about politics and had independent views on the subject before becoming mentally ill, or if he or she was the innocent victim of psychological trauma arising from political attacks, then he or she might engage in negative political speech and action after falling ill. For example, if those who become mentally abnormal as a result of suffering political persecution then develop delusions of persecution, the content of these delusions may have a negative political coloration, and such people can therefore develop hostile feelings toward the political environment. However, the fact that such a history existed before the mental illness arose by no means implies that the negative political speech and action expressed by the mentally ill person concerned is necessarily rational in nature. For sufferers of this kind, the influence of the pre-illness history acts at the unconscious level. Second, they may have been influenced and affected by other people's negative political speech and action. Some mentally ill people suffering from impaired powers of recognition can be unwittingly influenced by other people, and may simply copy them and ape whatever they say. Third, some mentally ill people, under the influence of their external environment, may be interested in politics and yet their mental conditions render them incapable of thinking correctly, and this can sometimes lead them to engage in negative political speech and action.

We should also consider one other point: while the speech and actions *per se* of some mentally ill people may be devoid of any real political meaning or significance, they may nonetheless, under certain specific kinds of circumstances, be elevated in the minds of others to the high realm of politics. For example, schizophrenics suffering from delusions of grandeur sometimes believe and declare themselves to be the Emperor or the President; in normal times, people would pay little or no attention to statements like that, but during periods when the political atmosphere is tense, such statements may well be seen as constituting "counterrevolutionary speech." Similarly, if an epilepsy sufferer kills someone in the course of an epileptic seizure in which they have lost normal consciousness, their choice of target in the attack will be quite random; during the Cultural Revolution era, however, if the victim happened to be a Party member or a cadre, it would likely have been viewed as a case of "counterrevolutionary murder."

We should now try to analyze further the specific situations and circumstances in which mentally ill people engage in negative political speech and action. This is by no means an easy task, since the case materials in this area are quite fragmentary and there are very few studies by others that one can consult. In comparison with the categories of violent crime and sexual crime, research into the topic of negative political speech and action by the mentally ill has thus far been a much-neglected area of study. The following analysis, therefore, can probably only supply a few clues that may promote more thoroughgoing research into this question in the future.

The kinds of mentally ill people who engage in negative political speech and action for pathological reasons are, primarily, those suffering from schizophrenia, paranoid psychosis, manic-depressive illness, reactive psychosis or mental retardation. The mental states directly leading to negative political speech and action include, in most cases, delusions of persecution, delusions of grandeur, delusions of reference, impairments of thought and logic, auditory hallucinations, and disturbances of the intellect. According to the above-mentioned report by Shen Muci *et al*, the types of mental illness identified among the 103 cases of a political nature they examined were as follows: 55 cases of schizophrenia; nine cases of reactive psychosis; eight cases of manic depression; five cases of mental retardation; one case each of prison psychosis, organic brain damage *sequela*, and other psychosis; together with seven cases of personality disorder and 16 cases where no mental illness was found. The various psychiatric symptoms displayed were as follows: in 13 cases, delusions of persecution; in 15 cases, impairments of thought and logic; nine cases of auditory hallucination; in five cases, delusions of reference; and one case of delusions of jealousy and one of disturbance of consciousness; in addition, there were 31 cases of pathological behavior, including eight cases [identified as being due to] personality disorder and 20 that were non-pathological [in origin].

Furthermore, in the report by Luo Jiming *et al* regarding 41 cases of a political nature, the types of mental illnesses involved were listed as follows: 30 cases of paranoid schizophrenia; three cases each of paranoid psychosis and of psychogenic mental disorder; two cases of depression and two of mania; and one case of mental retardation. The various psychiatric symptoms in these cases were as follows: in 15 cases, delusions of persecution; eight cases of auditory hallucination; in five cases, impairment of thought and logic; in three cases, delusions of reference; two cases each of delusions of grandeur, delusions of non-bloodline relationship; two each of emotional depression and disturbance of consciousness; and one case each of delusions of physical influence and pathological lying.[346] Evidently, the pathological causal factors leading to negative political speech and action by the mentally ill are different in each case, and because this is so, the specific situation and circumstances whereby mentally ill people engage in negative political speech and action will also, of necessity, have their own specific hallmarks.

Foremost among the pathological factors leading mentally ill people to engage in negative political speech and action are delusions, and impairments of thought and logic. The content of the delusions that can lead to negative political speech and action is always related, directly or indirectly, to questions of politics. Among the various categories of delusion, the ones that most readily give rise to negative political speech and action are delusions of persecution and delusions of grandeur. If the identity of the persecutor that is fabricated [in the mind of the detainee] by virtue of the delusions of persecution happens to be either the ruling political party, the state institutions, or individual members of the leadership, then inevitably the sufferer will develop feelings of hostility and over-vigilance toward the ruling political party, the state institutions or individual leaders, and they may then start "exposing," "denouncing" and "condemning" the latter's various "conspiracies" and "crimes." In general, the targets of these delusions of persecution are limited to certain specific individuals, but in some cases the scope of hostility may become constantly amplified in the sufferer's mind, progressing from one individual to a number of different people, and then onward to include a whole organization, the government, or even the whole of society.

For example, some sufferers initially only make accusations against the leader of their work unit and demand that the government department concerned punish him or her, but when they fail in this objective, they become convinced that the government is acting in collusion with the leader of their work unit. Others, suffering from delusions of grandeur, may develop political mania [*zhengzhi kuangre*] and become excessively interested in political matters –

---

[346] Luo Jiming, Li Shenlu and Tang Xiaofeng, "An Analysis of 41 Mental Illness Sufferers Involved in Cases of a Political Nature," *Journal of Clinical Psychological Medicine* (*Linchuang Jingshen Yixue Zazhi*), no. 6 (1996). (See Document 10, above, for the full text of this article.)

believing, for example, that they themselves have some political mission to fulfill and that they are destined to become (or already are) political leaders. If they proceed to propagate such views publicly, they will come into sharp conflict with the actual environment around them. In some cases, the sufferers not only exaggerate their own importance, but also seek to deny or negate that of others, and they may even try to usurp the latter's role, so leading to even greater complications. Usually, the various types of delusions relating to politics result only in the sufferer making and distributing speeches that attack the ruling political party, the state institutions or individual leaders; but if allowed to continue unchecked, such behavior can lead to extreme consequences, and the sufferer may then resort to dangerous measures, such as attempting to assassinate the perceived persecutor or anyone else he believes is trying to obstruct him from carrying out his political mission.

In addition, persons suffering from paranoid psychosis, paranoid schizophrenia, mania, and also organic psychosis accompanied by symptoms of delusion, are all liable, by virtue of the above-mentioned delusory symptoms, to engage in negative political speech and action. That carried out by paranoid psychotics has one common and persistent characteristic, namely that the behavior in question always seems to be "based on real facts" [*shi chu you yin*], whereas in reality it is motivated by pathological factors. The negative political-speech-and-action behavior of such people may seem, on the face of it, just like normal behavior, and so long as it does not impinge upon the delusory notions *per se*, these people can appear to be quite normal. They cleave stubbornly to their opinions, they regard themselves as being in the right, they dare to conduct their activities openly and make no attempt to conceal their identities or give false names, and they are not afraid of being arrested and brought to justice. Unless careful discrimination is exercised with [mental illness] sufferers of this type, miscarriages of justice can easily arise.[347]

Certain sufferers are highly fluent speakers and proficient at weaving stories, so some mentally normal people can become convinced that what they say is true and may even end up spreading the ideas further. In the case of those suffering from paranoid schizophrenia, the negative political speech and action may be caused not only by their delusions, but also by impairments in their thought and logic, or by a combination of both factors. The impaired thought and logic of some sufferers who are fascinated by politics can lead to their espousing the most strained, anomalous, bizarre and sometimes even ridiculous kinds of political viewpoints. Also, the role of auditory hallucinations should not

---

[347] "*Dui zhelei huanzhe, ruguo bu jiayi zixi shibie, keneng zaocheng cuo'an.*"

be underestimated. Manic illness sufferers who engage in negative political speech and action while under the dominance of their delusions are usually in a state of emotional excitement and mania at the time, and their behavior can be especially sudden and unpredictable. Also, the delusions of persecution and grandeur displayed by those suffering from organic psychotic disorders are, in terms simply of their behavior, quite hard to distinguish from those of people suffering from the functional psychoses, although the delusions may be either looser in structure or more systematic and entrenched. For this reason, people with organic psychosis can engage in negative political speech and action in much the same way as those with functional psychosis.

Case No. 224:

Mr. A, a local-level cadre. A family history of mental illness (both grandfather and father were sufferers). Joined the revolution at the start of the War of Liberation [1945-49]. In 1958, he opposed the "tide of exaggeration,"[348] and for this was dismissed from his leadership post in 1960 (he was officially rehabilitated in 1962). Because of the stress caused by this, from 1961 onwards he developed schizophrenia and was then given medical treatment and placed under the guardianship of his family; he lacked either self-awareness or the ability to look after himself, and at times when his illness worsened he would walk around naked and without any sense of shame. Over a several-year period prior to the Cultural Revolution, he wrote numerous letters to Chairman Mao and the Party Central Committee, all filled with incomprehensible nonsense. After carrying out several investigations, the authorities ascertained that he had written these letters because he was mentally ill, and thereafter the local post office used to destroy the letters whenever they found them. Everyone around him knew that he was mentally ill. During the early part of the Cultural Revolution, he wrote a series of letters to Premier Zhou [Enlai], saying: "The United Nations should quickly send troops to crush [the protests]," and other similar things. In December 1968, he was arrested as an "active counterrevolutionary," and a month or so later was sentenced by the court to ten years' imprisonment. Because he kept on uttering strange and incomprehensible

---

[348] "*Fukua feng*": The term officially used in China today to denote the tendency by Party officials at all levels during the Great Leap Forward (1958-60) to grossly over-report production statistics (especially grain output) in their localities, as a means of convincing the central government that they were implementing Mao's Great Leap Forward directive to do everything "more, better, faster, and more economically" (*duo-kuai-hao-sheng*). This wholesale fabrication of production figures is acknowledged to have been the main reason for the disastrous famine that ensued in China in the early 1960s, in which at least 27 million people died of starvation and related causes.

statements while in prison, in 1974 he was given a death sentence for engaging in [further] "active counterrevolution"; the death sentence was not approved by the provincial high court, however, and Mr. A died in prison in 1977.

Case No. 225:

Mr. Liu, 47 years old, a university graduate and returned overseas Chinese. After immigrating to China in 1962, he went to one of Beijing's most famous universities, graduating in 1968. That year was the harshest phase of the Cultural Revolution, and because of his class status and family background he was sent down to a state farm to perform manual labor. In 1972, he was sent to work in a research institute. He was generally enthusiastic in his work and achieved outstanding results, but he kept himself to himself most of the time and also was stubborn and self-willed. Throughout his time at college, the state farm and the research institute, Liu applied several dozen times to join the Communist Party of China, but he was always turned down because of his overseas connections. Because of this, he wrote numerous letters to the leading officials concerned, stating that he himself was free from any [political] taint, that there must be dissidents within the Communist Party of China, and asking the Party Central Committee to clean up the membership. The relevant departments criticized and educated Liu many times on this account. He was even subjected to criticism and struggle sessions and sentenced to a period of reform through labor. But Liu continued to uphold his own viewpoints.

After the end of the Cultural Revolution, he again wrote numerous letters to the competent departments expressing these viewpoints. Later, he wrote another letter, saying that in the mid-1980s he had organized and set up a political party called the "China Party for Democratic National Reconstruction" (*Zhongguo Minzhu Jianguo Dang*). In addition, he wrote a detailed and tightly argued "Party Charter" that was tens of thousands of words in length, in which he declared his intention "to unite with all advanced intellectuals at home and abroad," in order to assist the Communist Party "to clean up the membership." Liu made many copies of this document and distributed them within society, and he also sent a copy to a leading official of the Communist Party Central Committee. He was subsequently taken into custody for criminal investigation. Suspecting that he was mentally ill, the authorities sent him for forensic psychiatric examination. Appraisal findings: paranoia; no capacity for criminal responsibility.[349]

---

[349] Sun Dongdong, *Jingshenbingren de Falü Nengli* (Legal Capacity of the Mentally Ill), (Xiandai Chubanshe, 1992), p.127.

Case No. 226:

Mr. L, 32 years old, a worker, educated to lower-middle school level. He became ill immediately after the Cultural Revolution, believing that he was "the son-in-law of a fourteenth-generation descendant of Zheng Chenggong" and that he could lead the whole of China in carrying out reforms. He proposed to replace the Chinese Communist Party with a "Labor Party of China" (*Zhongguo Laodong Dang*), with himself as "Chairman," and he proceeded to formulate a "Party Charter" and "Party Constitution" and also to recruit members into the party. Three ignorant youths joined this organization. He also drafted a "Law of the People," a "Cadres Law," a "Military Law" and a "Law on Science," the contents of which were a total mishmash and full of nonsense, so that no one could make head or tail of them. Later on, he and his collaborators distributed several thousand leaflets throughout all areas of the city, thereby creating an extremely bad influence. He was then arrested on charges of committing "counterrevolutionary crimes."

During his investigation and questioning, it was discovered that although he confessed unreservedly both about the events in question and about his criminal motives, there were certain absurd and unusual elements in his account. He was then sent for forensic psychiatric appraisal. In the course of the appraisal, it was ascertained that he had a family history of mental illness, with several of his relatives afflicted. Upon psychiatric examination, it was found that while his consciousness was normal and his memory and intellect were both sound, he nonetheless had marked delusions of grandeur and his ideological outlook was fallacious and unrealistic. He requested the government not to destroy the various "laws" he had formulated, saying that although he had to go to prison and so would be unable to complete his "enterprise," these "laws" should still be preserved for the benefit of future generations, to serve as the basis for carrying out a scientific reformation of the country. Appraisal findings: paranoid schizophrenia; crime caused by delusions of grandeur during an active phase of the illness; no capacity for criminal responsibility.[350]

Case No. 227:

Ms. Li, 37 years old, a worker, educated to upper-middle school level. Normally quite introverted by character. In 1981, she and her husband were divorced on grounds of emotional incompatibility. In 1982, after she violated

---

[350] Jia Yicheng, ed., *Shiyong Sifa Jingshenbingxue* (*Applied Forensic Psychiatry*), (Anhui Renmin Chubanshe, 1988), pp.192-193.

labor regulations and undertook private work projects,[351] she was punished by being dismissed from her job but retained on payroll for a one-year probationary period. Thereafter she began to show signs of mental abnormality, suspecting her former husband, neighbors and work-unit leadership were saying insulting things about her, and she filed a court lawsuit making accusations against the leaders of her work unit; she also frequently got into arguments at her work unit, demanding that they revoke the punishment imposed upon her. She subsequently formed the belief that the government was putting poison into food and vegetables, as part of a plan to cause people's deaths from chronic poisoning and thereby to fulfill its goal of restricting China's population and allowing the ants to rule the world. On March 10, 1991, on a certain university campus, Li was caught red-handed while in the act of pasting up a small-character poster that had negative political content and was titled "Nuclear War in Peacetime"; a search of her person then produced a large quantity of other small-character posters. During the pre-trial criminal investigation, Li made a series of strange and incomprehensible statements and it was decided to send her for forensic psychiatric examination. Appraisal findings: schizophrenia; the small-character leaflets were posted up while she was in the grip of her delusions; no capacity for criminal responsibility.[352]

In some cases of negative political speech and action by the mentally ill, the capacity for discrimination and recognition of those concerned is fairly intact at the time they commit their offenses, but they are subject to the influence of other pathological factors. Cases of negative political speech and action by those suffering from minor manic disorders, for example, arise as a consequence of their reduced capacity for self-control. Minor mania sufferers have an unduly high opinion of themselves and are fond of arguing with others. While they may be dissatisfied with specific [government] policies, the criticisms they raise are not just restricted to the matter in hand but instead tend to go off in all directions at once, becoming high-flown and generalized in nature and striking out at random, so that such people often end up making extremist statements. They also enjoy propagating their viewpoints in public and in front of many onlookers, and they strive hard to convince people that they are correct, thereby

---

[351] "*si bao gongcheng.*" In 1982, before China's market economy began, citizens were normally not allowed to undertake paid work outside their state-appointed jobs.

[352] Lü Xianrong, ed., *Sifa Jingshen Yixue Anli Ji* (*A Compilation of Forensic Psychiatric Medical Cases*) (Ankang Hospital of the Wuhan Municipal Public Security Bureau, 1992), p.137.

giving rise to the impression that they are engaging in "counterrevolutionary propaganda and incitement." In the case of those suffering from depressive illness who engage in negative speech and action, sometimes their aim in doing so is to commit an indirect form of suicide (self-punishment). Some mentally ill people of this kind write letters to the relevant departments informing them that they're planning to carry out such-and-such an act which endangers state security, adding their real names and work-unit details to the letter, and they then sit back and await their punishment.

People suffering from impairments of the intellect can also engage in negative political speech and action. Such impairments impact, primarily, in two separate ways on the emergence of negative political speech and action. The first is that impairments of the intellect prevent those affected from being able to properly understand or construe the various items of political information they receive, with the result that they may uncritically adopt undesirable political ideas. The second is that these impairments prevent them from making appropriate judgments, on the basis of existing knowledge, in respect of the various political questions at issue, thereby leading them into careless and wild behavior. Whatever other people say or do, they will also say or do, although very few of them have any real insight into the nature and significance of their speech and actions. At certain times, they express "revolutionary" views, and at other times they express "counterrevolutionary" views; the listeners, however, will probably only notice the "counterrevolutionary" content of their statements and hence will regard them as being "counterrevolutionaries." While such people may have real or practical motives for engaging in negative political speech and action, nonetheless, not all of these will be directly related to politics; for the most part, they tend to be motivated by lower-level factors such as obtaining material gratification or getting attention from others. For example, one mildly mentally retarded person created and spread a horrifying political rumor, but he did so just because it amused him and he found it enjoyable.

Other mentally retarded people, despite having an impairment of the intellect as a whole, can still display special abilities and be able to accomplish certain tasks very skillfully, even when their motives for doing so are immature and the tasks themselves involve the wildest of fantasies. For example:

Case No. 228:
Male, mentally retarded. Suspected by his work unit of theft activities. After listening to radio broadcasts from Taiwan, and using a specified liaison point, he compiled an encryption system and wrote five coded letters to enemy espionage organizations in Taiwan and Hong Kong using a false name. He stated in the letters that he had established a counterrevolutionary group, and asked the

recipient organizations to recognize his group and provide it with funds, weapons and intercom communications devices; he also asked them to send him a fully competent female assistant who would become his wife and would take instructions from him, and he specified a contact address and a password to be used for this purpose. After he was arrested, he confessed to having the following motives for doing all this: "I wanted to prove that I hadn't actually stolen anything, so I thought up the idea of contacting Taiwan by letter and tricking them into sending over enemy agents and large amounts of money, weapons, ammunition and radio transmitters, so they could all be captured in one big net, as a way of proving that I was innocent and well-intentioned." He had firmly believed he could prove his innocence in this way, and at the same time get himself a wife.[353]

The incidence and investigation rates for cases of negative political speech and action by mentally ill persons suffering from marked impairments of the intellect vary, to a very great extent, in accordance with the [prevailing] political climate. At times when the influence of politics is all-pervasive, such people tend to engage in negative political speech and action quite frequently; while during more normal periods they do so rather rarely, since they are not inherently interested in politics. When the political atmosphere is harsh and restrictive, their negative political speech and action will be taken very seriously, and moreover will be investigated by the legal authorities; whereas at normal times people will tend not to pay any particular attention to such speech or action, since they know the person concerned is "crazy." Two sets of statistics appear to confirm this point. According to the first, between 1960 and 1976 a certain hospital dealt with a total of 40 mentally retarded persons who had committed crimes, and ten of these were cases of a political nature, making this the most frequent of all the various categories of offense. According to the second set of figures, between 1989 and 1992 another hospital dealt with altogether 116 cases involving mentally retarded persons, of whom 75 had committed crimes; among the latter, only three cases involved public disturbances that were probably linked to politics.[354]

---

[353] Shen Zheng, *Sifa Jingshenbingxue* (*Legal Psychiatry*), (Zhongguo Zheng-Fa Daxue Chubanshe), p.220.

[354] Wang Zenghui, "An Analysis of 116 Cases of Forensic Psychiatric Appraisal of the Mentally Retarded," *Linchuang Jingshen Yixue Zazhi* (*Journal of Clinical Psychological Medicine*), no. 6 (1996).

Negative political speech and action by those with personality disorders is an intentional and deliberate form of behavior, and is prompted by authentic motives. If we analyze the matter on a deeper level, however, we find that the personality disorders exert a distinct influence in causing such people to engage in this kind of speech and action. For example, people with anti-social personality disorders are frequently punished because they often break the law, but more often than not, instead of learning from these punishments and reforming their evil ways, their rebellious character type is such that they become even more hostile, and moreover start directing their feelings of hostility toward the state and the social system. A person suffering from anti-social personality disorder who had committed theft and mugging, for example, was sentenced to forced reeducation through labor, but during his time in reeducation he made the wildly arrogant statement: "It's no big deal for me to spend several years in jail; I'm planning to tussle with the dictatorship of the proletariat and I fully expect to be shot."[355] Similarly, people with paranoid personality disorders usually fail to look at problems in a complete and objective way, and if they are dissatisfied with a particular policy this will often develop into a sense of dissatisfaction with the government itself; and once such prejudices have formed in these people's minds it is very difficult to change them.

Perhaps the hardest thing of all to appreciate is that negative political speech and action can, in certain cases, become compulsive in nature. In the compulsive neuroses, this can assume a particular form known as compulsive antithetical thought.[356] Whenever people suffering from this condition encounter a particular object or phrase, they feel compelled to react with a diametrically opposite concept or phrase, even if it clashes strongly with their normal understanding of things. With some sufferers, moreover, the compulsive antithetical thoughts extend to politics. In Tsarist Russia, for example, there was a government official who was normally quite timid and nervous, and who always took great pains over his work for fear of offending his superiors; after being criticized on one occasion, however, he developed compulsive antithetical thought syndrome. From then on, whenever his top boss, Ambassador So-and-so, used to enter the hall where important government meetings were being held, he felt impelled to make a speech denouncing the Ambassador for his reprehensible private life and to shout out slogans demanding his overthrow. He knew that if he did this he would bring disaster down upon his head, so he

---

[355] Li Congpei, ed., *Sifa Jingshenbingxue* (*Forensic Psychiatry*), (Renmin Weisheng Chubanshe, 1992), p.322.

[356] In Chinese: "*qiangpoxing duili siwei*," also translatable as "compulsive antagonistic mentality."

always made an enormous effort to control himself. But these compulsive antagonistic thoughts kept on reemerging time and time again, leaving him in an extreme state of fear and anxiety. After the Tsar was overthrown, the man again became preoccupied with thoughts of attacking and overthrowing a certain leading official of the new government; just as before, these thoughts just kept on recurring and was unable to free himself of their influence.

Provided the content of these compulsive thoughts is not actually expressed or put into action, no real harm can arise. In the course of China's past political campaigns, however, some afflicted people actually gave voice to their compulsive thoughts and intentions, and as a result they were subjected to mass criticism and struggle sessions for displaying "reactionary ideology."[357]

---

[357] Li Congpei, ed., *Sifa Jingshenbingxue* (Forensic Psychiatry), p.270.

APPENDIX III: CRACKDOWN ON FALUN GONG

DOCUMENT 12: **Psychophysiological Reactions Associated with Qigong Therapy**

Xu Shenghan

Shanghai Mental Health Center, Psychiatric Department, Shanghai Medical University[358]

Fall 1994

Qigong as a part of the traditional Chinese medicine is similar to Western "meditation," Indian "Yoga" or Japanese "Zen," which can all be included in the category of traditional psychotherapy. A series of physiological and psychological effects occur in the course of Qigong training, but inappropriate training can lead to physical and mental disturbances. Physiological effects include changes in EEM, EMG, respiratory movement, heart rate, skin potential, skin temperature and fingertip volume, sympathetic nerve function, function in stomach and intestine, metabolism, endocrine and immunity systems. Psychological effects are motor phenomena and perceptual changes: patients experience warmness, chilliness, itching sensation in the skin, numbness, soreness, bloatedness, relaxation, tenseness, floating, dropping, enlargement or constriction of the body image, a sensation of rising to the sky, falling off, standing upside down, playing on the swing following respiration, circulation of the intrinsic Qi, electric shock, formication,[359] during Qigong exercise. Some patients experienced dreamland hallucinations, unreality and pseudohallucination. These phenomena were transient and vanished as the exercise terminated. Qigong deviation syndrome has become a diagnostic term and is now used widely in China.

Qigong is a traditional Chinese modality for promoting health and curing diseases. Qigong as part of traditional Chinese medicine is similar to western

---

[358] *Chinese Medical Journal* (Beijing), vol. 107, no. 3 (1994), pp.230-233. The journal is published in English and the present text is as it appears in the journal; no attempt has been made here to correct the English grammar.

[359] A crawling sensation on the skin, as if covered with ants.

"meditation," Indian "Yoga" or Japanese "Zen," which can all be included in the category of traditional psychotherapy.

A series of physiological and psychological effects occur in the course of Qigong training, which is somewhat similar in nature to biofeedback and some behavioral treatment in modern medicine. Inappropriate training can lead to physical and mental disturbances. More and more importance has been attached to the role of Qigong therapy in psychosomatic medicine. This article, from the viewpoints of medicine and psychology, deals with the role of Qigong therapy in physical and mental health problems.

Traditional Chinese medicine believes that Qigong is a self-training through "spirit" (*jing*), "vital energy" (*qi*) and "mind" (*shen*) of the human body, which balances Yin and Yang (negative and positive), circulating the vital energy and the blood, coordinates internal organs, clears and activates the main and collateral channels, so as to adjust physical and mental state.

Physiological Effects

The research in modern science proves that Qigong training has extensive effects and influences on various systems of the human body. It includes the changes in EEC, electromyogram EMG, respiratory movement as well as the declining of such physiological indices as heart rate, skin potential, skin temperature and fingertip volume, which reflects the changes of physiological functions, functional changes of autonomic, especially sympathetic nerve systems. During Qigong training, there exhibit a lot of physiological effects such as improvement of stomach and intestine function and the changes in metabolism, endocrine and immunity functioning. [1]

These effects represent an integration of multidimensional functions of the physiological systems in a special state of consciousness induced by Qigong. The integrated effects appear to have close correlation and synchronism with the activities of human body systems. Qigong functional state produced by relaxation and meditation in a special state of consciousness provides favorable conditions to regulate the physiological functioning either in a single system or between various systems, so as to achieve proper synchronism and good equilibrium. Body oxygen consumption decreases in this Qigong state, which implies relaxation and meditation may help adjust the energy metabolism and decrease the energy expenditure, which is favorable to energy accumulation. [2]

Psychological Effects

The state of "Rujing" (entering into the state of total calmness) in Qigong obtained through relaxation and meditation is a peculiar mental state. Through self-adjustment, the trainee finds himself in a functional state different from sleeping, waking or dreaming. During this time, the internal functions are supposed to be highly coordinated and in good order, which may exert some changes on mental activities with the effect of dampening psychological stress.

The author reported the clinical phenomena during Qigong exercise, i.e., 1) motor phenomena: jerking, twitching, tremulous and spontaneous movement; 2) perceptual changes: patients experiences warmness, chilliness, skin-itching, numbness, bloatedness, relaxation, tenseness, floating, dropping, enlargement or constriction of the body image, changing of the body image along with respiration, disappearance of body image, a sensation of rising to the sky, falling off, standing upside down, playing on the swing following respiration, loss of cognition of space–time continuum, circulation of the intrinsic Qi, electric shock sensation and formication during Qigong exercise. Some patients also had dreamland experience, feeling of unreality and some motor-sensory disturbances. Moreover, a variety of pseudohallucination may occur. [3] However, all these phenomena were transient and vanished as the exercise terminated.

Qigong healing modality can be regarded as a typical psychophysical therapy, and people will naturally consider applying it to the treatment of psychosomatic diseases. There have been many reports in this aspect, including the treatment of hypertension, asthma, coronary heart disease, gastric and duodenal ulcer, and allergic colitis. Besides, therapeutic effects on insomnia, depression, anxiety, neurosis, and childhood attention deficit syndrome have been reported.

Qigong Deviation Syndrome

Incorrect performance of Qigong exercise can lead to some somatic or psychological disturbances, just like what appeared during the early phase of over-meditation reported by Otis in 1973. [4] Such syndrome manifested during or after the Qigong exercise may be called "Qigong deviation," which has become a diagnostic term now widely used in China. It has also been included in the Chinese Classification of Mental Disorders (1989.) [5]

The mental disturbances initiated by Qigong exercise has aroused wide interests and discussion now among Chinese psychiatrists and Qigong researchers.

The diagnosis of "Qigong deviation syndrome" showed the following criteria: 1) normal behavior before doing Qigong exercise; 2) psychological and physiological reactions appear during or after Qigong exercise; suggestion and autosuggestion may play an important role; 3) the manifestation of Qigong deviation syndrome does not meet the diagnostic criteria of schizophrenia, affective disorder and neuroses.

The clinically common symptom of Qigong deviation is the uncontrolled flow of "Qi" (energy) in the body. All of the cases has such complaints as "Qi moving and dashing within the body" or "Qi dashing and rushing into the head," often stagnating somewhere and leading to pain, with some strange perception in the lower abdominal area called "Dan Tian" (elixir field.) The incessant movement of the vital energy may give rise to an unusual malaise as well as various physical symptoms such as headache, insomnia, discomfort, abdominal distension and others. Owing to the exercisers' overemphasis upon the experience of "arrival of Qi," many interesting psychic phenomena may be derived from: Qi being "stolen" – for instance, an elderly woman was furious when the instructor removed her Qi to another exerciser. She gave that exerciser a box on the ear and asked him to return her Qi. "Induction" of Qi – once there were two exercisers (patients with chronic physical illness) who were in the same ward. One day, one of them gave a puff inadvertently to the other, the latter soon began to dance elegantly. After a little while he told the other mysteriously: "Oh, this is caused by the communication between my Qi and yours." The psychic problem may arise on account of the attitude of the exerciser to the Zi Fa Gong (spontaneous skill), which manifests itself as fast, strenuous and irregular movement with large motions. Some schools of Qigong (as in the crane-flying Qigong) emphasize that the earlier, the larger and the faster the spontaneous skill emerges, the better results will ensue, therefore the exercisers spare no efforts to seek for the spontaneous skill. [6] In most of the exercisers, sensation of Qi, as well as the spontaneous skill were caused by suggestion and autosuggestion and they are prone to develop psychic disorders.

The common symptoms in mental disturbance are anxiety, nervousness, depression, etc. Seriously ill patients cannot control their own behavior. Some patients are found to have hallucination or delusion, and some even have the impulse of committing suicide.

Qigong deviation syndrome is a mental disorder closely related to the cultural background, and also to superstition or witchcraft (Case 2).

The mental and physical disturbances caused by Qigong deviation have the characteristics different from other psychotic disorders. Their causes are rather complicated. The author has done some tentative study on their clinical and causative factors.

Of the patients, 25 psychotic cases were assessed by Brief Psychiatric Rating Scale (total mean score of BPRS: 44.89 ± 9.42), and 50 neurotic cases were assessed by Hamilton Rating Scale (total mean score of HAMA [Hamilton depression]: 16.82 ± 6.90; total mean score of HAMD [Hamilton rating scale for depression]: 16.00 ± 8.30). There are significant differences between the Qigong deviation group and the control group (mean score of HAMD: 2.58 ± 2.22, $t = 11.04$, $P<0.001$; mean score of HAMA: 1.94 ± 1.66, $t = 11.83$, $P<0.001$).

Case Report

Case 1: Mr. A is a 22-year-old unmarried worker. He began to learn himself from Qigong books the "Wu Qin Xi" (exercise mimicking the gestures of five animals) on November 26, 1984 for the treatment of lumbago. Ten days later, he suddenly had "special cenesthesiopathy" with "Qi" flowing adversely in the head and abdomen. When "Qi" flowed into his head, he felt fullness of head and chest distress. When showing a Qigong gesture, he suffered agony and anxiety, even attempting to commit suicide. Two hours later he was sent to Shanghai Institute of Qigong for help. Guided by a Qigong master he recovered. The next day he became delirious and claimed that he could hear the voice of evil spirits; he prayed to Buddha for help but only lost his self control. During the intervals of the attacks, the patient was normal. But he could not work normally due to insomnia and difficulty in coping with Qigong deviation.

On January 15, 1985, the patient got upset because he was prevented by his family from doing Qigong exercise. He felt so hopeless that he attempted to commit suicide by bumping his head into a car. He was then sent to a hospital for psychiatric treatment. There were no abnormal findings in his physical and laboratory check-up. There was no history of psychosis in his family either. He was treated timely by ECT. Two days later, his father took him back home. Now he is followed up by a Qigong master and is so far in good health state.

Case 2: Mr. B is a 44-year-old married painter. He learned on his own the "He Xiang Zhuang" (crane-flying Qigong), another school of Qigong in February 1984, attempting to treat his ailment, the hypertrophy of cervical vertebra. He had no personal psychiatric history, neither his family. Several days after Qigong exercise, he was suddenly agitated with hyperthymia. He claimed that he knew everything in the world, "water is associated with the sea," when he talked about the sea, he would "think of the American continent."

Three days later, he was diagnosed as schizophrenia-like disorder and was treated in Shanghai Psychiatric Hospital. One month later he had remission.

Later he turned to learn the "Long Men Five Flow," another school of Qigong. On the third morning he suddenly began to cry and dance, still doing Qigong exercise in bed. He thought that his dead mother would be brought back to life whereas he would become a ghost. He said that he could see Buddha and God, and he believed in religion. He also smelt something unusual. He was again admitted to Shanghai Psychiatric Hospital.

Mental examination: the patient has emotional instability, with no delusion and hallucination, sometimes posing in a Qigong gesture and has intermittent attacks. EPG: extroversion. MMPI: schizophrenic character. He was given 100 mg CPZ *im*, *bid*. A week later, he recovered from his illness and now works as before.

Attention should be paid to the prevention and treatment of various mental and physical disturbances due to Qigong deviation.

References

1. Lin YG. Progress of combined traditional Chinese and Western medicine in the field of Qigong. Chin J Integ Trad West Med 1988; 8:82.
2. Lin YG. Study on the physiological effects of meditation in Qigong. International Conference on Trad Chin Med & Pharm Proceedings. China Academic Publishers 1987; 1014.
3. Xu SH. Analysis of the clinical phenomena of Qigong therapy in 100 cases. J Trad Chin Med 1961; 5:34.
4. Michael West. Meditation. Brit J Psychiat 1979; 135: 457.
5. China Neuro & Psychiat Association. Chinese classification and diagnostic criteria of mental disorders (CCMD-2). Beijing: CNPA, 1989: 66.
6. Zhai ST, Zhang XB. Psychological problems in Crane-Flying Qigong. The Asian Pacific Regional Symposium on Psychosocial & Cultural Aspects WPA/Nanjing China, 1985: 387.

DOCUMENT 13: A First Look at the Forensic Psychiatric Evaluation of Falun Gong Cases

Shen Jun and Gong Yantao[360]

October 2000

In this article, we explore various issues regarding the forensic psychiatric assessment of [criminal] cases involving the Falun Gong.

Case 1:
Female, 45 years old, a worker, educated to lower middle-school level. She first started practicing Falun Gong in 1996 because she had chronic colitis and hyperplasia of the lumbar vertebrae. She gradually became obsessed with Falun Gong, practicing it all day long, rarely eating, unwilling to see a doctor or take medicine when she fell ill, growing ever more estranged from her family, her health declining markedly, and yet she flagrantly told everyone how much she was benefiting from her practice of Falun Gong. Even after the government declared Falun Gong to be an evil cult, she refused to be dissuaded from her beliefs and continued gathering people to practice Falun Gong. Moreover, she went to Beijing to petition the authorities[361] [about the suppression of the group] and was then placed under criminal detention, but still she persisted in practicing Falun Gong; and she stopped sleeping.

Psychiatric examination: Consciousness clear and alert; markedly excited and loquacious; declared that since taking up Falun Gong she had been able to overcome all the tests and tribulations of life, though not yet to the point of having opened up her "heaven's eye";[362] regarded herself as currently being in excellent health and said that she felt very energetic even after not eating for several days; and insisted that her original ailments had been cured without taking any medicine. Furthermore, she said that she could see three suns in the sky and also a five-colored auspicious cloud, and that the "Master" [i.e. Li Hongzhi] was protecting her at all times. Sometimes when no one was present, she could hear someone telling her to "go to Beijing, and once you have

---

[360] Journal of Clinical Psychological Medicine (*Linchuang Jingshen Yixue Zazhi*), vol. 10, no. 5 (2000), pp.313-314.

[361] "*shangfang.*"

[362] "*tian mu*": in Falun Gong philosophy, a point located in the center of the forehead and equivalent to the "third eye" of other popular religions or sectarian belief systems.

overcome the three trials then your merit will be complete,"[363] and saying, "if
you're going, then go quickly." She said that her bloodstream was filled with
constantly revolving tiny gems made up of high-energy cosmic matter, and that
this caused her skin to shine with a special glow. Her emotional responses were
also inappropriate.

Forensic finding: mental disorder caused by practicing an evil cult; no
capacity to bear legal responsibility; recommend medical treatment.

Case 2:
Male, 62 years old, educated to upper middle-school level, a department
manager in an electrical equipment factory. After suffering from insomnia for a
long time, in 1995 he took up practicing various kinds of qigong, and in 1997 he
became besotted with the practice of Falun Gong. He soon became solitary and
untalkative, and he began giving people valuable presents for no reason. He
always ate less than other people and would buy the cheapest of foods, to the
point even of buying and taking home items that other people had turned down.
He said that [this was because] he wanted to be a genuinely "truthful,
compassionate and forbearing"[364] person. After the government declared Falun
Gong to be an evil cult, she not only ignored all efforts to dissuade him from
continuing to practice Falun Gong, but also joined with other practitioners in
traveling to Beijing to "uphold the dharma"[365] on behalf of Falun Gong.

Psychiatric examination: Consciousness clear and alert; declared that since
practicing Falun Gong all his previous illnesses had been cured, and that if
allowed to practice for just one more month his white hair would all turn black
once again, his skin would become softer and clearer, and he would become
"thoroughly rejuvenated."

Diagnosis: mental disorder caused by practicing an evil cult; should bear
partial legal responsibility for his crimes.

Case 3:
Male, 3 years old, a worker. In 1992 he began to show signs of mental
abnormality, with frequent recurrence of symptoms. In 1997, after his family
heard that one could cure illnesses by practicing qigong, they told him to take up
Falun Gong. Moreover, he then frequently participated in, and gathered others to

---

[363] "*guole san-guan jiu gongde yuanmanle.*"

[364] See Note 15, above.

[365] "*hu fa*": also translatable as "defend the teachings."

take part in, trips to Beijing to petition [against the suppression of the group], thereby exerting an extremely bad influence in society.

Psychiatric examination: Consciousness clear and alert; constantly over-excited; declared that since taking up Falun Gong he had gained even greater superhuman abilities than before; that he could summon the winds and rain at will; that he could tell what was going on in people's minds without the use of any instruments of detection; and that his soul had been fully realized and he was able to maintain frequent contact with aliens from outer space. He said that his purpose in going to Beijing was to use his qigong-acquired merit to make Tiananmen Square become a better and smaller place. His thinking was extremely chaotic.

Diagnosis: schizophrenia; behavior and actions completely dominated by pathological factors, and hence no capacity to bear legal responsibility.

Case 4:
Female, 41 years old, a cadre, college educated. She began practicing Falun Gong in 1996 and gradually became a die-hard element within her collective practice group. After the government ordered the banning of Falun Gong, and rejecting all efforts to persuade and educate her away from the cult, she continued to organize groups of practitioners to carry out petitioning activities on its behalf.

Psychiatric examination: Consciousness clear and alert; thinking logical and well-ordered; she defended with extreme vigor the various advantages of practicing Falun Gong, and in so doing slandered and vilified [China's] present social realities; apart from being emotionally over-excited, she showed no signs of hallucination, delusions or other conspicuous mental abnormalities.

Forensic finding: not mentally ill; should be held legally responsible for her crimes.

Discussion
Falun Gong is entirely different from ordinary kinds of body cultivation techniques, and no clear definition of the type of mental disorders that it produces can be found within China's currently used body of diagnostic criteria for mental illness. This creates distinct difficulties for us in the conduct of forensic psychiatric assessments work. Since the number of Falun Gong practitioners is relatively great, their scope and distribution is relatively broad and hence they exert a rather strong sociopolitical influence, it is essential that we strictly adhere both to psychiatric-medical criteria and also to legal-scientific criteria when carrying out forensic psychiatric assessments work in this area. This means carefully distinguishing between the following subjects of forensic

appraisal: ordinary practitioners who were tricked and deceived into taking up Falun Gong; people who were previously suffering from mental illness and then began practicing Falun Gong as a consequence of their psychiatric symptoms; people who were not previously mentally ill but have since developed mental abnormalities as a result of their obsession with Falun Gong; and the die-hard Falun Gong elements who are mentally quite normal and who have obstinately persisted in their erroneous beliefs and actions.

As can be seen from the forensic case examples given above, mental disorders caused by evil cults usually have the following characteristics:

1) Prior to commencing Falun Gong practice, in most affected cases certain socio-psychological factors were already in evidence (including varying degrees of personality defect, certain physical ailments or various unhappy life experiences), but there was no clear history of mental illness of any kind.

2) In most cases, those affected had been practicing Falun Gong for one year or more, they had become severely infatuated with it, and no amount of repeated education or persuasion, in whatever form, had succeeded in bringing them to their senses.

3) In most cases, the mental abnormalities emerged slowly and then gradually worsened (although there were also cases in which the symptoms arose suddenly and very conspicuously); and by contrast with the kinds of temporary, minor and partial changes in mental activity that can arise in the cases of those entering special qigong states,[366] these mental abnormalities were protracted in duration.

4) There were certain similarities between the manifestations of these mental disorders and the kinds of mental disorders that can be induced by popular body cultivation techniques, for example, disturbances of sensory perception and of behavior. But there were also differences, namely that in the case of Falun Gong-induced mental disorder both delusions and impairments of logical reasoning could also be found, often mixed in together with elements of objective reality or proximate reality, and moreover these were all closely interconnected with the evil cultic influence of Falun Gong's doctrine of "Truthfulness, Compassion and Forbearance." [1]

---

[366] The authors are probably referring here to "qigong-induced mental disorder" (also known as "qigong deviation"), a psychiatric diagnosis that was formally included in the Chinese Classification of Mental Disorders (CCMD-II) in 1989; for a detailed discussion of this Chinese-style "culture-bound disorder," see Document 12, above.

5) The social functioning of those affected was more severely damaged, and their response to specialist medical treatment was much poorer, as compared to those suffering from mental disorders caused by popular body cultivation techniques.

6) The original objective of those starting Falun Gong practice is usually self-improvement – for example, curing illnesses, physical cultivation or escaping from psychological difficulties – and in most cases their behavior is not premeditated or driven by any deep-seated social motive.

If we exercise comprehensive judgment [based on the above points], it is usually not difficult to make a diagnosis of evil cult-induced mental disorder.[367] At the same time, [these criteria] will help us to identify, and to maintain our guard against, any die-hard Falun Gong elements who might try to feign mental illness as a way of escaping legal punishment for their activities.

On the question of how to ascertain the capacity for legal responsibility in Falun Gong cases: although there are as yet no clear, government-stipulated legal criteria for forensic evaluations in this area, we nonetheless feel that the same principles should be applied as in other types of criminal cases. That is to say, we should first of all determine whether or not the person being appraised is mentally ill, and if so, the degree of severity of their illness, and then establish whether their behavior was prompted by pathological factors or by authentic criminal motives. [2] This requires that we comprehensively investigate the situation, make an overall objective analysis, and provide a thorough scientific verification of our findings. [3]

• In cases where the examinee has become so obsessed with Falun Gong that their entire mental activity has fallen under evil cultic control and they have lost the capacity to ascertain reality and control themselves, a finding of no capacity to bear legal responsibility for their crimes should be made.

• On the other hand, in cases where only temporary or minor mental disorders arise following the practice of Falun Gong, and where those concerned have retained or only partially lost their capacity to ascertain reality and control themselves, a finding of either ability or partial capacity to bear legal responsibility should be made.

• And in cases where mental abnormality is not pronounced, and where the examinees' activities have been primarily directed against society

---

[367] "*xie jiao suo zhi de jingshen zhang'ai.*"

and they have been able, moreover, to painstakingly plot and organize illegal activities, a finding of full legal responsibility should be made, as a means both of striking out hard against evil cults and of safeguarding the effective implementation of our national laws.

In view of the fact that Falun Gong practitioners constitute a special social group, but there has so far been an insufficiency of case material, and not enough investigation done, either to clarify the diagnostic criteria that should be used in the forensic psychiatric evaluation of Falun Gong cases or to indicate what the correct determination of legal responsibility should be, we furthermore propose that the relevant experts in this field should set up a special task force to study these various issues and to provide guidance for the future development of this work.

References:

1. Wu Caiyun, "A Clinical Analysis of 76 Cases of Qigong-induced Mental Disorder Characterized Mainly by Hallucination and Delusion," *Journal of Clinical Psychological Medicine (Linchuang Jingshen Yixue Zazhi)*, 1991, 2:7.
2. Xu [characters unclear], "A Discussion of Several Questions Relating to the Forensic Assessment of Mental Disease," *Shanghai Archives of Psychiatry (Shanghai Jingshen Yixue)*, 1999, (New) 11:9.
3. Zheng Zhanpei, "On the Evaluation of Degree of Mental Injury, and Some Issues for Attention in Practical Work," *Chinese Journal of Psychiatry (Zhonghua Jingshenke Zazhi)*, 2000, 1:6.

APPENDIX IV: PRC DRAFT LEGISLATION

DOCUMENT 14: **Mental Health Law of the People's Republic of China**

Draft of Ninth Revision in English[368]
October 15-24, 1990

Chapter 1. General Provisions

Article 1. The purpose of the Mental Health Act is to facilitate the development and improved management of mental health work in China; to facilitate the improved care and treatment of mentally ill persons; and to protect the legal rights of the mentally ill.

Article 2. To develop mental health services, to provide active treatment of mental illness and to prevent mental illness are the guiding principles of mental health work in our country. The program of developing mental health services shall be included in the global program and yearly plans of governments at various level; facilities for mental health services shall be improved; and scientific research on mental health shall be undertaken and full utilization of the results of such research shall be encouraged in the treatment and prevention of mental disorders and in the management of mental health services, in order to guarantee the effective implementation of the guiding principles being. [sic]

Chapter 2. Mental Health Facilities

Article 3. Mental health centers, mental hospitals or mental health care institutions (or stations), mainly undertaking diagnosis, treatment and prevention

---

[368] This English translation of the ninth draft of China's Mental Health Law appears as Annex 3 in a WHO report of January 28, 2000 describing the results of a WHO mission to China in September 1999 to discuss issues relating to mental health and law. As part of this mission, the WHO delegation and China's Ministry of Public Health jointly convened in Beijing a National Workshop on Mental Health Law. According to a note attached to Annex 3 of the WHO report, this ninth draft of the Mental Health Law was written "after the MPH/WHO National Workshop on Mental Health and Law, Chengdu, Sichuan, PRC, October 15-24, 1990." The inclusion of this draft of the Mental Health Law in the January 2000 report by the WHO almost certainly means that it was still the most recent draft of the Law, despite having been drafted some nine years previously. According to recent articles in the Chinese medical literature, a tenth draft of the Law is currently circulating for discussion in China, but no copy of the draft has as yet come to light.

of various mental disorders in local areas, shall be organized and led by bureaus of public health in the provinces, autonomous regions and cities.

Article 4. Mental health rehabilitation centers, mental rehabilitation hospitals or facilities, mainly admitting and taking care of the mentally ill in convalescent or chronic stages in order to promote their rehabilitation, shall be organized and led by bureaus of Civil Administration, in the provinces, autonomous regions and cities.

Article 5. Security mental hospitals, mainly admitting and taking care of the mentally ill under compulsory treatment and strict control according to legal provisions, shall be organized and led by bureaus of Social Security[369] in the provinces, autonomous regions and cities.

Article 6. Departments of mental health, for carrying out mental health services shall be set up in general hospitals of counties or at higher level.
    Psychiatric units or mental hospitals, mainly admitting mentally ill persons under penalty, shall be set up in the hospitals of prison or correctional institutions as required.

Article 7. Mental health facilities of provinces or cities shall be set up in quiet places with easy access, in order to facilitate the patients to get necessary care and treatment.

Article 8. The ration of personnel to psychiatric beds shall be determined according to the scales and the roles of the mental health facilities. The ratio of personnel to psychiatric beds in mental health centers and mental hospitals shall not be lower than 1:1; in mental rehabilitation centers or in security mental hospitals the ration shall not be lower than 0.6:1; and in teaching hospitals or research institutions, the ration shall be higher than 1:1.
    The component of mental health professional staff in the total number of personnel of the mental health organizations shall not be less than 70 percent.

---

[369] NB: China's network of secure mental hospitals, or "Ankang," is entirely under the control and administration of the Ministry of *Public* Security (*Gong'an Bu*, i.e. the police). It is unclear why, in this and other Articles of the present translation, the term Gong'an was rendered as "Social Security"; elsewhere in the document (Article 17, item 3) it was correctly translated as "public security."

Article 9. In various mental health facilities, doctors and nurses shall have been professionally trained and qualified. Psychiatric wards shall be quiet and comfortable. The environment inside the ward shall be clean and decorated, and outside there should be enough space for the daily activities of the patients. Facilities for occupational therapy shall be available. Various routine work systems, protection measures for patients and management systems including open wards or semi-open wards shall be established.

Article 10. Various mental health facilities shall be under the quality control supervision and regular review by the local authorities. Facilities failing to pass such reviews shall be ordered to be improved within a limited time period.

Article 11. Departments of Mental Health or Psychiatry and Departments of Medical Psychology or Behavioral Sciences shall be set up in medical universities or medical colleges. In some universities with adequate facilities, specialty or faculty of mental health shall be set up for training teachers, specialists and professionals in mental health.

Chapter 3. Management of Mental Health Work

Article 12. A National Mental Health Committee, consisting of members from Ministries of Public Health, Civil Administration, Social Security,[370] Justice, National Education Committee, and leading mental health workers of the country, shall be organized by the State Council.

Article 13. Mental Health Committees, consisting of members from Departments of Public Health, Civil Administration, Social Security, Justice, and mental health experts, shall be organized by the governments of provinces, autonomous regions and cities, respectively.

The leading groups of mental health shall be organized by the county government.

Article 14. The duty for mental health committee at various levels and mental health leading groups shall be:

1) To formulate mental health programs that will be subject to regular review, and to promote their implementation by relevant departments.

---

[370] See previous Note.

2) To coordinate opinions and actions related to mental health work of Departments of Public Health, Civil Administration, Social Security,[371] and Justice.

3) To study and evaluate implementation of the Mental Health Act.

4) To accept appeals from the mentally ill, their close relatives or guardians, and with authority to investigate activities violating provisions of the Mental Health Act, and to make appropriate decisions. If the decisions are not accepted, the case shall be reviewed and decided by the court.

5) To actively promote the development of community based mental health services, in urban and rural areas.

Chapter 4. Treatment of the Mentally Ill

Article 15. The treatment and hospitalization of the mentally ill shall principally be on a voluntary basis. Patients who consent to be admitted to mental health facilities shall fill a voluntary admission form according to the written recommendations of the evaluating or referring psychiatrist. In the hospital patients shall hold the same rights as patients in medical wards. Patients can be discharged on their own request.

Article 16. For the best health of mentally ill persons, any who shows florid symptoms severe enough to impair their capacity to work, study or living skills, but who refuse to be voluntarily hospitalized or receive treatment, shall be taken to the mental health facility by their close family members or guardians for treatment for the purpose of preventing further deterioration. Following evaluation by the psychiatrist and confirmation of the need for hospitalization, patients can be taken by their close family members or guardians with the certification by the psychiatrist and admitted. The discharge of patients shall be with the agreement of close family members or guardians, and shall follow the proper process stated in this Act.

Article 17. Persons who are diagnosed as mentally ill can be involuntarily hospitalized by their close family members or guardians, or the working unit, or local police, with the admitting certification by a psychiatrist for the purpose of treatment and custody, if they show one of the following:

---

[371] Ditto.

1) Violence toward others;
2) Evidence of dangerous intents to commit suicide, injury to self or to others, or other seriously dangerous behavior;
3) Disturbing social order or endangering public security.

When the psychiatrist in charge of the treatment testifies that the patient's mental disorder is in remission and that the danger of harm to other or to himself is no longer present, the person who took the patient to the hospital can take him out after following the prescribed process.

Article 18. Mental patients shall be treated, as far as possible, in the community or outpatient facilities. When hospitalization is needed, they shall be placed in the least restrictive facilities such as the psychiatric department in a general hospital or a mental health facility. Involuntary admission to a security hospital shall be used only for those patients with clear evidence of dangerous intention and behavior.

Article 19. In the hospital, the rights of mentally ill persons to correspond, to purchase or receive items for daily living, to receive visits from relatives, friends and others, and to keep their privacy, shall be guaranteed.
     Mental health professionals shall not insult, physically or mentally abuse patients or act in any way that harms or injures patients.

Article 20. Mental health professionals are obliged to put the patient under temporary protective restraint only when the patient is likely to hurt himself or others in the hospital. Such action can only be ordered by a psychiatrist, and the reasons and procedures of restraint shall be recorded in the patient's chart.

Article 21. Mental patients themselves and their family members have the right to be informed about the treatment and its possible side-effects, and the doctors shall tell them the truth, and unless it is involuntary treatment, patients and their family members have the right to decide whether or not to take the treatment. Before applying electric convulsive therapy or psychosurgery, written permission in written form [sic] by patient himself or his family members is required.

Article 22. Mental patients, their family members or guardians have the right to file a complaint against the superintendent or professionals in the mental health facility to the local Mental Health Committee or leading group and request an investigation and suitable intervention, when the rights of the patients are infringed. They also have right of appeal to the local court if not satisfied with the decision made by the local Mental Health Committee or leading group.

Article 23. Mental patients have the right to receive adequate treatment. Those who need treatment but lack the resources to cover their expenses for treatment, shall be provided financial support or access to treatment by local welfare agency or local authority.

Article 24. Mental patients who had a job before the illness have the right to get mental health care and welfare free of charge as other ill person do.

Chapter 5. Rights of the Mentally Ill

Article 25. Mentally ill persons shall be treated with respect for human dignity. They shall not be expose to teasing, discrimination, insult, and abuse of any kind.

Article 26. The right of mentally ill persons to vote or be elected, if suspended by court because of their illness, shall be restored as soon as their illness is in remission and upon such certification by a psychiatrist.

Article 27. Mentally ill persons who had jobs before their illness have the right to return to their former position, or to be placed in a more suitable one upon the recommendation of a psychiatrist when their illness is in remission.

Article 28. Mentally ill persons who have no job shall be provided opportunity for work by the local government and agencies in such places as welfare factories, occupational workshops when they recover from their illness and are able to work. Welfare factories and occupational workshops in which more than 50 percent of the workers are mental patients are exempted from taxation.

Article 29. Mentally ill persons who lost their ability to work and have no living resources shall be [eligible for][372] social welfare provided by local authorities, as other handicapped persons.

---

[372] The original translation states here: "shall be no social welfare..."; this was presumably a misprint.

Article 30. Mentally ill students, who discontinue their study under the recommendation of a psychiatrist based on the nature and severity of their illness, can return to their studies under the recommendation of the mental health facility and school regulations when they recover from their illness.

Article 31. School or classes providing special education and training shall be set up for mentally retarded children, to enhance their ability to live and work.

Article 32. Mentally ill persons who are in remission and who are competent to make the decision shall be allowed to marry under the Marriage Law of the PRC. Their right to have children shall not be denied solely for reason of mental illness.

Article 33. When the spouse of a mentally ill person wants a divorce, under provisions of Article 25 of the Marriage Law of the PRC, the living, treatment, and guardianship arrangements shall be made by the court.

Article 34. The right of mentally ill persons to inherit under provisions of the Inheritance Law of the PRC shall not be taken away for reason of their illness.

Article 35. Mentally ill persons who are involved in mental health teaching or as research subjects shall be given information about the purpose, procedures and related matters in clear and understandable form, and their informed consent shall be obtained.

Chapter 6. The Criminal Process

Article 36. In the criminal process, the proceedings shall be suspended when the defendant is declared incompetent to stand trial because of mental illness; the proceeding will continue when the defendant is restored to competency. Anyone found to be mentally ill and not able to serve the penal sentence, shall be transferred to mental health facility or put on probation under the guardianship of the family members to receive the needed treatment.

Article 37. During the penalty, the days spent in mental health facilities for treatment shall be counted in the time to be served.

Article 38. In security mental hospital, the patient's mental condition shall be reviewed at least once every six months. When a remission is confirmed by a psychiatrist and the symptoms endangering others and himself are no longer present, the patient can be discharged and put under the care of his family members or guardians.

Patients transferred from the judicial system shall be transferred back at discharge.

If mentally ill persons, their family members, or guardians have any objections to involuntary hospitalization, involuntary treatment, and detention of the patient, they can appeal to the Mental Health Committee or leading group, asking for review by mental health experts. The Committee or leading group can review the matter and make an appropriate decision in light of the experts' opinion. Further objection or appeals can be made to a court.

Chapter 7. Forensic Mental Health Assessments

Article 39. The forensic mental health evaluator should be qualified as a psychiatrist (or "attending psychiatrist" so called in China) or as a forensic physician with knowledge and clinical experience in the field of psychiatry.

Article 40. The rights and duties of forensic mental health evaluators:

1) Right to review the relevant case materials, to join the investigation and to interview or question the concerned persons or witnesses with the consent of the referring agency;
2) Right to request additional materials which are essential for assessment;
3) Right to refuse to do assessments for sound reasons;
4) Right to request the referring agency to provide complete and reliable case materials that can provide factual evidence for the forensic assessment;
5) Right to request the referring agency or judicial organizations to provide protection to forensic mental health evaluators when their personal safety is threatened because of involvement in forensic assessment.
6) No organization, agency or individual shall intervene or influence the forensic assessment, so long as the evaluators conduct the assessments according to law.
7) The referring agency shall pay for the assessment according to stipulation.

The duties of the forensic mental health evaluators:

1) Forensic mental health evaluators have a duty to safeguard the confidentiality of the case materials reviewed.
2) The assessments should be objective, fair and honest. The evaluator found to be engaging in fraud might be criminally liable pursuant to Article 36 of the Criminal Procedure Law of the PRC.
3) Forensic mental health evaluators should adhere to professional and scientific principles in the assessment, and base their conclusions on sufficient evidence.

Article 41. Definite conclusions regarding the mental state of the defendant at the time of the alleged offence or action, and written opinions about the criminal responsibility of the assessed person should be included in the report of the forensic mental health evaluation. Different opinions in the assessment or conclusion should also be indicated in the report.

If questioned by the referring agency regarding differing opinions or conclusions in the report, the evaluator has the duty to explain. If the referring agency considers it necessary, a re-evaluation can be conducted by the original evaluators or other evaluators based on additional materials. However, the conclusions should not be revised under any coercion or pressure.

The evaluators provide reports of their assessment only to the referring agency, and testify in court by request. They have no obligation to provide or to explain conclusions to their[373] agencies or persons.

Article 42. The assessed person, or his legal representative or lawyer has the right to know the results and conclusions of the assessment and the evidences on which they are based. When the conclusions of the assessment are believed to be incorrect or unfair, the assessed persons, their family members or guardians have the right to request the court to review the conclusion or request another agency to re-evaluate. The payment to the re-evaluator should be provided by the applicant.

---

[373] This word is probably a typographical error and should read: "other."

Chapter 8. Legal Responsibility

Article 43. Persons who engage in any of the following acts shall be investigated and have legal responsibility under Article 134 of the PRC Criminal Law:

1) Acts that threaten, menace, blackmail or inflict violence on a person, and which directly induce a severe mental disorder.
2) Acts of discrimination, insult, open or disguised abuse of the mentally ill, which increase the physical or mental suffering of the mentally ill or aggravate their illness.

Article 44. Rape or seduction of the mentally ill or mentally retarded persons who lack the ability to protect themselves by means of cheating, luring, or use of force, shall be prosecuted under provisions of Article 139 of the PRC Criminal Law.

Article 45. The intentional infliction of physical harm on a mentally disabled person resulting in organic mental disorders, or intellectual impairment, or severe personality change with significant impairment of the ability to work, study and live, shall be punished as severe injury, under provisions of the PRC Criminal Law.

Article 46. The Mental Health Committees or leading groups have the right to give criticism, warnings, or penalties to agencies or persons who severely violate the Mental Health Law. If grave consequences are induced, the legal responsibilities will be investigated and prosecuted under the Criminal Law.

Chapter 9. Definitions

Article 47. The terms in this law are defined as follows:

Mental Disorders: Referring to psychosis, neurosis, developmental disorders, personality disorders, psychosexual disorders and other mentally abnormal states.

Mentally Disordered Persons: Persons who suffered from a mental disorder or disorders.

Mental Health Services: The programs and resources supplied for diagnosis, treatment, rehabilitation and prevention of mental disorders, and for the promotion of mental health of normal persons.

Mental Health Facilities: The facilities provided for mental health services, such as mental health centers, mental rehabilitation centers, security mental hospitals, mental hospitals, departments of psychiatry in general hospital, mental health care institutions, psychological consultation clinics, rehabilitation stations, occupational therapy stations, day care centers, welfare shops for the mentally ill, and other facilities for mental health care of children and aging persons.

Community-based Mental Health Services: Services provided by the primary mental health facilities for the mentally ill in the community. These facilities include the following: day hospitals where patients stay during the day; rehabilitation stations or occupational therapy stations where the patients take part in occupational therapy; home beds refer to visits by or social workers to interview and treat mental patients in their homes and give advice on treatment and nursing to patients and their relatives.

Open-door Ward: Wards where the patients have the right to determine whether they should be admitted and discharged, or should accept any treatment. The patients may be participating freely in any activity in the hospital. Psychiatric in-patients have the same rights as the in-patients in general hospital.

Half-open Wards: Wards where the relatives or the guardians of the patient have the right to determine whether the patient should be admitted and discharged, and the patient should accept any treatment. The patient may be allowed to move about in the ward or outside; however, for reasons of safety, the patient is allowed to take part in only some activities in the hospital.

Chapter 10. Appendix

Article 48. Appropriate implementation clauses or other regulations may be formulated by the concerned Departments in the State Council.

Article 49. The date of the beginning of the implementation of this law is ___.

(Note: This Draft was reviewed and discussed by all participants and WHO experts, especially Dr. Saleem Shah,[374] during the MPH/WHO National Workshop on Mental Health and Law, Chengdu, Sichuan, China, People's Republic of China, October 21-24, 1990.)

---

[374] Dr. Shah, who had very wide knowledge and experience of psychiatry in China, tragically died in a car crash in the early 1990s.

DANGEROUS MINDS

POLITICAL PSYCHIATRY IN CHINA TODAY

AND ITS ORIGINS IN THE MAO ERA

HUMAN RIGHTS WATCH

350 Fifth Avenue, 34ᵗʰ Floor
New York, NY 10118-3299
http://www.hrw.org

**GENEVA INITIATIVE
ON PSYCHIATRY**

P.O. Box 1282
1200 BG Hilversum
The Netherlands
www.geneva-initiative.org

For the past forty years in China, non-violent political and re-
gious dissidents have run the risk not only of being sent
prison for their alleged crimes, but also – as used to occur in th
former Soviet Union – of being falsely diagnosed as sufferi
from severe forms of mental illness and then subjected to invo
untary psychiatric treatment in custodial mental asylums. Eve
in today's economically more open China, numerous dissiden
and nonconformists – including Falun Gong activists, ind
pendent labor organizers, whistleblowers, and complainan
against political persecution or official misconduct – contin
to encounter this highly sinister form of repression.

The main evidence compiled by Human Rights Watch an
the Geneva Initiative on Psychiatry in *Dangerous Mind
Political Psychiatry in China Today and its Origins in the Mao E*
is drawn from hundreds of legal and psychiatric studies pu
lished officially in China since 1949. The report reconstructs th
shadowy history of politically abusive psychiatry in China, wi
a focus on the Cultural Revolution decade, when virtually a
forms of mental illness were said to be caused by politica
deviant thoughts; and it examines the reasons for the persis
ence of political psychiatry into the post-Mao reform era, whe
the official theory has been that some dissidents commit the
"crimes against the people" because of mental illness.

The report also outlines the steps that the Chinese go
ernment should adopt in order to end these abuses, as well a
measures that the international community – notably the Wor
Psychiatric Association – should take in support of the ethical
minded mainstream of contemporary Chinese psychiatry.

Cover Design by Rafael Jiménez

ISBN 1-56432-278-5

90000

9 781564 322784